CW00793842

Seawall Design

CIRIA
6 Storey's Gate, Westminster
London SW1P 3AU
Tel. 071–222–8891
Fax. 071–222 1708

SEAWALL DESIGN

R. S. Thomas BEngSc, CEng, MICE

and

B. Hall FICE, FIWEM
Posford Duvivier

Butterworth-Heinemann Ltd
Linacre House, Jordan Hill, Oxford OX2 8DP

OXFORD LONDON BOSTON
MUNICH NEW DELHI SINGAPORE SYDNEY
TOKYO TORONTO WELLINGTON

First published 1992

British Library Cataloguing in Publication Data
A catalogue record for this book is
available from the British Library

Library of Congress Cataloguing in Publication Data
A catalogue record for this book is
available from the Library of Congress

ISBN 0 7506 1053 0

Typeset by Latimer Trend & Company Ltd, Plymouth
Printed and bound in Great Britain by Redwood Press

Contents

Glossary

Accretion	Build-up of material solely by the action of the forces of nature by the deposition of waterborne or airborne material.
Alongshore	See **Longshore**
Apron	Layer of stone, concrete or other material to protect the toe of the seawall against scour.
Armour unit	Large quarrystone or special concrete shape used as primary wave protection.
Artificial nourishment, beach replenishment, beach feeding	Supplementing the natural supply of beach material to a **beach**, using imported material.
Bastion	A massive **groyne**, or projecting section of seawall, normally constructed with its crest above water level.
Beach	By common usage, the zone of granular sediments that extends landward from the lowest water line to the place beyond the high water line where there is a marked change in material or physiographic form, or to the line of permanent vegetation.
Beach material	Granular sediments, usually sand or shingle, in the beach zone.
Breastwork	Timber structure generally parallel to coast.
Bulkhead	Structural partition within a seawall.
Bull nose	Substantial lip or protuberance at the top of the seaward face of a wall, to deflect waves seaward.

Bypassing Movement of **beach material** from the accumulating updrift side to the eroding downdrift side of an obstruction to longshore transport, e.g. in inlet or harbour.

Cliff stabilization Works to halt and prevent instability and erosion of cliffs. Causes of instability can include both external **coastal processes** and geotechnical factors within the cliffs.

Coastal defences, coastal works Collective terms covering protection provided to the coastline. These include **coast protection** and **sea defences**.

Coastal processes Collective term covering the action of natural forces on the coastline and adjoining seabed.

Coastal regime The overall system resulting from the interaction of the various **coastal processes** and their action on the coast and seabed.

Coast protection Works to protect land against **erosion** or encroachment by the sea.

Cribwork A technique of construction, for **groynes** or seawalls, where stones/rubble are retained by an open network of vertical or horizontal members.

Deep water Water so deep that waves are little affected by the bottom. Generally, water deeper than one half the surface **wave length** is considered to be **deep water**.

Design storm Seawalls will often be designed to withstand wave attack by the extreme **design storm**. The severity of the storm (i.e. **return period**) is chosen in view of the acceptable level of risk of damage or failure.

Diffraction Process by which energy is transmitted laterally along a wave crest. Propagation of waves into the sheltered region behind a barrier such as a breakwater.

Downdrift The direction of predominant movement of **littoral drift** along the shore.

Erosion The removal of material by the action of natural forces.

Fetch	Relative to a particular point (on the sea), the distance over which the wind can blow on the sea and so generate waves at the point.
Flood wall, splash wall	Wall, retired from the seaward edge of the seawall crest, to prevent water from flowing onto the land behind.
Foreshore	The part of the shore lying between **mean high water** and **mean low water** level in England and Wales and between **mean high water springs** and **mean low water springs** in Scotland.
Freeboard	The height of a structure above **still water level.**
Geotextile	A synthetic fabric which may be woven or non-woven.
Groyne	A structure generally perpendicular to the shoreline built to control the movement of **beach material.**
Hard defences	In common usage, normally taken to describe concrete, timber, steel, asphalt, rubble or similar shoreline structures.
Littoral drift, littoral transport	The movement of **beach material** in the **littoral zone** by waves and currents. Includes movement parallel (longshore transport) and perpendicular (onshore – offshore transport) to the shore.
Littoral zone	**Beach** and **surf zone.**
Longshore	Along the shore.
Maintenance	Repair or replacement of components of a structure whose life is less than that of the overall structure, or of a localized area.
Mean High Water (MHW), Mean Low Water (MLW)	See **Tides**
Monochromatic waves	A series of waves, each of which has the same wave period.
Offshore breakwater	A breakwater built towards the seaward limit of the **littoral zone**, parallel (or near parallel) to the shore.

Orthogonal (wave ray)	In a wave refraction/diffraction diagram, a line drawn perpendicular to the wave crest.
Overtopping	Water passing over the top of the seawall.
Parapet	Solid wall at crest of seawall projecting above deck level.
Porous	In terms of **revetments** and **armour**, cladding that allows rapid movement of water into and out of it during wave action (many geotextiles and sand asphalt can be non-porous under the action of waves but porous in soil mechanics terms).
Prototype	The actual structure or condition being simulated in a model.
Random waves	The laboratory simulation of irregular sea states that occur in nature.
Recurved	The concave face of a wave wall designed to throw back the waves (thrown-back).
Reflected wave	A wave that is returned seaward when a wave impinges on a **beach**, seawall or other reflecting surface.
Refraction (of water waves)	The process by which the direction of a wave moving in **shallow water**, at an angle to the contours, is changed.
Refurbishment, renovation	Restoring the seawall to its original function and level of protection.
Rehabilitation	Works to an existing wall which may include **upgrading** as well as **renovation.**
Replacement	Process of demolition and reconstruction.
Return period	In statistical analysis an event with a **return period** of *N* years is likely, on average, to be exceeded only once in every *N* years.
Revetment	A cladding of stone, concrete or other material used to protect the sloping surface of an embankment, natural coast or shoreline against **erosion**.

Rip-rap	Well-graded quarry stone normally used as a protective layer to prevent **erosion.**
Rubble mound structure	A mound of random-shaped and random-placed stones.
Run-down	The seaward return of the water following **run-up.**
Run-up	The rush of water up a structure or **beach** as a result of wave action.
Salting (salt marsh)	An area of soft, wet land periodically flooded by saline water; usually characterized by salt-tolerant grasses and other low vegetation.
Sea defences	Works along the coast whose principal function is to prevent or alleviate flooding by the sea.
Secular change	Long-term changes in sea level.
Shallow water	Commonly, water of such depth that surface waves are noticeably affected by bottom topography. It is customary to consider water of depths less than half the surface wave length as shallow water.
Significant wave height	The average height of the highest one third of the waves in a given sea state. (see also Section 4.4)
Significant wave period	An arbitrary period generally taken as the period of one of the highest waves within a given sea state. (see also Section 4.4)
Soft defences	Defences which consist of sand or shingle (beaches, dunes or banks), which may be natural or man-made.
Still water level	Water level which would exist in the absence of waves.
Storm surge	A change in water level on the open coast due to the action of wind stress as well as atmospheric pressure on the sea surface.
Surf zone	The area between the seawardmost breaker and the limit of wave **run-up.**
Suspended load	The material moving in suspension in a fluid, kept up

by the upward components of the turbulent currents or by colloidal suspension.

Swell (waves)

Wind-generated waves that have travelled out of their generating area. **Swell** characteristically exhibits a more regular and longer period and has flatter crests than waves within their **fetch.**

Synoptic chart

A chart showing the distribution of meteorological conditions over a given area or a given time.

Tides

Highest astronomical tide (HAT), **Lowest astronomical tide** (LAT). The highest and lowest levels, respectively, which can be predicted to occur under average meteorological conditions and under any combination of astronomical ones. These levels will not be reached every year.

HAT and LAT are not the extreme levels which can be reached, as **storm surges** may cause considerably higher and lower levels to occur.

Mean high water springs (MHWS), **mean low water springs** (MLWS). The heights of mean high water springs is the average, throughout a year when the average maximum declination of the moon is $23\frac{1}{2}°$, of the heights of two successive high waters during those periods of 24 hours (approximately once a fortnight) when the range of the tide is greatest. The height of **mean low water springs** is the average height obtained by the two successive low waters during the same periods.

Tombolo

A bar or spit that connects an island or offshore structure to the shoreline.

Upgrading

Work to an existing defence to provide improved performance.

Foreword

This book is the culmination of CIRIA Research Project 353. It follows the publication, in 1986, of CIRIA's Technical Note 125 'Seawalls: survey of performance and design practice'. That report, as well as presenting the results of a survey of the performance and design of seawalls, identified the need for and scope of these guidelines.

Research Project 353 was carried out by Posford Duvivier under contract to CIRIA. The technical authors of this book were Dick Thomas (of Posford Duvivier) and Brian Hall (consultant to Posford Duvivier). Under their overall authorship, contributions were also made by M. W. Owen, Dr A. Brampton and W. Allsop of HR Wallingford, Professor E. Penning-Rowsell of Middlesex Polytechnic and M. L. Lings of Bristol University. Throughout the project's implementation, the Steering Group, as listed in the acknowledgements, provided guidance and valuable input.

The report covers all aspects of seawall design from the broader issues of coastal management and other options for coastal defence and environmental assessment, through to problem definition, project planning, data collection and interpretation, conceptual and detailed design, design for construction and maintenance, materials, financial and economic considerations. As a result, the report makes extensive reference to a wide range of publications, particularly those of the British Standards Institution and the *Shore Protection Manual* published by the US Army Corps of Engineers.

The book guides the reader in respect of the various potential problems, their definition, possible solutions, the establishment of key functional requirements of a seawall, and the methods of designing to take due account of engineering, environmental and economic considerations. The book is intended to publicize and assist with good design practice, to identify limitations in design, to give guidance on data collection, and thus assist the user of the book to develop soundly based site-specific solutions.

Acknowledgements

This book was written by R. S. Thomas and B. Hall (Posford Duvivier) under contract to CIRIA.

The CIRIA project was carried out with the guidance and assistance of the Steering Group listed below:

Mr N. Pallett (Chairman)	Babtie Dobbie
Mr A. J. Allison	Ministry of Agriculture, Fisheries and Food
Dr P. C. Barber	Consultant
Mr M. G. Barrett	Posford Duvivier
Mr M. E. Bramley	CIRIA (to Autumn 1989)
Mr T. S. Hedges	Department of Civil Engineering, University of Liverpool
Dr S. W. Huntington	Hydraulics Research Limited
Dr P. Kemp	Consultant
Mr H. R. Payne	Water and Environmental Protection Division, Welsh Office
Mr P. Lacey	Ove Arup & Partners
Mr A. G. Roberts	Canterbury City Council
Mr G. Stephenson	CIRIA (from Autumn 1989)
Mr I. W. Stickland	Posford Duvivier
Mr T. J. Walker	Edmund Nuttall Limited
Mr P. Wright	Scottish Development Department

The project was funded by:
Ministry of Agriculture, Fisheries and Food

CIRIA acknowledges the US Corp of Engineers, Coastal Engineering Research Centre, Vicksburg, USA and Chris Browne for figures reproduced within this book.

1 Introduction

1.1 Definition of a seawall

The principal function of a seawall is to:

- Protect the coast against erosion;
- Alleviate flooding by the sea.

In some cases it may fulfil both functions, and can additionally be used for amenity purposes or to protect reclaimed land. In the majority of cases the effect of wave action is of prime importance.

The shoreline is an environment hostile to structures placed there. It is also a valuable and sensitive part of the environment. Therefore, while the seawall should be durable it must also be integrated into the coastline without causing permanent damage to the environment.

1.2 The guidelines

These guidelines are intended for engineers involved in the planning and design of seawalls, with some experience in coastal works. They cover all relevant considerations including environmental aspects, constructiuon and long-term management, but do not contain all the material that would be necessary to provide a full understanding of all the aspects covered. The book aims to provide the engineer with an appreciation of the principles and procedures involved in seawall design and how these should be used to develop a design appropriate to a specific site. In identifying all relevant considerations, it will help the engineer to identify areas where specialist advice should be sought.

The authors have drawn strongly on UK practice and, where codes and regulations are quoted, these are normally British, although the underlying principles and procedures clearly have a wider application.

It should be noted that seawall design covers both the development of completely new coastal defences as well as the rehabilitation of existing seawalls. In this context, rehabilitation can cover either upgrading to an improved standard of protection or simple restoration to the original standard.

A seawall should be considered as merely an element, possibly a dominant one, in a scheme of coastal defence works. Whether a seawall is indeed an appropriate element should be evaluated within a planned system of coastal management. This book makes reference to coastal management and to alternative or additional coastal defence works, such as groynes, but detailed consideration is beyond its scope.

The particular aims of the book are as follows:

1. To collate existing technical information and practical experience in order to facilitate their better use and dissemination;
2. To publicize good current design practice, and its limitations;
3. To set out a basic framework for data collection, planning and design activities;
4. To indicate the range of possible design solutions and give the engineer a basis on which to select the optimum.

Compilation of the book has been supported by a literature review[1] and surveys of types, performance and design practice related to UK seawalls[2].

With coastal engineering works, the design process necessarily involves identification of the most appropriate strategies for construction (e.g. form of contract, method of specification) and management (e.g. monitoring of performance, maintenance procedures). These aspects are not covered *per se*. It is emphasized that the success of coastal engineering works is dependent on the effectiveness of construction and subsequent management.

Because of the site-specific nature of coastal works and the wide variation between different sites, it is not possible to provide indications of the cost of the seawalls, although guidance on assessing capital and ongoing costs is given. A summary of cost-benefit methodology is included so that it forms an interface with approaches developed by the UK Ministry of Agriculture, Fisheries and Food.

1.3 Use of the guidelines

Since the guidelines cover a wide range of design projects ranging from major to minor works, the use of all chapters of the guidelines may not always be necessary. The engineer, however, should use discretion in omitting some steps or procedures and is advised in any case to consider carefully the contents of Chapters 2 and 3. To assist with setting each of the chapters in the context of the overall design process, the same flow diagram prefaces each chapter. Those parts of the design process that are dealt with in the chapter are highlighted in the figure as appropriate.

The figure is necessarily general, and shows a straightforward flow from identifying the need through to final design. However, in practice the design process is not linear, as this might suggest. It is iterative, going repeatedly through various stages of data assessment, preliminary design, data acquisition, further design, and so on until the final scheme is reached.

The reader will note that the depth of coverage of the book varies from chapter to chapter. This is unavoidable due to:

- Availability of information published elsewhere, particularly in BS 6349[3] and the US Army Corps of Engineers *Shore Protection Manual*[4];
- The desire to avoid excessive duplication;
- Relative importance for seawall design;
- Variations in the level of current knowledge.

In order to limit the variation in detail within a section, 'boxed' text is used to present levels of detail different from the general run of the text. Further detail or more information may be found in the References at the end of the book.

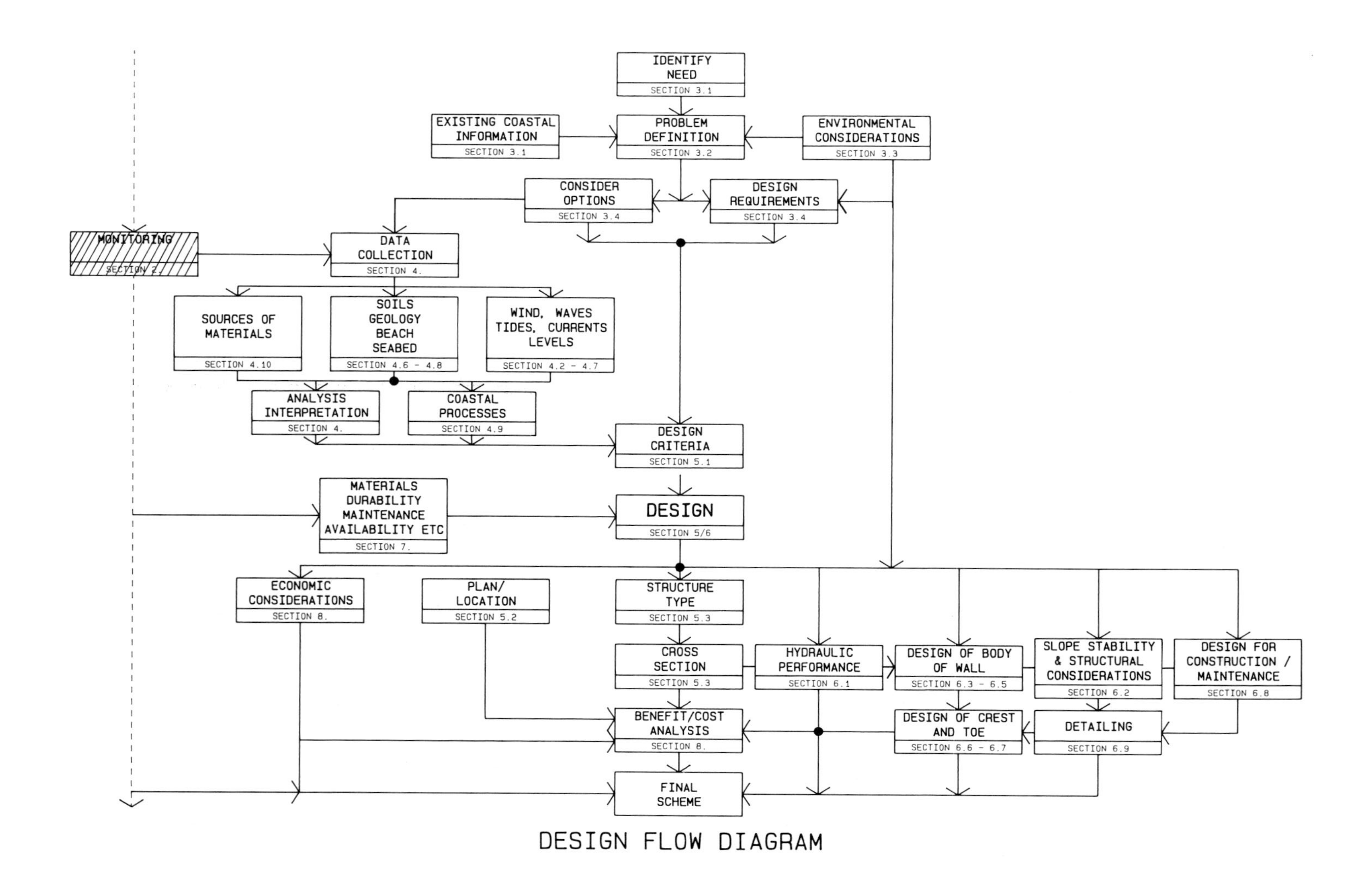

DESIGN FLOW DIAGRAM

2 Coastal management

The coastal regime is complex, fluid, dynamic and rarely in a state of equilibrium. In this context, works carried out in the coastal zone can have major impacts elsewhere. Moreover, there are many differing demands on this zone, including those associated with:

- Property (buildings, highways, land);
- Tourism (beaches, amenity);
- Fishing;
- Commercial (harbours, sand and gravel extraction);
- Environmental (flora, fauna, local amenity);
- Outfalls (sewage, industrial).

The coordination of the various demands, in the light of the impact that each has on the other and on the coastal regime, all within a broad planning strategy, is termed coastal management. An invaluable tool in the implementation of such a strategy is a sound understanding of the coastal regime based upon investigations, measurement and monitoring. Furthermore, such an understanding allows the impact of individual works, for example, coastal defences, outfalls, or dredging to be assessed and so reduces the need for extensive studies related to individual projects. Coastal management therefore requires a knowledge of all types of existing and proposed coastal structures, and environmental and planning requirements, and of the response of the coastal regime to the various works that take place.

Where coastal effects extend beyond the administrative boundary of a controlling authority in whose area a problem has been identified, it may well be technically and economically desirable to promote a joint study and/or management strategy with adjoining authorities within a coastal cell. A coastal cell is defined as a section of coastline bounded by relevant discontinuities in the coastal processes (such as headlands or estuaries).

2.1 Monitoring

The benefits of regular monitoring for coastal management cannot be overemphasized. While monitoring does cost money, in many cases it is very cost-effective because:

- Acquisition and analysis of long-term data (e.g. beach profiles) can be cheaper and more reliable than intensive short-term measurement and modelling;
- It can provide warning of problems before they become serious and costly to repair;
- It allows an assessment of the performance of existing and new defence systems enabling successive improvements to be made in the management strategy.

To support effective coastal management, monitoring needs to be extensive. Data on engineering factors (such as winds, waves, etc., as discussed in Chapter 4) are likely to be of direct value, but monitoring may need to extend to less obvious characteristics such as ecology, water quality, gravel-extraction effects, etc.

2.2 Options for coastal defence

Coastal defence works can broadly be divided into two groups as follows:

1. Indirect measures to take away the cause of the problem (such as stopping the quarrying of sand from the beach);
2. Direct measures which confront the problem.

Direct measures, which include seawalls, are discussed below. With the exception of seawalls, many of the options can be classified as 'beach management' or 'beach control' in that their aim is to ensure a healthy beach as a means to solving the problem whether it is erosion, flooding or cliff instability.

As a first step, before deciding on which option is the most appropriate, the engineer should confirm that works are indeed necessary. Estimating the likely damage in the 'do nothing' case will demonstrate the justification for carrying out works. Estimating the economic losses of such damage will form the basis of economic assessment (see Chapter 8).

2.2.1 Seawalls

In the past these have been the most widely used option for coastal defence. Ranging from massive vertical retaining walls to sloping revetments, they are built along the shore in order directly to protect the land from the sea. Because of their potential vulnerability to toe scour, they are frequently used together with some system of beach control such as groynes and/or beach nourishment. Exceptions to this may include:

- Stable foreshores of exposed rock;
- Beaches stabilized by natural controls (e.g. between headlands);
- Beaches stabilized by adequate littoral drift;
- Beaches where the potential for future erosion is limited and can be accommodated in the seawall design.

Seawalls are essentially rigid and steep (i.e. 'hard') in relation to a mobile foreshore, and so can have a substantial impact on the shoreline both in visual or amenity terms and in their effect on coastal processes. The latter can be by wave reflection or the removal of littoral material from the sediment transport system.

2.2.2 Dune stabilization

Over long lengths of the UK coastline the prime protection against the sea is provided by sand dunes. Their deterioration can pose a substantial problem, particularly as they are a valuable reservoir of beach material in times of storms. There are a number of techniques which preserve or enhance the dunes, including the planting of grass, construction of fences, and restriction of access, which improve their ability to trap and retain windblown sand. Dune stabilization has clear conservation benefits in that it merely enhances the natural system and does not introduce hard elements to the coastal regime.

2.2.3 Beach nourishment

Beach nourishment or replenishment is the import of granular material to form or augment a beach. Material used ranges in size from sand to cobbles, and requires selection on the basis of grading, shape, durability, drainage and compaction properties.

Nourishment schemes extend from those involving small quantities to make up local deficiencies to schemes which involve major beach changes to provide protection against erosion and/or flooding. The type of material used depends upon various factors, including:

- Availability;
- Cost;
- Environmental requirements;
- Required profile;
- Required stability in relation to onshore–offshore and alongshore movements.

In areas not subject to natural controls (such as that provided by headlands) the movement of artificial nourishment can be reduced by groynes or offshore breakwaters, or can be accommodated by recirculation or recharge. Recirculation involves the collection of material at some downdrift location and transporting it to the updrift end of the frontage on a routine basis while recharge consists of the regular supply of additional material from an outside source. Recirculation systems sometimes incorporate a large terminal groyne at the downdrift end to reduce losses.

2.2.4 **Groynes** (Figure 2.1(a))

Groynes are linear structures, aligned approximately perpendicular to the shore, which reduce the longshore movement of beach material under wave and current action. At their landward end they should either terminate against a seawall or extend beyond the normal zone of beach movement, while at their seaward end they usually extend beyond the low-water neap tides but rarely beyond the low-water spring tides. They may be constructed singly for a particular purpose (as discussed above) but are more generally built as part of a continuous system – a groyne field.

The current and wave patterns created by groynes are complex. However, in the right circumstances their overall effect is straightforward and is to slow down the rate of longshore transport until such time as the bays between groynes become full and transport is restored by movement over and to seaward of them. In the absence of artificial nourishment, they can only retain or redistribute the existing supply, and on a long beach they may be expected to create a deficiency at the downdrift end which will remain at least until the longshore transport is restored by movement over and to seaward of them. This has, in places, led to problems of erosion. Without an adequate supply of either natural or artificial beach material, groynes are not effective in raising beach levels. Simple groynes do not reduce the loss of beach material to the offshore.

In addition to their normal function of reducing longshore transport, groynes are used:

- To control the distribution of beach material along a frontage;
- To limit effects of drift reversal;
- For diverting currents away from the shore.

The performance of groynes in coarse beach material such as shingle is reasonably well established. However, with finer material (sand) the effect of wave-generated currents and turbulence within the groyne bays becomes more significant in terms of potential scour, and their effects are less well understood.

The most common type of groyne is of imported hardwood, comprising piles with planking and/or sheet piles. Planks can be removed and the groyne height 'tuned' to give optimum effect. Where rock is available at reasonable cost and variations in beach level are not extreme, then rock mound groynes may provide a more efficient solution. Other forms of construction include steel piling, concrete armour, solid concrete, asphalt and cribwork. Permeable groynes in timber, steel and concrete have also been used. The visual impact of groynes is considerable, particularly when viewed from the downdrift side and, if high, they make access alongshore difficult and potentially dangerous. On the other hand, they can preserve a valuable amenity and provide interest and shelter on an otherwise featureless beach. For further details see CIRIA Report No. R119 and TN135[1,2].

2.2.5 **Offshore breakwaters** (Figure 2.1(b))

Offshore breakwaters are built parallel to the shore just to seaward of it. They are placed either singly to protect a specific coastal location, or as a series to provide

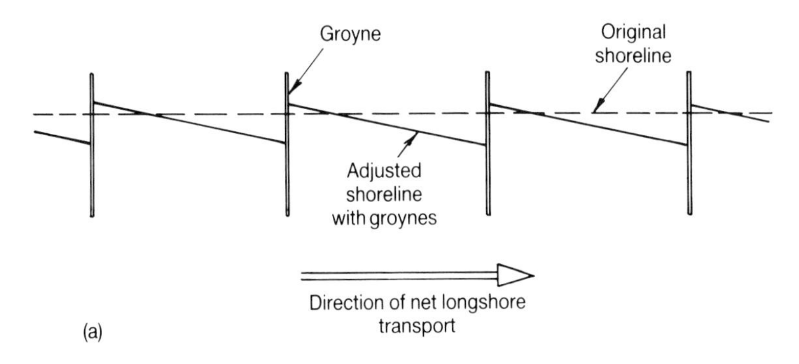

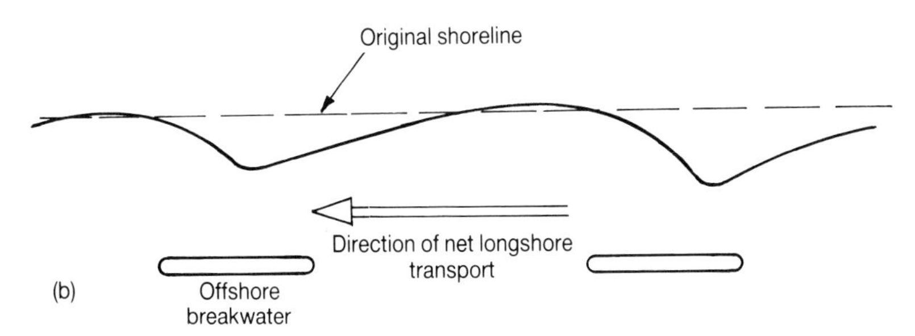

Figure 2.1 (a) General beach configuration with groynes; **(b)** General beach configuration with offshore breakwaters

protection to longer frontages. They have been used extensively in Southern France, Italy, Israel and Japan, but only since 1980 have they been adopted on the coastline of the UK. The tidal range in countries where they have been used is, for the most part, much less than in the UK, so it has been difficult to apply overseas field experience directly to situations in this country. However, the greater understanding of coastal processes that has developed, particularly with advances in computational modelling, has reduced this difficulty.

The breakwaters are normally rubble with concrete or rock armour to minimize wave reflection. They may or may not be tall enough to extend above the sea level at all states of the tide. They serve to reduce the amount of wave energy reaching the shore and have the following related effects:

- Reducing longshore transport, particularly in the lee of the breakwaters;
- Reducing offshore transport and so allowing/encouraging the formation of a beach, or reducing the rate at which nourishment is lost offshore;
- Reducing wave heights at the shore;
- Producing a beach which grows towards the lee of the breakwater.

Offshore breakwaters can produce very strong local changes to the coastal process regime and so a thorough understanding of their likely impact is a prerequisite to

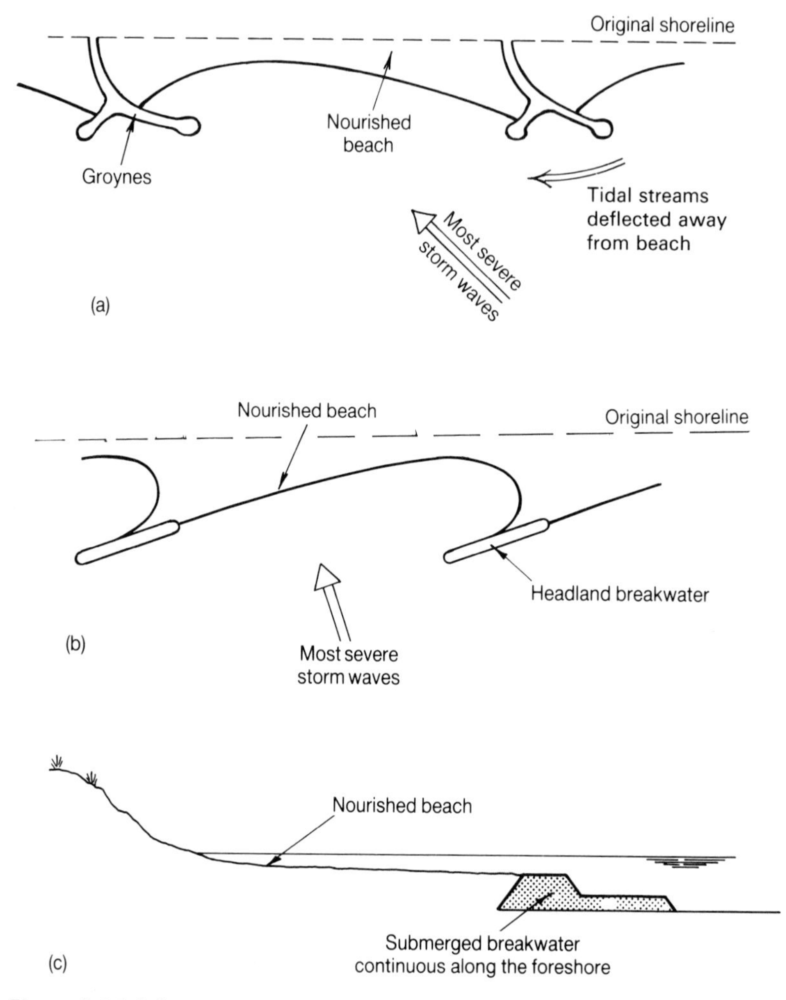

Figure 2.2 (a) General layout of fishtail groynes; **(b)** General layout of headland breakwaters; **(c)** General section through perched beach

their use. They do, however, offer a sound 'method' for stabilizing a shoreline, while providing a recreational beach with considerable visual interest and potential amenity value.

2.2.6 Other beach-control structures

Coastal defences should be tailored to suit the specific problem and the engineer is thus not restricted by the discrete options listed above but should develop appropriate site-specific solutions which may combine aspects of groynes, seawalls and offshore breakwaters. Fishtail groynes (Figure 2.2(a)) have been used in the UK. The rubble groynes retain beach material in bays between them, and deflect tidal currents away from the beach, thus reducing beach losses and trapping new material.

Headland breakwaters (Figure 2.2(b)) have been used in the United States and in Singapore, particularly as a means of retaining reclamation fill. The breakwaters themselves are normally rubble. Care is required in design to avoid erosion around the headlands.

Perched beaches (Figure 2.2(c)) offer potential as a good solution although they have suffered sometimes from loss of beach fill. They are also possibly less attractive as an amenity than the headland breakwater and fishtail groyne systems since they can constitute a submerged hazard to bathers and boats.

2.3 Phased works

In an emergency when immediate work is required to safeguard a length of coast, works will not be undertaken in a single stage and the first, emergency stage may have to be carried out without the full design procedure. This work may subsequently be incorporated into a more permanent solution. Equally, budgetary constraints may require that construction be phased over a number of years. Clearly, the intermediate stages need to be assessed with respect to their impact on the coast, for the coastal zone is sufficiently dynamic to suffer major changes within periods of time of much less than a year. In the emergency case certain environmental aspects, such as access, may have to be sacrificed temporarily.

Phased works incorporating pilot schemes can also be of considerable value. Much emphasis is placed in these guidelines on the need to understand the coastal regime. Unfortunately, certain areas of seawall performance cannot be fully and confidently assessed in advance. A pilot scheme to assess the *in-situ* performance of new materials or new designs both in terms of their durability and their environmental impact can be very useful. The possibilities and consequences of failure should be considered in advance and the new element should be well monitored. This latter need is likely to require thorough hydrographic measurements (waves, currents, water level, foreshore and bed levels) as well as structural surveys, so that the significance of relative short-term behaviour can be assessed. Pilot schemes have been particularly useful in the case of beach-control structures such as groynes and offshore breakwaters. The monitoring of such schemes has both increased confidence in the design of subsequent works and provided data with which to calibrate numerical or physical models.

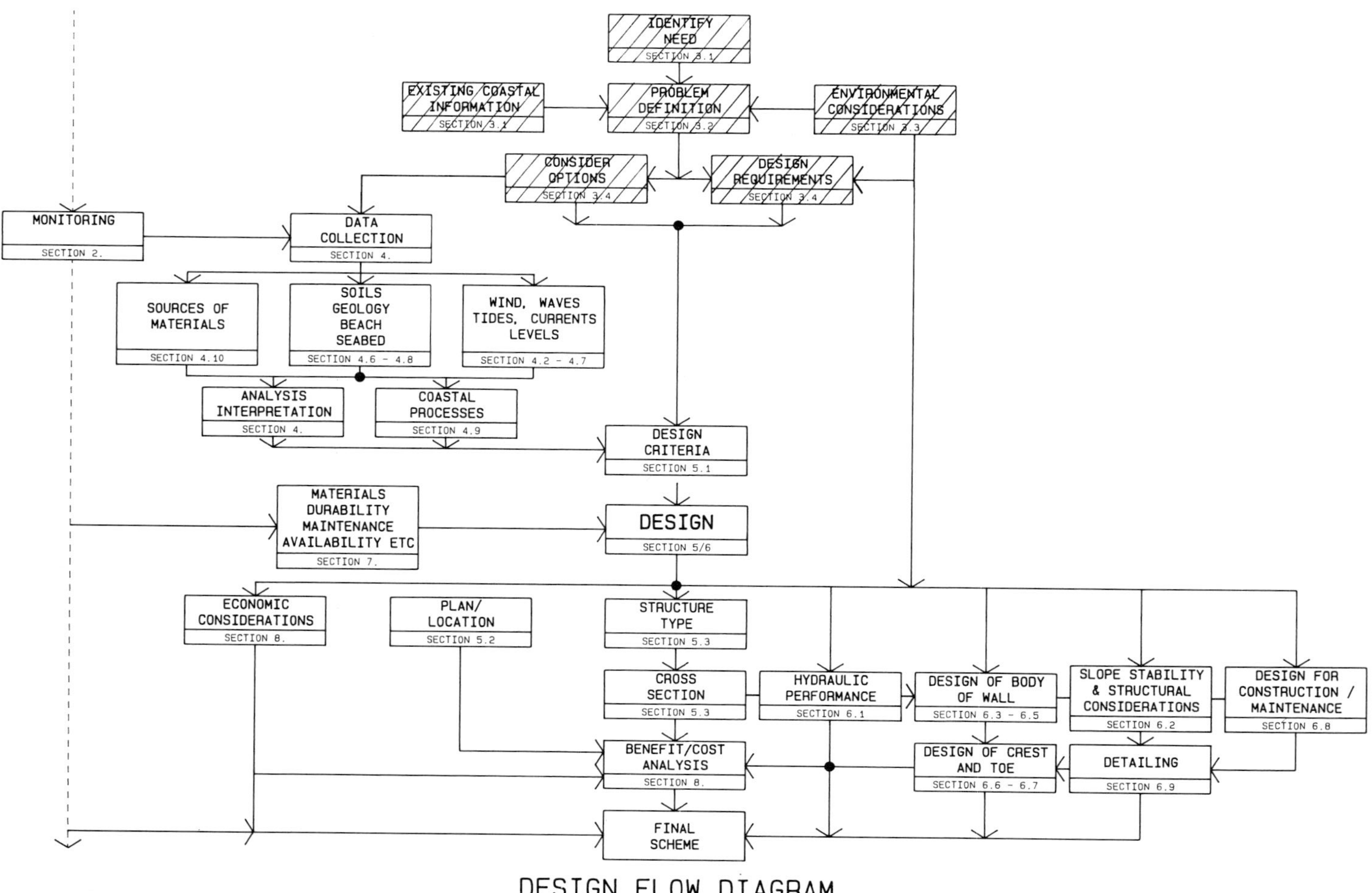

DESIGN FLOW DIAGRAM

3 Project planning and environmental aspects

This chapter sets down a broad framework for planning, giving general examples. A fundamental need, particularly in the early stages of the project, is to determine the actual problem to be solved. This, together with the extent of available information, dictates the subsequent work that is required.

The potential for environmental change is large because of the fluid and unstable nature of the coastal regime. Environmental aspects should therefore be considered throughout the design process. Possible environmental impacts are discussed in this chapter in order to give guidance on those areas that may be particularly pertinent to a site.

3.1 Existing coastal information

The assembly and review of existing relevant data is the first and an important step towards identification of the basic problem to be solved. An analysis of existing data will provide an initial appreciation of the problem which, in turn, will indicate the need for particular information and allow planning of the design and development process.

An initial overview of the general coastal situation and processes can usually be obtained from information which is readily available. This should include a preliminary site visit and, in the case of outside organizations, reference to the controlling authority, followed by a study of maps, charts, drawings, aerial photographs and the tide tables of the general area. The engineer should be aware that, as discussed further in Section 3.2, he should not necessarily confine himself to the local area as the causes of the problem and the effects of the solution may extend well beyond.

Existing coastal information can provide outline data on:

- Coastal topography and areas liable to flooding;
- General geology and its relationship with coastal topography;
- General offshore aspects including contours and wave climate;
- Tidal information, levels and currents;
- Existing coastal defences, harbour works and other coastal structures;

- Initial assessment of littoral processes, including drift direction and coastal discontinuities;
- Nature and likely source of beach material;
- History of erosion and flooding including surges;
- Planning and environmental considerations.

Existing coastal information can be obtained relatively simply and cheaply. It can often provide useful pointers for further investigations and for the design of the seawall itself. An inspection of the site of the proposed works by an experienced engineer can reveal much valuable information.

3.1.1 Site inspection

First-hand knowledge of the site is most important. To obtain full value from a site visit, the engineer should be sufficiently experienced to recognize, interpret and record the conditions or effects observed, and should not be misled by isolated observations which may be untypical. The inspections should cover, if possible, a low and a high water period. The observations which should be made fall broadly into three categories:

- Offshore;
- The coastal zone;
- The backshore area, coastal slope and hinterland.

Conditions offshore and in the coastal zone vary from day to day and the dangers of extrapolating a few observations into conclusions on the coastal process should be recognized. This can be particularly the case when making observations of littoral drift from accumulation patterns on the beach. A check on recent local weather conditions will assist in establishing the significance of the observations. Points which should be noted are as follows:

1. *Plan shape of coastline.* This may give a good indicator to the local coastal regime. Natural or artificial features such as cliffs, rocky outcrops, rivers, harbours, large outfalls or bastion groynes can act as barriers to littoral drift. A setback in the coastline to one end of such a feature, or of groynes, can be identified as lee scour, thus indicating the net longshore drift.
2. *Nature and depth of beach material.* Identifying the type of beach material will assist in locating its source and potential for erosion/deposition (Section 4.9.7).
3. *Underlying strata.* Where exposed, the nature of the underlying strata should be noted. This can be further identified by reference to geological maps and records (Section 4.8).
4. *Existing defences.* An inspection of the existing coastal defences is useful in providing the benefit of previous experience and in indicating the extent to which they may be relied on in the future. The identification of signs of distress in a seawall is discussed further in Section 4.11.

5. *Existing beach profile.* The significance of the beach profile as observed should be judged alongside other data such as meteorological and wave records together with details of past beach levels where available. (See also Section 4.9.6.)
6. *Severity of wave action.* It is often possible to identify areas which are more exposed to waves than others. Such conditions can occur, for example, on natural or artificial promontories and re-entrant angles (local indentation in the coast) which might encourage wave set-up and foreshore scour. Changes in coastline orientation with respect to the dominant wave direction will tend to result in variations in exposure to wave action and in longshore drift.

Observations which come within the backshore category should include:

- Stability of the coastal slope;
- General nature of the backshore area, land use, vegetation, industry;
- General ground elevation and extent of low-lying ground;
- Access to the site for construction and maintenance work.

3.1.2 Study of historical information

Historical information is useful in identifying:

- Accretion or erosion of the coastline;
- Temporal variations in bathymetry;
- Information on existing or previous structures;
- Pre-existing coastal features.

Accretion and erosion may be assessed by comparison of maps issued at different dates.

Maps of the British Isles, issued by the Ordnance Survey, have been available since the latter half of the nineteenth century. The maps have been published in three distinct editions. The latest metric edition was introduced in 1974, based on the earlier imperial survey information to scales of 1:50 000, 1:10 000 and 1:2500. These are currently being revised. The Ordnance Survey at Southampton and the British Museum Map Library will make maps of relevant areas available for inspection upon request. Further details on Ordnance Survey information is given in BS 5930[1].

Interpretation of the earlier maps, particularly with respect to identification of tide lines, should be carried out with care. Levels of specific tidal elevations differ between editions, as does Ordnance Datum.

More recently, aerial surveys have been carried out. Information on aerial surveys is stored by the Central Register of Air Photography, UK. Information on aerial surveys in Scotland and Wales is kept by the Scottish and Welsh Offices. The extent and frequency of coverage varies between locations, but the data enable a general overview of the coastline processes to be made and may highlight some coastal feature not evident from a land inspection. Care must be taken in a comparative study to allow for differences in tidal elevation. Comparative tidal elevations can be estimated by consideration of fixed sloping faces such as the groynes and slipways, etc. If the photographs are taken on a calm day, absolute levels may be obtained by photogrammetry on water level adjacent to a fixed structure of known elevation. Where the time is given on the photograph, levels may be arrived at by reference to tide gauge readings.

Historical hydrographic data can be obtained from the Curator at the Admiralty Archives, Taunton. The first accurate charts were produced in the latter half of the nineteenth century. Again, care must be taken to ensure the charts are corrected to a consistent datum and scale before any comparative study is undertaken. It should be remembered that Admiralty Charts are produced for the purposes of safe navigation, and as such, the selected soundings tend to indicate minimum depths. For detailed studies it is advisable to revert to the collector charts (showing the basic soundings) to ensure that the bathymetry is correctly represented.

Information on previous or existing works may also be gleaned from older maps and charts, and in some cases these may indeed provide the only evidence of early structures. There may be other sources of information on existing works for which a measure of patient research is required, such as:

- Local libraries and museums;
- Local and drainage authority records;
- Local societies with interests in the coastline;
- Published papers, e.g. Institution of Civil Engineers proceedings;
- Consulting engineers' records;
- Picture postcards and photographic collections.

The performance and effect of previous works can provide a valuable indicator for the design of any new work. Pre-existing coastal features such as old river outlets, marshes or saltings which no longer appear on current maps may be identified on earlier versions. Among other things, this may give an early indication of bad ground which might be encountered and be a guide to where site investigation work might be necessary.

3.1.3 Local knowledge

Discussions with local fishermen and seamen (especially pilots) may provide a useful insight into the coastal processes. This information is, by its nature, highly subjective and should be used with caution, but it can in some situations provide the only data available initially, especially in the offshore area. The engineer should not confine himself to engineering matters. Discussion with the local planning authority will give information on environmental aspects, including the location of Sites of Special Scientific Interest (SSSIs), Areas of Outstanding Natural Beauty and other environmentally sensitive areas.

3.1.4 Existing structures

A study of adjoining coastal defences and marine structures can provide a useful insight into the likely problems which will have to be overcome and give an indication of potential solutions. However, no two sites are the same, and the apparent success of a solution at one place cannot be assumed to apply at an adjoining site.

The analysis of any damage or deficiency of any existing structures directly affected or involved in the planned works is clearly important. A survey to ensure that the existing structure at least outwardly conforms to construction drawings (if available) is usually necessary. Total failures of seawalls are not common, and the problem is often a deficiency in hydraulic performance or structural soundness not necessarily associated with a total collapse. Where failure has occurred, further detailed study will be required to establish the causes. (See Section 4.11.)

If the failure or damage is associated with an extreme event then all possible data should be collected relating to the build-up and occurrence of the event, and this might include:

- Predicted tide level;
- Recorded sea levels;
- Wind records and synoptic charts;
- Wave records or observations;
- Records of flooding;
- Newspaper articles or other records.

Coastal structures are often interdependent (e.g. the relationship between a groyne system, beach levels and the performance of a seawall). The appraisal should therefore not be confined to the seawall itself (see Section 3.1.1) nor restricted to the structure under immediate consideration.

An overview of the visual impact of existing structures should be taken as an initial basis for evaluating the visual impact of new works.

3.1.5 Previous studies

Considerable data on the coastal regime, structures and environmental aspects may already be available for the length of coastline under consideration. A number of coastline studies have been undertaken by research organizations and some universities. The majority of this work is published, but there are a number of unpublished PhD theses which can be obtained by direct reference to the universities concerned.

In addition, development of marine structures such as sea outfalls and harbour works involve detailed feasibility studies prior to their construction. Contact should be made with the developing authority or body for access to such data.

Perhaps the most extensive study of the UK coastline is the Royal Commission on Coast Erosion, which was carried out between 1906 and 1911[2]. Less comprehensive surveys were made for England in 1980, commissioned by the Department of the

Environment[3] and for Wales in 1982 by the Welsh Office[4]. A further review of the coast of England and Wales has been carried out by Hydraulics Research Limited[5].

3.1.6 Geology and soils

Preliminary geological data may be obtained by examining published geological maps and memoirs which are available from the British Geological Survey (BGS). BGS also holds records of borehole data some of which have been published while others are available for reference. Further information on the availability of geological maps and memoirs is given in BS 5930[1].

Information on geology and soils may also be available from adjoining sites. This may give an indication of the strata to be encountered but will not necessarily eliminate the need for more thorough site investigation work for detailed design. Local geological societies may also be a useful source of information.

3.1.7 Published hydrographic, meteorological and topographic data

Considerable amounts of data are available in the UK from national institutions, as indicated below:

1. Topographic data – from Ordnance Survey and local authorities (see Section 4.6.1);
2. Soundings (bathymetric) data – from The Hydrographer of the Navy (see Section 4.7.1);
3. Tidal data – on tide levels and tidal streams from Admiralty tide tables (see Section 4.2.1);
4. Wind and wave data – from Marine Information and Advisory Service and Meteorological Office (see Sections 4.3 and 4.4.2);
5. Extreme sea levels – from the Proudman Oceanographic Laboratory (see Section 4.2.5).

3.2 Problem definition

An assessment of existing coastal information forms a basis for an initial identification of the problems to be solved. These may not be confined to the primary ones which require the use of or improvements to a seawall.

Examples of primary problems which may lead to the use of a seawall are:

- Loss of land area or property as a result of erosion;
- Damage or risk of damage due to flooding;
- Ground instability arising primarily from erosion;
- Physical damage from wave action;
- Damage or nuisance from spray, shingle or blown sand;
- Loss of amenity or adverse environmental effects;

- Lack of space for access or development;
- Damage to or deterioration of existing coastal defence structures;
- Potential failure of existing structures.

3.2.1 Initial assessment of coastal regime

Coastal processes are discussed in more detail in Section 4.9. Where the primary problem is merely one of extending the life of an existing wall, and the proposed works will have no significant secondary effects on the existing coastal regime or the environment, the need for an assessment of the coastal regime may be limited. Examples are when replacing worn-out components of an existing wall or marginally raising a clay bank with local materials. However, even in such cases the possible impact of the works should be evaluated, and in most cases a full understanding of the regime will be desirable and necessary. Where the proposed seawall is on a coast which is already the subject of planned coastal management (Chapter 2), this task is readily achieved within the management strategy. In the absence of such a strategy the existing coastal information should be drawn together to give a general picture of the coastal regime. The topics involved in this process are as follows:

1. *Tidal streams and currents*. Data on tidal streams and currents should be collated to provide an overall picture of the strength, direction and general pattern of currents in the area.
2. *Waves*. Data can be gathered in the form of actual wave data or simple hindcasts on the basis of wind data. This should be used to determine:

- Likely typical directional wave climate and if good data exist this may allow the production of wave roses (see Section 4.4.3). If this is not the case, the assessment may be confined to identifying the directions from which waves most frequently arrive, and their range of wave heights (see Section 4.4.7);
- Quantitative information regarding particularly severe events which may have caused damage at the site.

3. *Tides*. Mean spring and neap tide ranges should be determined from published documents and specific data may be obtained for particularly severe events.
4. *Coastal sediments*. A map should be annotated to indicate the nature of surface sediments on the beach and seabed, using data on geology and soils and site observations. Particular note should be taken of areas of seabed, beach and coast that are erodible (i.e. soft rock, sand and silts).
5. *Coastal changes*. The assessment of historical changes will indicate past trends of erosion and accretion. The site observations, supplemented by past studies, can give useful information on the present pattern of erosion and accretion as well as the impact of coastal structures.
6. *Sediment transport*. Consideration of the data in (2) and (4) above, plus information on coastal changes (5), will give indications of the predominant direction of longshore drift. Estimates of drift quantities are discussed in Section 4.9.6.

Consideration of data in (1), (2) and (4) will give indications of the general patterns of seabed transport and deposition which may be supported by the assessment of seabed changes in (5).

7. *Isolated events*. Where an isolated severe event has produced significant damage or caused changes to the coast, collation of points (1)–(6) above may well give useful information on why that particular event was so severe in its effect. For example, it might indicate a particular combination of wave direction, water level and low beach levels, or merely the culmination of a long-term trend of changes identified in (5).

3.2.2 Identification of causes

The cause of the primary problem to be solved should be investigated using the assessment of the coastal regime derived in Section 3.2.1. Detailed aspects to be considered will vary from site to site, depending on the relevance of various factors. Two examples are considered below – erosion and flooding.

1. *Erosion*. A key element of this analysis is the sediment budget, which is discussed in more detail in Section 4.9.6. This uses the simple logic that, if erosion is taking place within an area, it follows that losses from the area must exceed supply into it. This logic can be used to derive a network (Figure 3.1) which demonstrates possible causes of erosion. The knowledge of the coastal regime and of development can thus be used to explore possible causes.

   Such an analysis begins with an assessment of whether the problem is local (related to a specific location or structure) or general, and whether the cause is a long-term problem, an isolated severe event (such as a particular combination of waves and high water level) or a new problem which resulted from a change to the previous situation. Knowledge of the direction and paths of sediment transport can indicate links between the problem and events elsewhere on the coast or seabed.
2. *Flooding*. The nature of the problem should be identified, i.e. whether it is one of seepage through or under the existing defences (Figure 3.2) or of overtopping. Further, it is important to assess whether the problem is long-term insofar as the defences may have always been inadequate, or whether they have become inadequate as a result of progressive increase in severity in hydraulic conditions (e.g. due to rise in mean sea level) or as a result of deterioration in the condition of the defences. Where conditions have become more severe due to erosion (perhaps due to loss of beach in front of an existing seawall), the engineer should assess the likely cause as discussed in (1).

3.3 Environmental assessment

Seawalls are often necessarily large structures and can have a marked effect on the environment. They are built as a long-term investment; and it is important that the

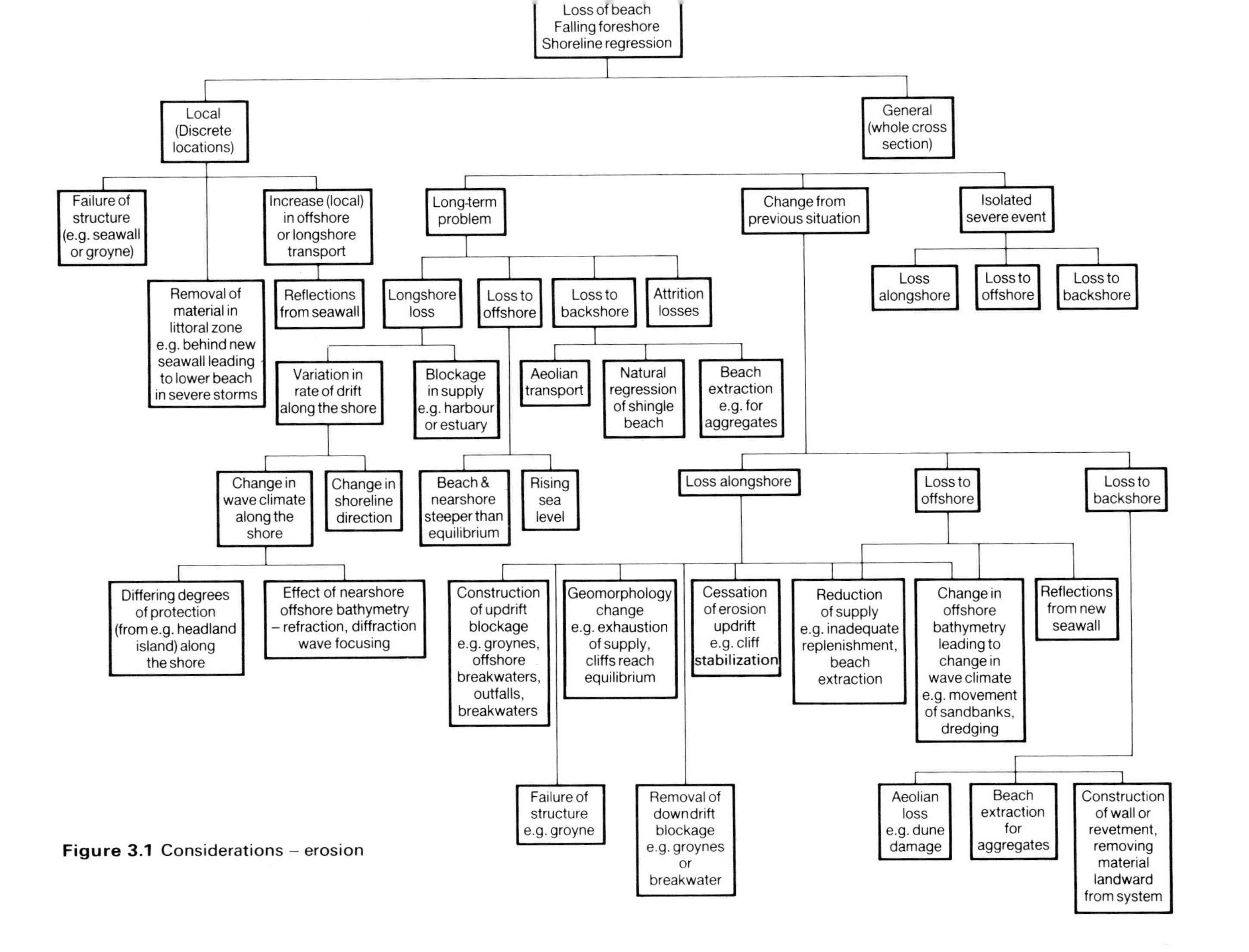

Figure 3.1 Considerations – erosion

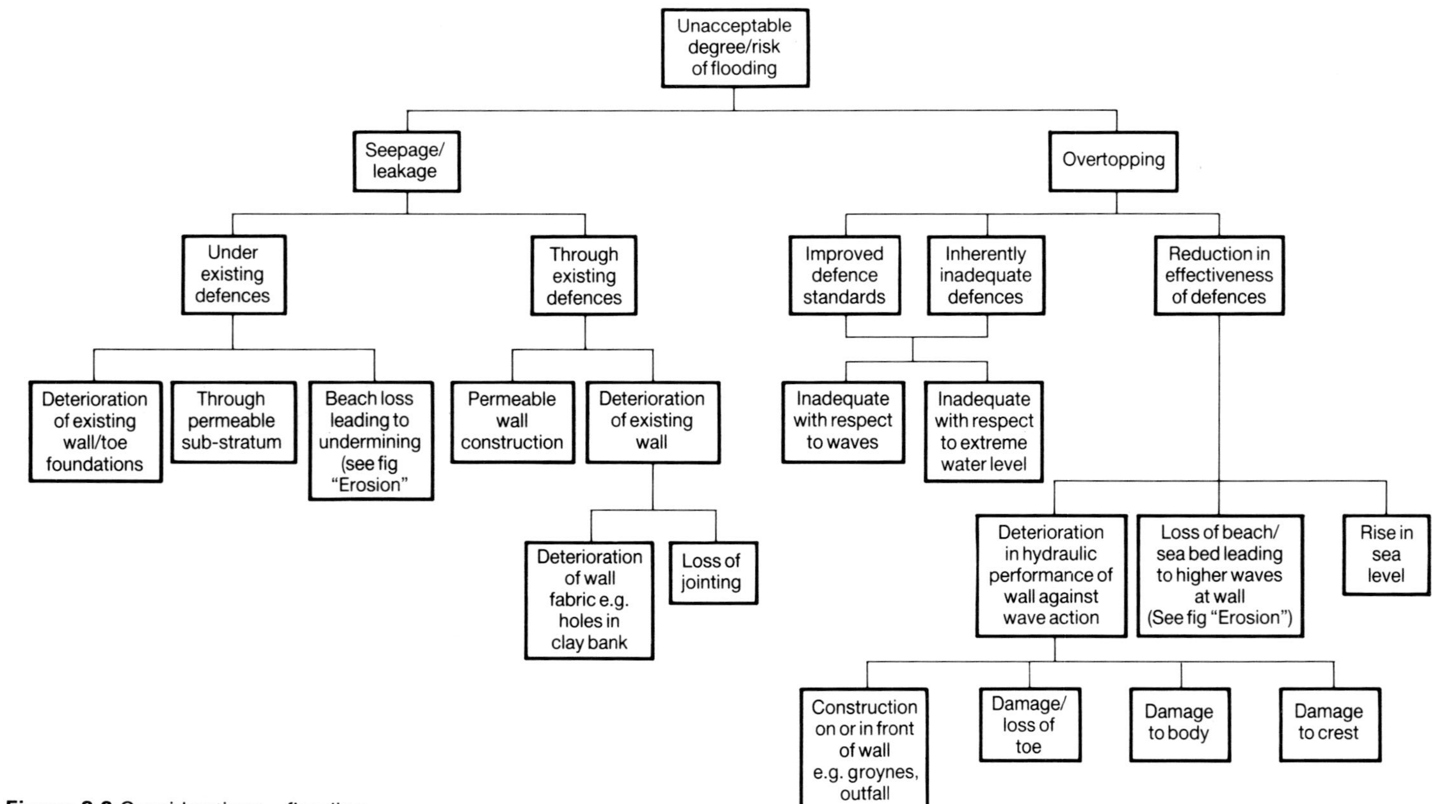

Figure 3.2 Considerations – flooding

environmental impact of a seawall should be considered in the same context. A seawall may be hydraulically and structurally sound, but if it has undesirable environmental impacts it will rightly be criticized. Environmental assessment is a subject requiring specialist knowledge in a number of areas and it is therefore likely that the engineer will require specialist help.

Environmental considerations should be brought into the design process right from the start. While in many cases it is now a legal requirement to carry out an independent environmental impact assessment (see Appendix A), this should not relieve the engineer from taking into account environmental factors throughout the design. The environmental assessment (EA) therefore starts in the initial stages of the project but should continue on to completion of the works.

A typical procedure for assessment of the environmental effect is as follows:

1. Define the existing environment, with emphasis on significant and valuable aspects (baseline survey), as input to the key functional requirements.
2. Identify the probable effects of the proposed works on the existing environment.
3. Where effects are likely to be adverse, investigate practical measures whereby the proposed works can be modified to mitigate those impacts.
4. Project the existing environmental trends beyond the construction period of the proposed works to demonstrate the probable effect of not proceeding with the works (e.g. a consequence of the 'do nothing' option could be widespread flooding, which will have its own environmental impacts).

The environmental effects of the construction of a seawall fall broadly into:

- Coastal processes;
- Flora and fauna;
- Human sensory;
- Social and socio-economics;
- Geology, archaeology and history;
- Pollution.

These are discussed in Section 3.3.1–3.3.6. In each case the effect can range from beneficial through to destructive. Much of the assessment of the environmental impact is subjective and some of the wider environmental aspects may be decided by others. There should be preliminary consultation with interested parties as this can save abortive work (Section 3.1.3).

In many cases enlightened design and minor modifications can achieve environmentally beneficial results at little extra cost. In certain cases, though, the designer may be constrained by rules applied to the procurement of grant aid which may preclude money for environmental aspects, particularly amenity. Where modifications are necessary to achieve an environmentally sensitive scheme it may be that such constraints would not be applied. On the other hand, if additions are introduced for purely amenity functions, which are not essential for the purpose of coast protection or sea defence, then additional sources of finance may become necessary.

3.3.1 Coastal processes

Section 3.2 has outlined how the cause or causes of the problem(s) should be identified. In a similar way, the understanding of the coastal regime should be used to identify locations or processes which may be affected by the proposed works. For example, prevention of erosion may lead to a reduction in longshore supply of material so that a beach downdrift may erode as a result. While the precise impact of a seawall on the wave, current and sediment transport regime is difficult to assess (and this is particularly so at an early stage, when working on the basis of existing data), these considerations will nonetheless allow an initial assessment of some of the functional requirements of the works. They will also help to identify the need for further more detailed data acquisition and analysis.

As the further studies proceed, the impact of the works can be better defined, and modifications can be made to the design to minimize undesirable impacts or to achieve desirable effects (see Sections 4.9.7 and 5.1–5.3).

3.3.2 Flora and fauna

The baseline survey should identify the nature of flora and fauna in the zone which could be influenced by the works, taking note of any particularly sensitive or valuable areas, and bearing in mind the possible effects of the works on other areas of the coast. The possibility that the wall might alter the existing ecology to the benefit or detriment of existing flora and fauna should be assessed. Aspects which might be considered include:

- Effect of any changes of the ecosystem in the cliff slope behind the seawall;
- Effect on saltings and wetlands;
- Foreshore changes;
- Effect on natural habitat;
- Effect on rare and protected species;
- Temporary effects during construction and the extent to which any damage caused might be recoverable.

While other flora and fauna might appear following the construction of a wall, it has to be recognized that any significant change, particularly when rare species are involved, is quite likely to be irreversible.

3.3.3 Human sensory

Human sensory considerations are: visual impact, noise, odour and vibration. Visual assessment concerns both the long- and short-range views. The former takes into consideration the impact on the general landscape and might suggest the overall lines and type of wall which might be most appropriate, while the short-range view covers points of detail, shape, height and general appearance.

Visual aspects of a seawall are considered in Chapters 5 and 6, but examples of typical considerations relevant to both long- and short-range visual impact are as follows:

1. The type, shape and layout of a new wall, its relation and compatibility in general to the coastline and any existing structure, are relevant in terms of both the view of the structures as well as the view from them. An artistic impression or photomontage is useful if a proposal is to be put to the general public.
2. The level of the crest of the splash wall should be considered in relation to the visual obstruction which might be created.
3. Large areas of fair-faced shuttered concrete rarely turn out to be visually attractive. Use of shutter liners to produce a textured finish, grit blasting or bush hammering together with feature joints to mask construction and movement joints can transform an otherwise dull and unsightly structure. Raised features, masonry facing and flint insets can also be used to enhance the appearance but sometimes at significant cost. Facings and insets can be chosen to have the advantage of being resistant to abrasion. Attention should be given to detail in order to avoid defects such as unsightly cracks and spalling, etc.
4. The temporary visual effect of intrusion during construction should be considered.
5. Materials such as rock and, to a lesser degree, timber have become associated with the coastline and may be visually acceptable in locations where steel sheet piling or extensive areas of plain concrete would be intrusive and unacceptable.

The problem of noise and vibration is common to all building and civil engineering works. Seawall construction has the further disadvantage that, in order to coincide with low tide periods, it may be necessary to start work earlier and finish later. Night-time working may be necessary.

Odour problems may arise from shellfish beds or rotting seaweed. In certain situations hydrogen sulphide can be released when the beach is disturbed. This latter phenomenon is, however, short-term.

3.3.4 Social and socio-economic

Tourism, industry and leisure considerations are, to varying degrees, linked under this broad heading. The extent to which the coast is of value as an amenity, for such aspects as bathing and boating, should be identified. It may well also be important from the point of view of commerce, such as boat building, fishing, and retail trade to tourists, all of which require access across the shore.

Aspects of the works which should be considered, and which are discussed further in Chapters 5 and 6 are:

- The overall effect on the local communities which might result following the construction of the wall;
- Effect on local life during construction such as nuisance, noise and temporary loss of trade to local businesses or increase in trade as a result of public interest in the works;

- Effect on the foreshore as a recreational area;
- Matters of public safety generally (such as rock armouring on a public beach);
- Provision of access to the foreshore and escape routes in emergencies;
- Access ramps for maintenance, small pleasure and fishing boats, wheelchairs and prams, etc.;
- The use of steps as seats and of a splash deck as a promenade, incorporation of seats into the rear splash wall;
- Creation of amenity areas behind the wall.

3.3.5 Geology, archaeology and history

*A number of coastal sites contain geological outcrops which are of considerable academic and scientific interest. The UK Joint Nature Conservation Committee (JNCC) seeks to retain outcrops in an exposed condition. The case it makes is particularly strong where the area is designated as an SSSI. There is also a fear that the elimination of toe erosion will reduce the weathering of a cliff face and encourage the growth of vegetation, thus obscuring the outcrop of special interest.

Archaeological and historical considerations might include the need to excavate for and identify relics during the construction programme. It may be necessary in some cases to incorporate archaeological or historical structures within the works to the extent that they are preserved. Early discussions with local societies can be invaluable in identifying such areas.

3.3.6 Pollution

Problems can arise where the construction of a seawall might affect the discharge from existing or proposed outfalls. These should be identified early and possible effects on effluent dispersal assessed on the basis of the understanding of the coastal regime. The potential for pollution resulting directly from a seawall is greatest during construction. Contaminated fill material should be avoided and, in any case, the works should be designed, planned and constructed so as to minimize losses (see Section 6.4.5). In certain areas where contaminated landfill has been used in the past, a seawall may be used to protect it, thus providing an environmental benefit.

3.4 Project planning

The definition of the problem to be solved (Section 3.2), the consideration of environmental aspects (Section 3.3), and a preliminary cost/economic assessment (discussed in Section 3.4.1 below) should determine the key functional requirements of the wall. Different defence options can then be evaluated, although considerable additional data and analysis may be required before selection of options and subsequent design can be finalized. The approach suggested in Sections 3.4.2 and 3.4.3 will, however, allow a plan to be set down in order to undertake the design in an adequate and cost-effective manner.

* See page 32.

3.4.1 Preliminary cost/economic assessment

Financial and economic aspects are dealt with in Chapter 8 and a full economic evaluation may be undertaken in due course. However, an initial review of costs supplemented by a preliminary assessment of the likely benefits is of value for budgeting purposes and in assessing the priority of the work.

Costs of similar works elsewhere, taking account of the different characteristics of the site (such as water depth, exposure to wave action, construction access), can give an initial order of costs per metre run of construction. CIRIA Technical Note 125[6] gives ranges of costs in 1986. A preliminary benefit assessment may only be subjective and qualitative, but some degree of monetary assessment may be obtained by comparison with other sites.

3.4.2 Functional requirements

The functional requirements may be amended and refined as further data are gathered during design of the scheme, but this early assessment will be the basis for selection of options that are worth more detailed consideration. At this stage it may well be that the use of a seawall is found to be inappropriate, and that some other form of coastal defence is more suitable (see Chapter 2).

The subject areas that should be covered by the functional requirements are indicated in Figure 3.3. The main areas are:

- Cost/economics (Section 3.4.1);
- Environmental impact (Section 3.3);
- Structural performance;
- Principal function (based on the problem definition, Section 3.2).

3.4.3 Initial evaluation of options

The broad characteristics of various seawall types are discussed in Sections 5.1–5.4 and of other coastal defence options in Section 2.2. Comparison of the characteristics (e.g. ease of access to the beach, ability of a wall to withstand severe abrasion) of the different options in relation to the functional requirements will allow potentially successful options to be identified. The consequential effects in both the short and long term should be considered and the advantages and disadvantages of each alternative identified. Scheme selection depends not only upon the engineering and environmental merit of each option but also on an economic comparison (see Section 8.2). This should involve the comparison of high initial cost schemes requiring little maintenance with low initial cost ones of shorter life and/or requiring significant maintenance. To the extent that the choice of scheme depends on a policy decision by the controlling or funding agency, it may be necessary to select and present alternative options at an early stage, including economic assessments of each scheme.

The consequences of 'doing nothing' should also be assessed both for consideration as an option and also as a basis from which to assess the benefit derived from a scheme. This may involve extrapolating on the basis of previous erosion rates and

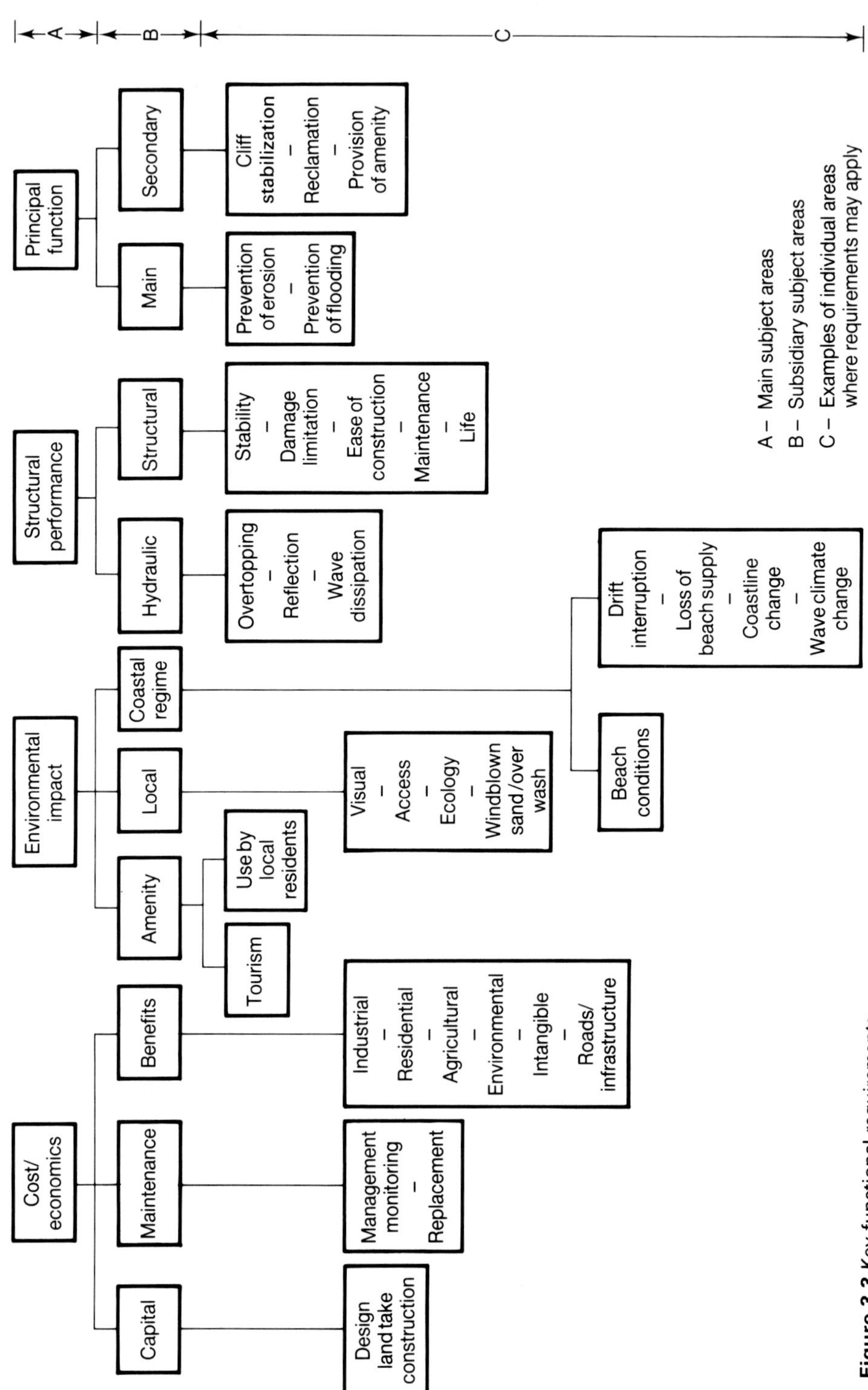

Figure 3.3 Key functional requirements

estimating future events using engineering judgement. Such events might include the collapse or breaching of a seawall, the accelerated erosion or flooding of the ground behind, or the failure of groynes with loss of beach (see Section 8.3).

3.4.4 Procedure

It is unlikely that the available data and the initial studies will be sufficient to identify only one possible option for the works. Further data and analysis will be required to complete the selection and also to allow detailed design to be carried out. At this stage, therefore, the engineer should identify where further data and analysis are required and set down a thorough plan which shows how he will proceed with the completion of the works. In broad terms, the procedure should incorporate the elements shown in Figure 3.4.

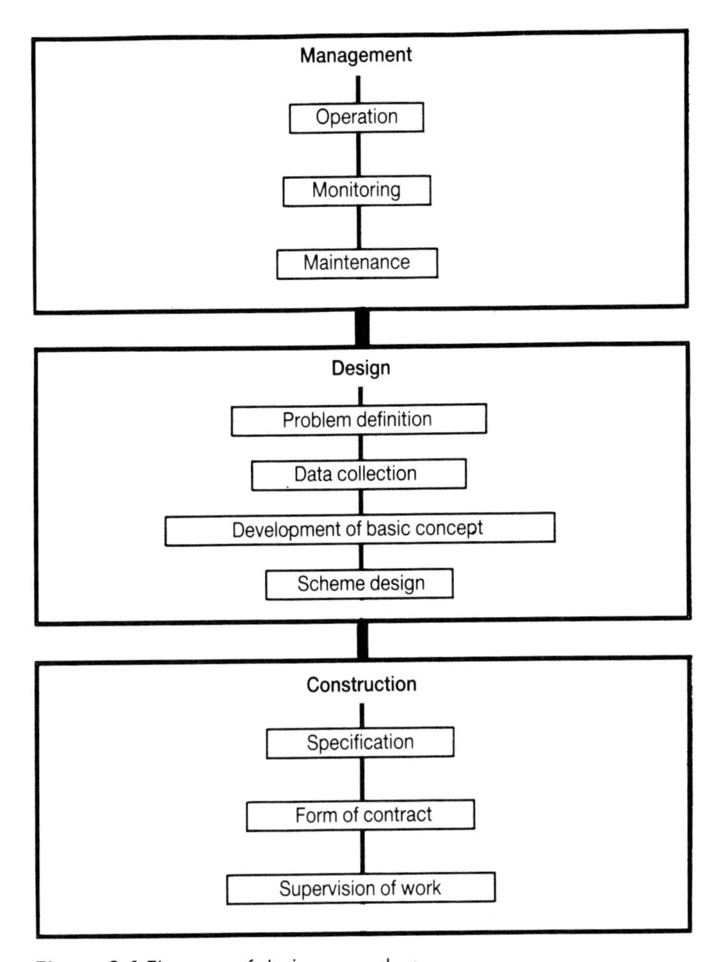

Figure 3.4 Elements of design procedure

In designing coastal defences the engineer should adopt a progressive, iterative approach to design. A step-by-step method provides a means of defining the problem, understanding the significant processes at work and possible options, assessing their impact and designing solutions. The procedure is indicated in Figure 3.5. Such a procedure is cost-effective in the way it enables the engineer to:

- Reach an initial decision on feasibility, whether in environmental, economic or engineering terms;
- Progress the project along lines which suit the required financial and statutory approvals;
- Tailor surveys, models and design work to suit the problems involved and solutions envisaged.

The first 'loop' in Figure 3.5 up to the initial evaluation of options has been covered in Sections 3.1–3.4. As discussed in Sections 3.4.1–3.4.3, it is at this stage where initial conclusions on the nature of the problem, functional requirements and possible options become evident. This allows a plan of implementation to be established which would include:

1. An environmental assessment (see Section 3.3);
2. An economic assessment (see Chapter 8);
3. Site investigation recording new data and modelling (Appendix B and Chapter 4);
4. Based on (1) and (3), a refinement of the understanding of the coastal regime (Section 4.9);
5. Based on (4) and the functional requirements, a review of options;
6. Recommendation of the preferred option.

At the time when this plan of implementation is set down, the initial evaluation of options (Section 3.4.3) is likely to have identified a number of possible solutions, not all of which will be seawalls. The earlier elements of work under items (1)–(4) should therefore be aimed at allowing a decision on the broad type of solution. Only when this decision has been reached can these items be completed.

The second stage therefore may well effectively be split into two or more phases, with the interim findings of (1)–(4) indicating that further work is required before items (5) and (6) can be completed. For example, in an area where a seawall already exists but requires upgrading in terms of its ability to prevent overtopping, investigation into possible sources of beach materials and calculations of longshore transport rates may rule out beach nourishment on the grounds of cost. Similarly, groynes or offshore breakwaters may prove too costly or environmentally unacceptable. This may lead to an interim finding in Stage 2 that works to the seawall are to be preferred. The remainder of Stage 2 should therefore be focused on determining the nature of these works, e.g. whether to improve the wall's ability to prevent overtopping by

Figure 3.5 Staged design procedure ▶

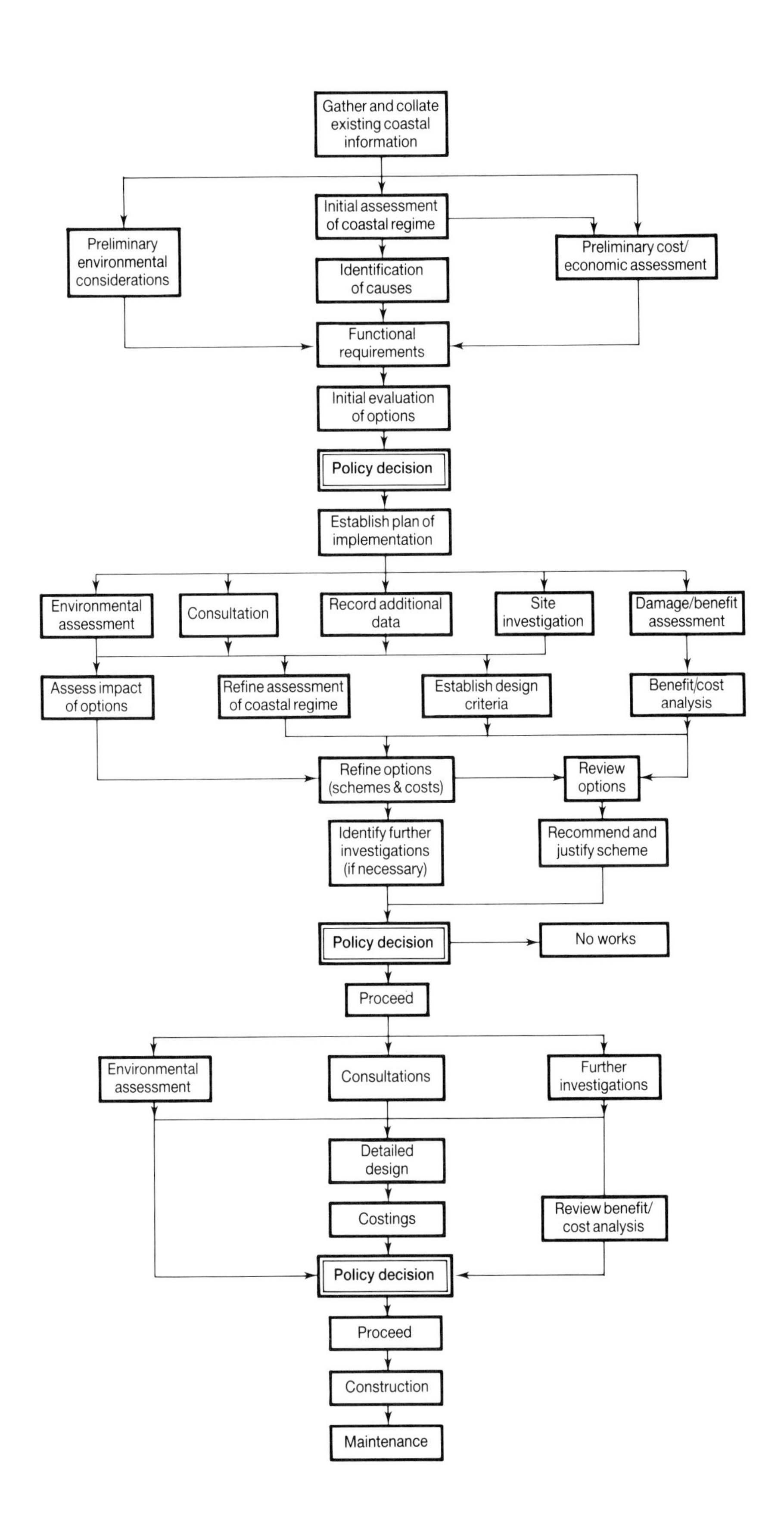

Gather and collate existing coastal information
Preliminary environmental considerations
Initial assessment of coastal regime
Identification of causes
Preliminary cost/ economic assessment
Functional requirements
Initial evaluation of options
Policy decision
Establish plan of implementation
Environmental assessment
Consultation
Record additional data
Site investigation
Damage/benefit assessment
Assess impact of options
Refine assessment of coastal regime
Establish design criteria
Benefit/cost analysis
Refine options (schemes & costs)
Review options
Identify further investigations (if necessary)
Recommend and justify scheme
Policy decision
No works
Proceed
Environmental assessment
Consultations
Further investigations
Detailed design
Costings
Review benefit/ cost analysis
Policy decision
Proceed
Construction
Maintenance

raising it or by placing rock in front of it or by other means of improving the hydraulic performance of the wall (see Section 5.7.5).

The findings of the second stage should therefore include:

1. Identification of the preferred option;
2. An economic assessment showing the justification for the work;
3. An environmental assessment showing the key points, possible impacts, and means of mitigating them;
4. Recommendations for further investigation necessary for detailed design.

The third stage should take the project through the investigations and detailed design, and recommend monitoring work. The works proposed, at least in the UK, may well be the subject of a formal environmental assessment procedure, and this will require extensive consultation and, where appropriate, measures taken to avoid or mitigate impacts. The consequences of significant changes in the design, as distinct from that envisaged at the end of the second stage, should be assessed in economic, environmental and engineering terms.

* The UK Joint Nature Conservation Committee (JNCC) was established by the Environmental Protection Act 1990 and coordinates three country councils: English Nature, the Scottish Natural Heritage (the Nature Conservancy Council for Scotland becomes a part of this last in April 1992) and the Countryside Council for Wales. JNCC and the three country councils carry forward duties previously undertaken by the Nature Conservancy Council (NCC). The Council for Nature Conservation and the Countryside representing Northern Ireland is based at the DoE Norther Ireland Conservation Service address in Belfast.

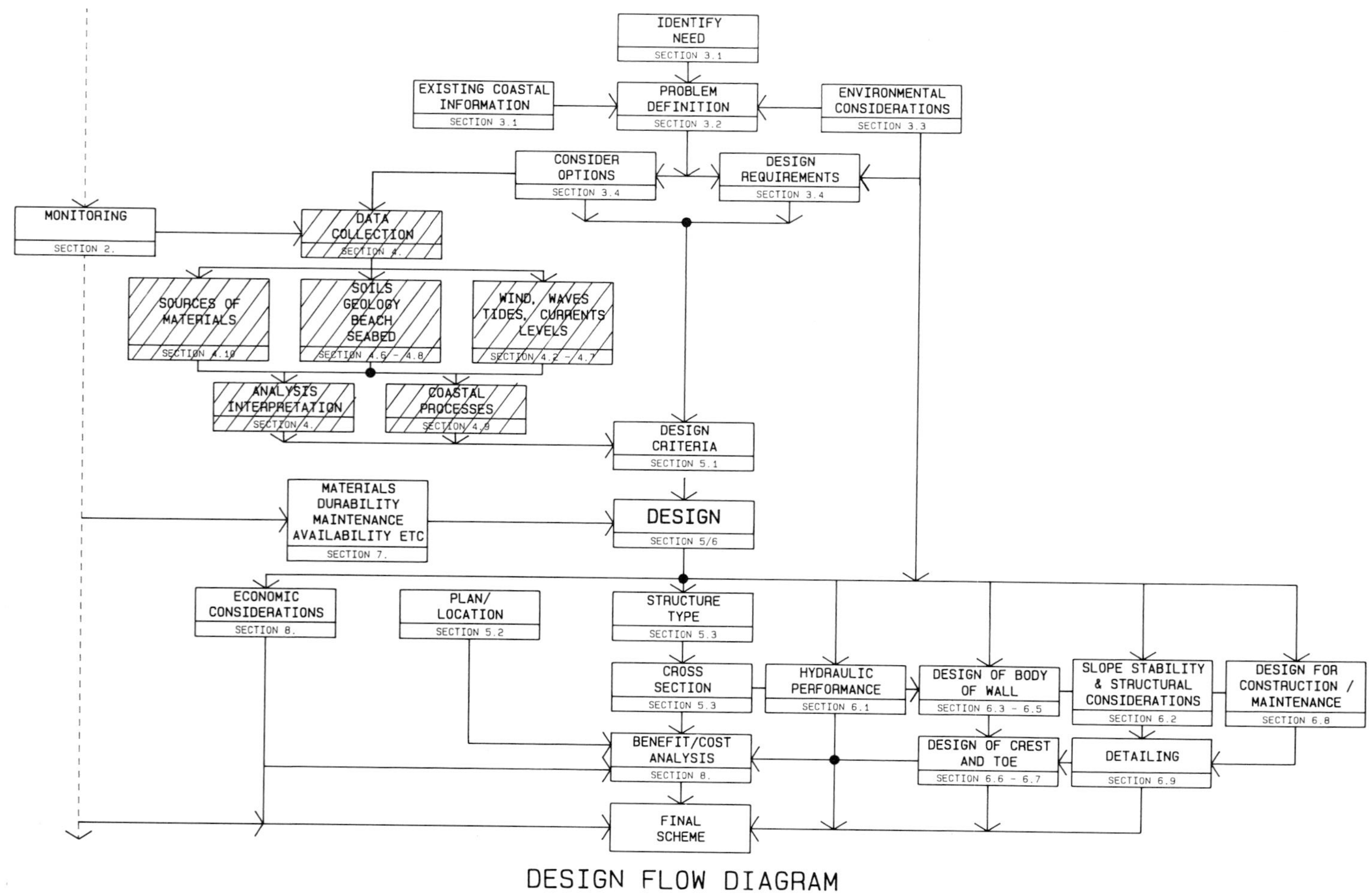

DESIGN FLOW DIAGRAM

4 Data collection, analysis and interpretation

The preliminary stages of a project will use existing data to assess the coastal regime, define the functional requirements of the works and establish requirements for additional information, as discussed in Chapter 3. The provision of data for project development is discussed in this section and covers:

- Sources of existing information;
- Acquisition of new data;
- Evaluation and analysis;
- Interpretation.

The chapter is subdivided into subject areas (such as water level, waves, soils). In addition, Section 4.5 discusses the joint occurrence of waves and water levels which is particularly important for design of sea defences. Section 4.9 shows how much of the data can be brought together to study coastal processes.

Clearly, the extent and reliability of data acquired will have a major bearing on the degree of design optimization and impact evaluation that is possible, and a lack of initial investigation, giving a short-term saving, can lead to long-term problems. Equally, the cost of site investigation and data acquisition, storage and analysis should be considered carefully in the light of potential savings that can arise from refinement of design.

The marine environment is changeable and often hostile. Surveying in and on the sea requires the right craft and equipment and experienced personnel. All too often, inexperience leads to loss of data and equipment, invalid data and danger to life.

4.1 General information on data acquisition

4.1.1 Data sources

For many of the subject areas there are established institutions (referenced in detail under the individual subject headings) charged with the responsibility for collating existing data, or of registering the type, source and extent of data available for the UK and surrounding sea areas. These 'data banks' depend for their success on the willingness of the parties to keep them informed. The search for data should, therefore, start with (but not be confined to) the existing data banks. For the continuing success of data banks, all newly recorded data should be made available to them. Other possible sources are discussed in Sections 4.2–4.11.

4.1.2 Validity

All data are subject to errors in varying degree. In the coastal zone, tides, waves, currents, etc. vary considerably from one site to another and from time to time, and there is frequently a lack of specific data relevant to the site. For both these reasons all available data should be critically evaluated with regard to validity, and hence usefulness, for the project under consideration. The engineer should neither take data at face value without evaluation nor simply discard them because they are not ideal whatever their source or nature. Techniques are available for adjusting and enhancing data, and all relevant data will tend to be of some use provided their limitations are appreciated.

The above points apply equally to the evaluation of existing data as they do to the evaluation and establishment of programmes for recording new data. Existing data have the advantage of normally being cheap and often having a longer duration than can be achieved for an individual project. New data, however, offer the possibility of eliminating measurement and recording errors by using the most appropriate system correctly located, but over a limited duration and at a substantial cost. Frequently, the best compromise is to carry out new records in such a way that they can be used to enhance existing data recorded over a longer time span.

Examples of aspects that should be included in the evaluation of data

Aspects of data	*Examples of factors affecting validity of data*
Location of measuring system	Evaluation or exposure of anemometer. Remoteness from site, when parameter being measured varies in space (e.g. winds and waves)
Measurement system	Visually observed data – subjectivity Calibration errors Response of system to rapid changes (e.g. oscillating currents)
Recording system	Interference on telemetered data Calibration errors Variability in chart speed
Measurement period	Too short a period for statistical reliability Too long an interval between samples Unrepresentative period (e.g. recording in summer and extrapolating to winter)

4.1.3 Analysis

Having assessed the validity of available data, the engineer should optimize their use by the most appropriate analysis. Carefully planned analysis is the key to optimizing limited available data. The increased use of computers has allowed greater sophistication in the treatment of data, but this can become costly and should be tailored to suit the needs of the project. Furthermore, the limitations and accuracy of data should be brought into the analysis with the use of confidence limits (see Section 4.5). The techniques of analysis are constantly progressing, and the engineer should ensure that the analysis is undertaken by suitably qualified and experienced personnel.

4.1.4 Acquisition of new data

The acquisition of new data is important but can be costly. Much of the equipment used in data acquisition is that with which an engineer is familiar, such as a level, theodolyte, staff, ranging rods, camera, etc. Other more specific equipment can be purchased such as wave recorders, tide recorders, anemometers, echo sounders, etc., but unless they are used as part of a continuing monitoring exercise, they may be best obtained by letting a survey contract with a specialist firm. The use of a specialist firm as opposed to purchase has the advantage of allowing the use of the most appropriate and up-to-date equipment and gives access to suitably experienced personnel.

Two of the prime problems with recording oceanographical data offshore are the remoteness of the recording location and the severity of the marine environment. As a consequence, much data is lost due to:

- Delays in finding faults;
- Damage in storms, or due to impact by flotsam or vessels;
- Theft or vandalism of instruments;
- Lack of durability.

The recording system should be reliable (well proven), thoroughly and frequently calibrated, well maintained, durable (both in terms of the instrument and its mountings/moorings) and adequately insured.

4.1.5 Monitoring

The value of new data will, in many cases, be a function of the time available for recording and the consequent duration of records. For this reason and because of its fundamental importance in the planning and design process, recording should commence early. The time scale of works (frequently in response to urgent need) is often too short to allow acquisition of data of adequate duration, and the value of good-quality, long-term coastal monitoring programmes is considerable (Section 2.1).

4.1.6 Specifications

Sections 4.2–4.4 and 4.6–4.8 indicate the type of equipment and recorders that are available for acquisition of data, and frequent references are made to BS 6349, Part 1: 1984 'Maritime Structures – General Criteria' which outlines the appropriate measurement techniques. Section 4.1.4 refers to the merit of using specialist contractors to undertake the survey work by contract. In this event, the contract conditions and specifications should be drawn up carefully to ensure that the correct data are gathered in the correct manner.

Guidance on specifications is available for hydrographic and marine geophysical surveying in references 2 and 3 and geotechnical work in reference 4. In any event, the engineer should ensure that before letting any survey contract he knows:

- The type and format of data required;
- The accuracy of survey work;
- The realistically attainable accuracy of survey work;
- The experience of contractors.

The accuracy required of the surveyors will have a great impact on cost. The specifications should ask for nothing more and nothing less than is necessary. They should ensure that the following are either specified or details requested from the surveyor:

- Data required;
- Overall level of accuracy;
- Method and frequency of calibration of equipment;
- Method of working;
- Analysis techniques;
- Format of results;
- Supervision on site (adequate level of staff supplied by contractor);
- Equipment (type and number);
- Provision of back-up in the event of breakdown (e.g. dedicated stand-by);
- Safety.

Data-acquisition techniques are advancing rapidly and vary greatly from firm to firm. The engineer should familiarize himself with the available techniques as far as possible before going to tender. In this respect a performance specification is frequently the best way to obtaining cost-effective pertinent data. Alternatively, the engineer can retain the services of a specialist firm of surveyors to advise him.

4.1.7 Level data

Coastal works bring together marine and land-levelling practice, and this can lead to confusion. Great care must be taken in evaluating level information to establish the correct data. In marine use the normal data are the Admiralty Chart Data. This is local, and varies along the coast with the tidal constituents. The level of Chart Data is normally close to the Lowest Astronomical Tide. Its precise level relative to Ordnance Data is published, for locations around the UK, in the Admiralty Tide Tables, Volume 1[5]. Near ports, levels are sometimes referred to local 'Dock Data', whose value may be obtained from the relevant port or harbour authority.

When assessing historical surveys care should be taken to establish the data accurately. Both Chart and Ordnance Data have been modified a number of times, sometimes within the last 20 years. In the UK details on the historical values of data can be obtained from the Hydrographer of the Navy and Ordnance Survey, respectively.

4.2 Water levels

The depth of water fronting a seawall can play a part in governing the wave action that impinges upon the wall and the degree to which the seabed is moved by wave action. Further, it clearly has an effect on the degree of run-up and overtopping, the hydraulic loads on the wall, and is important in planning construction in respect of tidal working. Data on water levels are therefore required for:

- The assessment of coastal processes;
- Design of slope protection;
- Hydraulic performance;
- Structural design;
- Economic evaluation;
- Design for construction;
- The derivation of inshore wave climate.

This section discusses the sources of documented data, techniques for assessing normal tidal rise and fall, means of recording and the estimation of extreme water levels.

4.2.1 Normal tides

Daily predictions of times of high and low waters at a selected number of Standard Ports are published by the Admiralty[5], who also lists data for Secondary Ports. These give values of mean high and low water levels for spring and neap tides, together with time differences relative to the Standard Port. In the case of Standard Ports, the level of highest and lowest astronomical tides is also listed.

The level of highest and lowest astronomical tides for Secondary Ports can be estimated with sufficient accuracy for many design purposes by the method described in the boxed section below.

Tide data for Secondary Ports

The estimation of highest and lowest astronomical tides at Secondary Ports can be obtained by plotting the full range of tidal levels of the nearest Standard Port on the vertical axis, and the mean spring and neap tides of the nearest Secondary Ports on the horizontal axis. By extrapolation of the best-fit straight line the appropriate astronomical levels can be read off, as shown in the example below.

	Standard Port (Aberdeen) (m above CD)	*Secondary Port* (Stonehaven) (m above CD)
HAT	+4.8	
MHWS	+4.3	+4.5
MHWN	+3.4	+3.6
MTL	+2.5	
MLWN	+1.6	+1.7
MLWS	+0.6	+0.6
LAT	0	

From the above, the estimated levels of astronomical tides and mean tide levels for Stonehaven are:

HAT	+5.0
MTL	+2.6
LAT	+0

Tide tables are also published by harbour authorities and other commercial organizations, the predictions being obtained from the Proudman Oceanographic Laboratory (POL) at Bidston, Birkenhead. It should be noted that it is common for locally produced tide tables to have the water levels referred to a local datum which may be different from Admiralty Chart Datum.

Requirements for specific tidal data other than those contained in the published tables should be referred to POL. Extensive data are held by POL, which is responsible (on behalf of the UK Ministry of Agriculture, Fisheries and Food) for the tide gauges of the UK National Network (Figure 4.1).

4.2.2 Tide recording

In certain circumstances it may be necessary to carry out tidal observations at a particular site, either on a temporary basis as part of a hydrographic survey (see Section 4.7) or on a more permanent one for long-duration records such as are necessary for the production of astronomical tidal harmonic constituents, the statistical analysis of extreme events or flood warning.

Figure 4.1 Tide gauges of the national network (UK) – January 1990

In either case, the selection of the most suitable instrument, its installation, calibration, levelling to datum, etc. are matters requiring experience and judgement. For more detailed information on types of gauges, duration of recordings and other factors affecting this, the engineer should consult BS 6349, paragraphs 10.4 to 10.4.2.8.

4.2.3 Surges

Actual water levels differ from those that are predicted in tide tables. The variations, or residual elevations, are due to meteorological effects and local oceanic factors. In UK waters meteorological effects dominate over oceanic factors, and give rise to storm surges through the action of wind and barometric pressure. The magnitude of a storm surge is determined not only by local conditions but also by the combined effect of winds and atmospheric pressure acting over the entire continental shelf and beyond.

Large surges are more frequent in the winter months, when storms usually occur. Surges may be positive, i.e. raising sea level to above the predicted value, or they may be negative. Large positive surges are more frequent than large negative ones. This is because depressions, which cause positive surges, tend to be more intense and associated with more severe winds than anticyclones.

Figure 4.2 shows the distribution of positive storm surge elevations which, on average, would be exceeded once in 50 years. The figure is based on the results of numerical model simulations, obtained by Flather[6] combined with data from observed surges at seven coastal sites.

Values from Figure 4.2 should only be used for the early design stage. For definitive values specific to a given site, reference should be made to the Proudman Oceanographic Laboratory or other authorities. POL holds hourly surge data from numerous coastal and offshore tide gauges. Other authorities, such as harbour and river authorities and the Storm Tide Warning Service at Bracknell, may also have surge data but they are likely to be at times of High Water only. The use of surge data to estimate extreme water level is discussed in Section 4.2.5.

It may be necessary to obtain advance warnings of surges, particularly during seawall construction, but also when responsible for maintenance and operation of sea defences. In the UK, the Storm Tide Warning Service at the Meteorological Office, Bracknell, provides warnings for the east coast of England from the English/Scottish border to the Thames Estuary. The warnings they issue are generally communicated through the police and the National Rivers Authority (NRA).

4.2.4 Secular changes

Secular changes are the long-term variations in sea level caused by a combination of climatic and/or geological effects over many decades. Briefly, the changes are due to the gradual increase in volume of the oceans through the melting of grounded ice, thermal expansion, variations in mean atmospheric pressure, and readjustment of the earth's surface.

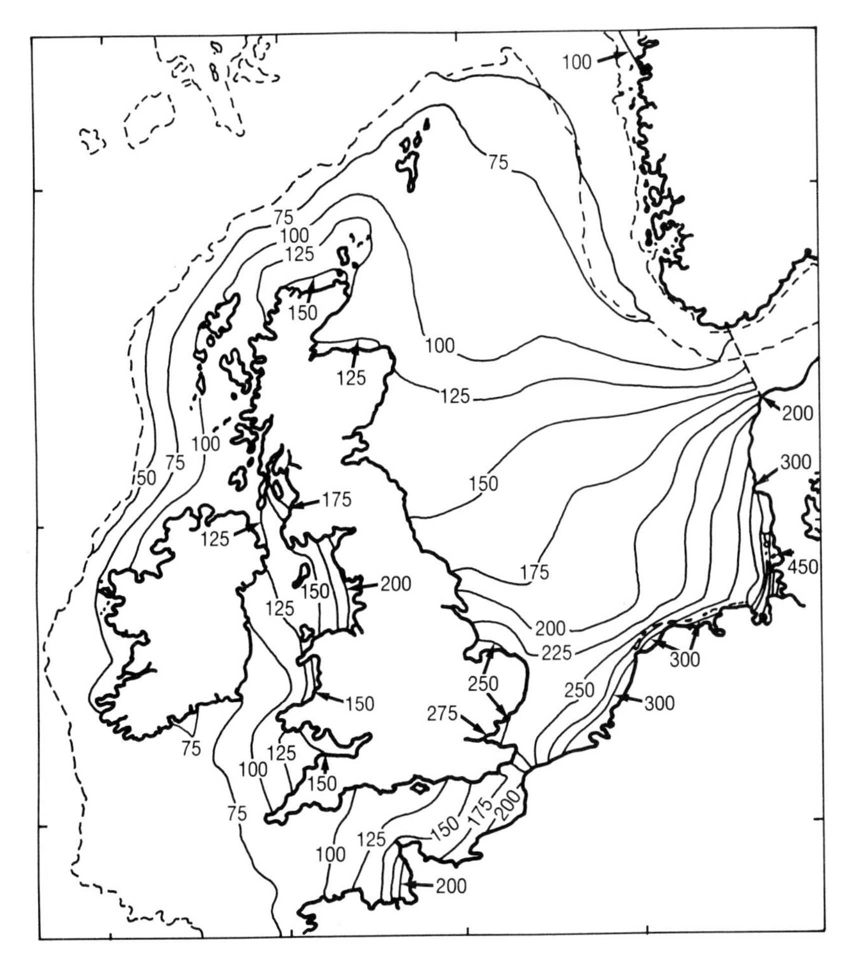

Figure 4.2 Storm surge elevation

Though the changes may be small in relation to the variations in sea level arising from tides and surges, they are important for the purpose of interpreting tide gauge readings, especially when these extend over several decades. Similarly, it is necessary to know the secular change that is likely to occur in years to come in order to determine long-term extreme water levels, which may apply towards the end of the design life of the seawall.

The global value for the secular change in mean sea level over the last century has been estimated as some 1.0 mm to 1.5 mm per year. However, there is evidence that rates of rise have increased considerably since about 1920, due to the 'greenhouse' effect caused by an increased carbon dioxide level in the atmosphere. These rates may well therefore increase over the next 100 to 150 years. Additional to the global effects, there are local influences due to long-term changes to local mean atmospheric pressure and readjustment of the earth's crust. Obviously, these vary from place to place.

Research on rising sea levels is advancing rapidly, and for the latest information and for information on specific sites, reference should be made to the Permanent Service on Mean Sea Level at the POL.

4.2.5 Extreme water levels

Sections 4.2.1–4.2.4 discuss the causes of water level variations together with means and sources of information for obtaining values for tide, surge and secular change. Ultimately, the designer of a seawall is faced with the problem of obtaining the design still water level for the seawall. Two methods are available for determining extreme values and these are discussed below. Before embarking on such an analysis, the engineer should consult the POL and local coast protection, sea defence and port authorities. The POL has carried out extensive work in deriving extreme sea level data which could limit the need for further analysis. Work by local authorities may be of value, although the engineer should first ensure that the work is valid.

Extrapolation of annual maxima

Traditionally, estimates of extreme still water levels have been derived from the frequency distribution of annual maxima (or minima). Graff[9] discusses some of the problems in this approach as well as presenting a comprehensive analysis of the observed sea levels at 67 ports around the British Isles. This method assumes combinations of tide, surge and secular change as they occurred during the years in which the water levels were measured. The confidence that can be ascribed to extrapolation depends upon the period of time over which observations were made. For confidence in the results, observations extending over a period of the order 100 years, giving a data set comprising 100 annual extremes, are desirable.

A linear trend in excess of the secular change is sometimes evident in the data, e.g. maximum levels becoming progressively higher over the years. This might be attributed to unnatural causes, such as instrumental drift or, possibly, man's activity such as dredging or canalization of rivers. The trend should be removed from the data set before it is analysed, and an allowance can subsequently be made on the extreme level.

If satisfactory data exist, the extrapolation to extreme levels can be undertaken (see Section 4.4.7). Methods of extrapolating extreme values are described in reference 10 and summarized by Graff. Recent work by Smith and Tawn[11,12] has used a limited number of extreme values from each year rather than the single annual maximum. Statistically more reliable (i.e. statistical errors are smaller), this allows extreme value estimates to be based on as little as 20 years of data. The engineer should refer to POL if he requires further information.

Joint probability

An alternative method to that of extrapolating annual extremes is joint probability, which should be used if the tide gauge records are of inadequate duration or when greater confidence is required in the extrapolation. The method makes more efficient use of the data and can give useful results from as little as one year of measurements under certain circumstances. In general, 5–10 years' data are required. This is achieved by considering hourly values of tide and surge, of which there are approximately 9000 in a single year compared with only one annual maximum. The method takes into account the fact that a prescribed total level can be reached as a result of many different combinations of tide and surge.

A time series of surge elevation, from which its frequency distribution can be derived, is obtained by removing the predicted tidal levels from a measured sea-level record. The surge frequency distribution can be generated from hourly records. Part years should be avoided, as there is a very definite season during the winter when surge activity is at its highest.

Special consideration needs to be given to shallow water areas where interaction between tide and surge renders invalid the fundamental assumption in the basic approach that tide and surge components are statistically independent.

The method is not applicable to areas that are surge dominated, where the surge component is large with respect to the tide (e.g. Lowestoft in the UK). A revision to this method by Tawn[13] allows a wider application. The technique has been applied by POL to sea levels at several coastal sites around the British Isles, deriving estimates for extreme surges, tides and total still water levels.

Joint probability of water levels in conjunction with the occurrence of waves is discussed in Section 4.5.1.

4.2.6 Fluvial flow

By virtue of the location of seawalls, fluvial flow, or flow originating from freshwater sources, tends to be a secondary consideration in relation to the dominant tidal currents and the dynamic effects resulting from wave action. Where seawalls are located upstream within estuaries, fluvial flow may need to be assessed and considered. This should be borne in mind when planning a current measurement exercise (see Section 4.7). Where fluvial flow contributes to the movement of sediments or the general estuarine regime, then the effects of constructing a seawall should be examined with respect to these phenomena. Information on freshwater discharges may generally be obtained from the National Rivers Authority (NRA) in England and Wales, or in Scotland, the appropriate river purification board.

4.3 Wind

The main application of wind data in the design of seawalls is its use in the evaluation (hindcasting) of wave climate. Good-quality long-term directional wind data are available from many more locations than similar wave data. Wind data are therefore required for:

- *Hindcasting of overall wave climate*: hourly wind records of speed and direction or percentage occurrence of winds by speed and direction;
- *Hindcasting of extreme waves*: estimates of extreme winds, speeds and associated durations and directions;
- *Assessment of seasonal variation in wave climate (for construction planning)*: hourly wind records of speed and direction or seasonal tables of percentage occurrence of winds by speed and direction.

Since wind data are normally only needed in seawall design for assessing wave climate, the precise requirement is a function of the available wave data and the extent of wave studies that are required (see Section 4.4).

4.3.1 Definitions

Whereas for structural design purposes wind speeds are calculated from the 'basic wind speed', which is the three second gust exceeded, on average, once in 50 years, and measured at 10 m above sea level/ground level, for wave hindcast purposes the hourly mean wind speed is often used. The Beaufort scale is often used to classify wind speed by numbers (forces) which correspond to identifiable effects. The Beaufort scale is given in Table 4.1. Wind direction is usually expressed to the nearest 10° or by compass point, the direction being that from which the wind blows.

4.3.2 Data sources

General information wind data in the UK is given in the *Observer's Handbook* published by the Meteorological Office. The 'Pilots' published by the Hydrographer of the Navy, obtainable from agents for the sale of Admiralty charts, give general wind data and wind roses. Methods of deriving extreme hourly wind speeds and wind loads for structural design are documented in the Code of basic data for the design of buildings, Part 1, 1972[3].

Data for specific sites (see Figure 4.3) may be obtained from the UK Meteorological Office at Bracknell. They hold wind records from anemometer stations around the British Isles and information can be obtained as wind roses, showing monthly, seasonal or yearly distributions of wind speeds and directions. Tabular formats are also available. For wave hindcast purposes, hourly data can be supplied on disk for direct input to computer facilities.

Useful wind data may also be obtained from airfields, ports and coastguards and the Meteorological Office often holds copies of these data. These, however, may not be in accordance with standard procedure (e.g. irregular records). Data are also available from offshore stations and from Voluntary Observing Ships (VOS data). The Meteorological Office holds copies of VOS data in computer data banks. When obtaining wind data, particularly from these secondary sources, the engineer should check on:

- The degree of exposure of the recording site, whether it is sheltered or particularly exposed;

Table 4.1 Beaufort wind scale

Beaufort force (knots)	*m/s*	*Beaufort wind scale at sea*	*Beaufort wind scale on land*
0 >1	0–0.2	*Calm:* Sea like a mirror	*Light:* Smoke rises vertically
1 1–3	0.3–1.5	*Light breeze:* Small wavelets, still short but more pronounced crests have a glassy appearance and do not break	*Light:* Wind felt on face; leaves rustle; ordinary wind vane moves
3 7–10	3.4–5.4	*Gentle breeze:* Large wavelets, crests begin to break. Foam of glassy appearance	*Gentle:* Leaves and small twigs in constant motion, wind extends light flags
4 11–16	5.5–7.9	*Moderate breeze:* Small waves, becoming longer; fairly frequent white horses	*Moderate:* Raises dust and loose paper; small branches move
5 17–21	8.0–10.7	*Fresh breeze:* Moderate waves, taking a more pronounced long form; many white horses are formed. Chance of some spray	*Fresh:* Small trees in leaf begin to sway; small-crest waves on inland waters
6 22–27	10.8–13.8	*Strong breeze:* Large waves begin to form; the white foam crests are more extensive everywhere. Probably some spray	*Strong:* Large branches in motion. Inconvenience in walking against the wind
7 28–33	13.9–17.1	*Near-gale:* Sea heaps up with white foam from breaking waves	*Strong:* Whole trees in motion. Inconvenience in walking against the wind
8 34–40	17.2–20.7	*Gale:* Moderately high waves of greater length; much foam	*Gale:* Twigs break off trees. Progress generally impeded
9 48–55	20.8–24.4	*Strong gale:* High waves. Dense streaks of foam along the direction of the wind	*Gale:* Slight structural damage; tiles or slates blown off roofs
10 48–44	24.5–28.4	*Storm:* Very high waves with long overhanging crests. Visibility affected	*Storm:* Trees uprooted; roofs damaged. Other structural damage
11 56–63	28.5–32.6	*Violent storm:* Exceptionally high waves. Visibility seriously affected	*Violent storm:* Widespread damage
12 64	>32.7	*Hurricane:* The air is filled with foam and spray. Visibility very seriously affected	*Hurricane:* Damage to 'Disaster' scale

- The reliability of the recording system, whether it is visual observations of wind speed based on sea state (as are VOS data), a hand-held anemometer, or a fully automated well-maintained anemograph;
- The height of the anemometer above ground (10 m is standard) and whether corrections need to be made;
- The length and frequency of records, e.g. whether it is a true mean hourly speed or an average over several minutes.

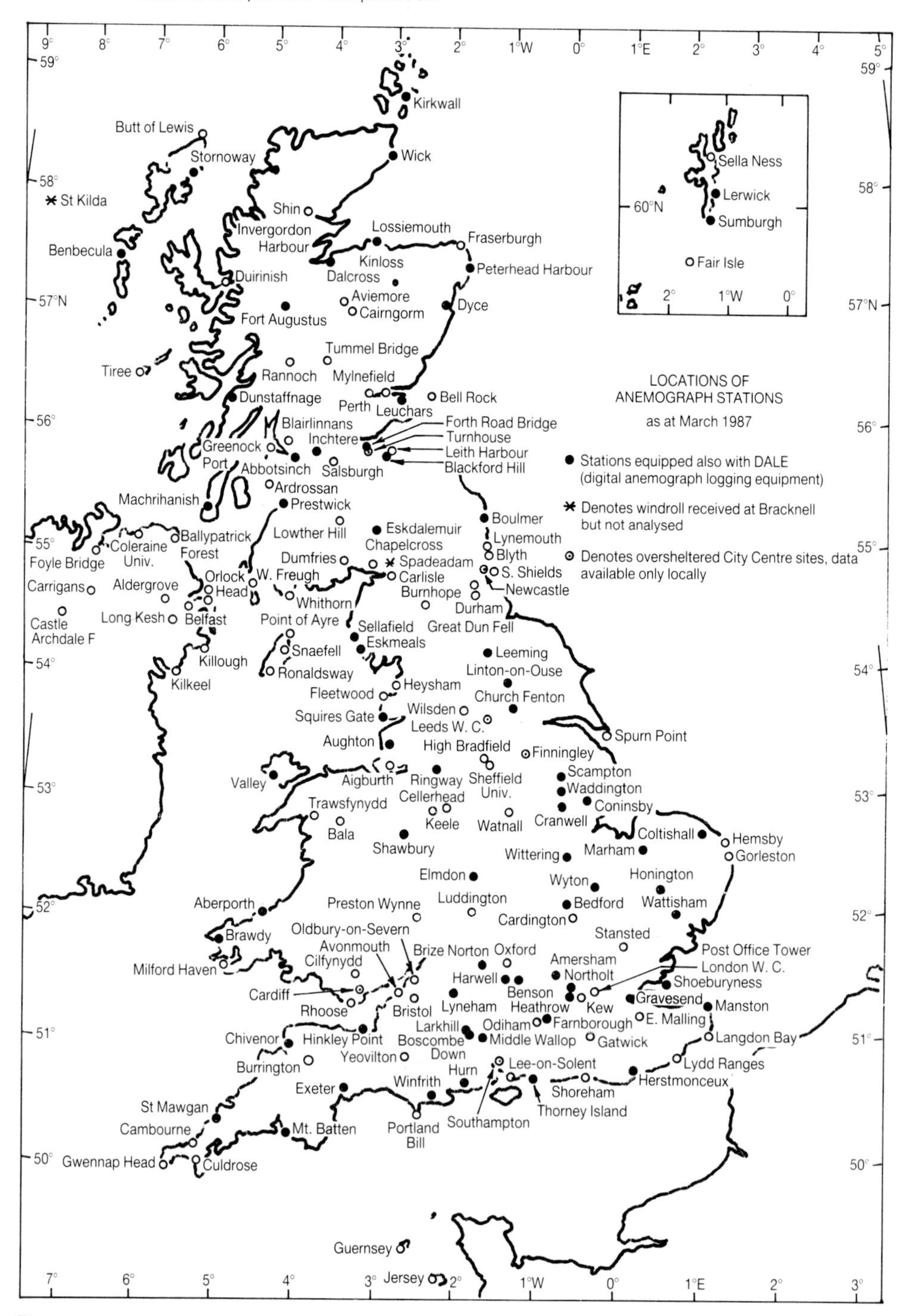

Figure 4.3 Locations of anemograph stations

4.3.3 Wind recording

Wind speeds and direction vary considerably from one site to another, and frequently good quality wind data are not available for a specific site. In assessing the appropriateness of available data to the site in question it should be remembered that, when required for hindcasting, it is the wind climate blowing over the sea area where waves are generated that is important, rather than the wind climate at the site. Nonetheless, in areas where good wind data are not available locally, it can be useful to record winds at the site, particularly when waves are locally generated.

Guidance on the type of wind sensors, their installation and the analysis of data is given by BS 6349[1], although, as stated, 'expert advice should be obtained before installation'. Given that the recorder is well installed, short-term (say, one year) local wind data can be very useful in supplementing existing wind records. They can provide a relationship between the site and long-term data elsewhere, thus allowing a long-term data set for the site to be synthesized.

4.4 Waves

A good knowledge of wave conditions is required for seawall design both directly, in terms of:

- An assessment of the type of wall that is appropriate;
- Hydraulic performance;
- Wave loads;
- Construction techniques and timing;

and indirectly:

- To understand the coastal regime;
- As input to hydraulic models.

This section deals with the gathering and analysis of wave data. As such, it includes guidance on the derivation of design wave conditions. Application of the data is dealt with in Section 4.9 and Chapter 6.

Sea waves are inherently irregular. A train of waves will tend to comprise waves of various heights, periods and direction. Because of this variability, waves are best described in statistical terms (e.g. mean wave period) as discussed in Section 4.4.2.

On UK shores, waves are wind generated, although not necessarily locally, e.g. they may be swells from distant storms. Wave conditions vary greatly with time, from season to season and year to year. The engineer should be wary, therefore, of assessing wave climate on the basis of a few months' records. General data on wave conditions off the coast can be obtained from various sources (Section 4.4.1).

Having established the offshore wave climate, further work is normally required to determine the wave conditions at the wall. The latter are likely to be modified as a result of shallow water effects (Section 4.4.6). Using the inshore wave climate the various wave height and period parameters can be determined for use in the design of the wall (Sections 4.4.2 and 4.4.7, respectively).

4.4.1 Procedure

Wave conditions at the wall are required for direct input to the design or, if model studies are used, those at the seaward limit of the area modelled may be more appropriate (Appendix B). For assessing coastal processes, wave heights just offshore (e.g. at the breaking zone) may be required for the simple analyses, whereas if numerical models are to be used offshore wave conditions may be required as input (Section 4.9). Before starting a study of waves, the engineer should, as far as is feasible, review the nature of information that is required and tailor the output to suit.

In the following general procedures it is assumed that the engineer needs to know wave conditions at the toe of the wall. Clearly, if he does not wish to study waves so far inshore (if he simply wants to define conditions at the boundary of an area to be modelled) then he should stop short of the full procedure outlined below.

Determining offshore wave conditions

The three potential sources of wave data are:

- Existing records (Section 4.4.2);
- Records taken specifically for the works (Section 4.4.3);
- Wind data and wave hindcasting (Section 4.4.5).

Existing wave wave data are somewhat limited in extent but should be researched thoroughly because they are likely to be cheap and available quickly. On the other hand, recording waves can be relatively costly and time-consuming, since minimum periods for recording may be of the order of one year. Therefore, any means of improving the validity of existing data (which may, for example, not be close to the site) or reducing the length of time required for records is potentially advantageous.

Wave hindcasting (the calculation of wave conditions based on wind records) can be very useful in this respect. In such a way, for example, a shorter period of wave records (say, six months) can be used to calibrate a wave hindcasting model, and thus 'extend' the wave records to the much longer period (ten years or more) for which wind records are often available. The engineer should review existing wave data and, if adequate, use them to establish offshore wave statistics in terms of direction, height (H_s) and period (T_p) (Section 4.4.4). If the extent of existing wave data is not adequate, then they could be used to calibrate a wave hindcasting model and thus produce a valid estimate of offshore wave statistics in terms of direction, height (H_s) and period (T_p) (Section 4.4.5).

Existing wave data could well be those available as part of a longer-term monitoring programme. The time scale for an individual project is unlikely to allow more than a few months for wave records, and this shows the value of monitoring.

If suitable existing wave data are not available, the engineer should evaluate whether a short period (say, six months) of wave recording supplemented by hindcasting is adequate (Section 4.4.5). To be reliable, hindcasting requires calibration, which is the purpose of the wave recording. It may be, however, that recording is not justified where one or more of the following apply:

- Water depths at the seawall are so small as to severely restrict the height of waves reaching the wall;
- The foreshore is such that it will be unaffected by changes in coastal processes (e.g. a hard rock platform);
- The wall is of such limited extent that the cost of wave recording is comparable with that incurred by a degree of overdesign. Great care should be exercised in this case since simply making the wall stronger may not be adequate in terms of 'overdesign'. A stronger wall may still fail if it is undermined, outflanked or if it produces an undesirable impact on coastal processes.

When using wave data in an assessment of coastal processes (e.g. looking at longshore drift) the offshore conditions will need to be presented as either:

- A table showing percentage occurrence of wave height, period and direction: such a table prepared to give long-term (say, ten years) annual average conditions can be used directly to estimate longshore transport (Section 4.9.6), and tables for individual seasons or years can be used to assess the significance of various periods which may have caused problems;
- A time series of hourly (or three-hourly, depending on availability and model requirements) values of wave height and period as direct input into a model.

Establishing design wave conditions

The offshore conditions appropriate to the design return period should be established

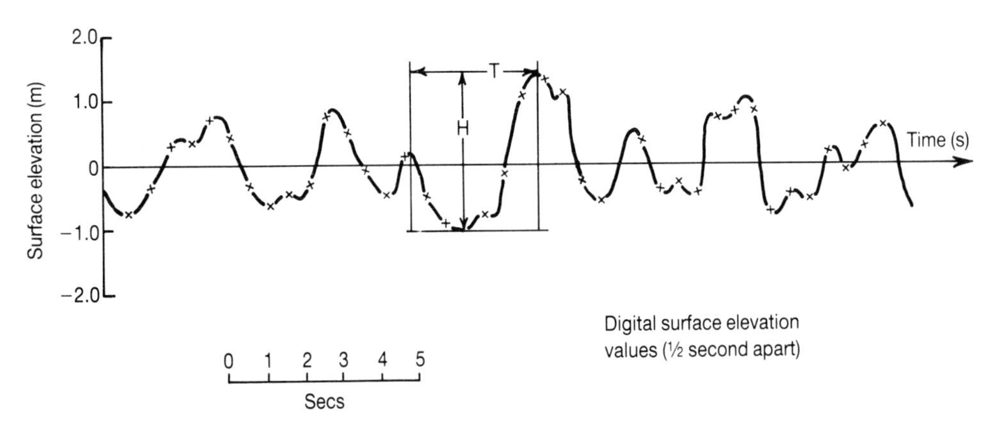

Figure 4.4 Wave trace of an irregular sea

Definitions and parameters

(a) Definitions

Relevant basic definitions given in BS 6349 Part 1[1] are as follows:

Wave height – the height of a wave crest above the preceding wave trough, and is denoted by H and in deep water by H_0 (see Figure 4.4)

Wave period – the period of time for two successive wave crests to pass a fixed point and is denoted by T (see Figure 4.4)

Wave length – the distance between consecutive wave crests and is denoted generally by L and in deep water by L_0

Wave celerity or velocity of wave propagation is the speed at which the wave travels. This is denoted generally by C and in deep water by C_0. Wave celerity is related to period and length by $C = L/T$.

Wave celerity is also a function of the water depth, d. C, L, T and d are related by the following expression:

$$C = \frac{g\,T}{2} \tanh \frac{2\,\pi\,d}{L}$$

When the water depth d is greater than half the wave length, the effect of depth becomes negligible. Water depths greater than half the wave length are called deep water since the wave does not 'feel' the seabed.

Further discussion of wave characteristics is given in references 1 and 15.

(b) Parameters

Because waves are inherently irregular it is necessary to describe them by wave height and period parameters, e.g. significant wave height and peak wave period. These are statistical parameters derived from the wave energy spectrum.

The main parameters that are required in design are:

H_s the significant wave height, i.e. the average height of the highest one third of waves in a given sea state. This approximates the wave height that would be estimated by an experienced observer. When using spectral techniques of wave analysis, significant wave height can be estimated from

$$H_s = 4\sqrt{E}$$

where E can be derived from the energy spectrum (see (c) below).

H_{max} maximum wave height, i.e. the maximum single wave height in a given period of time. Because of the random distribution of wave heights within a sea state the expected value of H_{max} will increase with increasing duration. Conventionally, in wave analysis a duration of 3 h is assumed. In shallow water the maximum wave height is often limited by breaking, but if it is not, then wave heights have been found to conform to a known statistical distribution such that

$$H_{max} = H_s \times (\tfrac{1}{2} \log_e N)^{\frac{1}{2}}$$

where N = number of waves in the chosen duration. For example, for a wave period of 4 s and duration 3 h, $N = 2700$ and $H_{max} = 2H_s$

$H_{1/m}$ the average wave height of the highest $1/m$th of waves in a given sea state

T_z, the mean zero crossing period of a wave record is the average wave period calculated as the duration of the record divided by the number of times the record crosses the mean water level line in an upward (or downward) direction

T_p, the peak wave period, derived from the energy spectrum, is the wave period at which there is maximum wave energy

T_s, the significant wave period, i.e. the average wave period of the highest one third of waves in a given sea state (T_s is often close to T_p).

(c) Wave spectra

A useful means of describing a sea state is the use of an energy spectrum. Spectral analysis of wave records can be performed easily and cheaply with the use of computers and specialist software (Section 4.4.5).

The principle of spectral analysis is that the sea state is composed of a large number of waves of different frequencies (frequency is the reciprocal of period) which propagate in various different directions distributed around the mean direction. Spectral density is a measure of the energy of the sea state expressed as a function of wave frequency and direction.

Presently, only rarely are directional wave data available, so the total wave energy ($S_{(f)}$), irrespective of wave direction, is calculated as a function of frequency. The plot of $S_{(f)}$ against frequency, f, is known as the one-dimensional energy spectrum, or more commonly as the energy spectrum.

Various standard forms of spectrum have been developed, based on analysis of extensive sets of wave records, notably JONSWAP[15] for non-fully developed seas and Pierson Moskowitz[16]. The various wave height parameters (H_s, H_{max}, T_p, etc.) can be determined directly from the energy spectrum.

(Section 4.4.7). Depending on the impact on the wall of water level and wave direction, a number of different combinations of wave conditions, direction and water level may be selected, each with the same joint probability of occurrence (Section 4.5).

Assessing shallow water effects

As waves approach the shore, they can be modified by refraction, shoaling, bed friction, breaking and wind. The engineer should, on the basis of experience, make a preliminary assessment of their significance in terms of the wave climate at the wall. Depending upon their significance, not all the factors need to be studied thoroughly whether by manual methods or by models (Appendix B). A study taking into account the relevant mechanisms will allow the design offshore conditions to be transferred inshore to give design conditions at the wall.

Deriving inshore wave height and period parameters

Knowing the inshore wave conditions, which should be in the form of significant wave height (H_s), peak wave period (T_p), direction and spectral shape, other wave height parameters such as $H_{1/100}$ can be determined as required for use in design formulae (Section 4.4 and Chapter 6).

4.4.2 Data sources

It should be stressed that, more often than not, existing wave data will not correspond exactly to the site location being studied. Data may relate to another nearshore site or to offshore conditions. In the latter case it will be necessary to analyse the shallow water processes (Section 4.4.6). When data are obtained from another nearshore site it will also be necessary to consider how those data might have been modified by the shallow water processes particular to that site.

The types of existing wave data can include the following:

1. Instrumentally recorded data;
2. Synthetic data from wind records;
3. Visually observed waves.

Instrumentally recorded data

The Deacon Oceanographic Laboratory (DOL), UK, holds the most comprehensive index of instrumentally recorded wave data for UK waters and worldwide. Because of the more recent nature of instrumental wave monitoring, the bulk of the measurements date from 1950. DOL can advise on the availability of data for a particular area. Procurement of the data can be arranged through the Deacon Laboratory or, in some instances, by arrangement with the originating organization.

Synthetic data from wind records

Since 1982 the UK Meteorological Office has been routinely running a computational model which forecasts wave conditions over a 25 km grid covering most of the north-west continental shelf of Europe. The model is used to predict wave conditions at three-hourly intervals and the results for the 12-hour increments are stored for each grid point. In addition to locally generated waves, the model also allows for waves originating in the Atlantic.

Results from the model can be obtained from the Marine Advisory Consultancy Service at Bracknell[21,22], who can abstract the data for any required grid point. In addition to the basic parameters (wave height, period and direction) they can also provide directional wave energy spectra.

Visually observed waves

The primary source of visually observed wave data in the UK is the Meteorological Office at Bracknell. This incorporates the Marine Advisory Consultancy Service, which specializes in providing advice on wave and wind conditions in the seas around the UK coastline and worldwide. Wave data held at Bracknell fall into two categories as follows:

1. Data from single stations. Some care must be taken, especially with data from light-ships, since the location of the observations is likely to be close to a substantial seabed feature which may lead to assumed results for the general area that are actually conditioned by the local feature.
2. Abstracts. The main data bank contains some 61 million entries, extracted from ships' logs, principally of wind and visually observed wave conditions. Data cover the period from 1854 to the present, although there is some bias in the data, as the majority of observations have been made since 1960. Despite the vast amount of data, there is sometimes difficulty in obtaining sufficient values in a particular area to provide a statistically sound description of the wave climate. In some cases this problem can be reduced by considering observations from a larger area (say, 5° of longitude by 5° of latitude) to obtain several thousand observations. Around the UK coast, however, this is not practical because the wave climate will vary markedly within such a large area due to the irregular shape of the seas and land masses.

Data from the main data bank are not continuous, and will have originated from a large number of different observers and have spanned many years. For the purposes of statistical analysis there is an advantage with this type of data in that they consist of a large number of independent values. There can, however, be problems in assigning return periods to the data because of uncertainty in the frequency of the observations (Section 4.4.7).

In addition to the Meteorological Office, visually observed wave data may also be obtained from other commercial organizations. These (and the Meteorological Office) provide services for further analysis of the data.

4.4.3 Wave recording

It is often desirable to have a record of wave data specific to the site of interest. This may be required if there are insufficient existing offshore data from which to gauge nearshore conditions, or if the complexity of the nearshore processes renders them not amenable to analytical methods.

Essentially, there are three methods for obtaining wave records: wave buoys, pressure recorders and wave staffs or similar devices.

Wave buoys

These are the most commonly used instruments for wave measurement. Each consists of a moored buoy containing a vertically positioned accelerometer and a radio transmitter. The measured vertical accelerations of the buoy are integrated electronically, transmitted as a radio signal to a shore-station and decoded to give a digital (or an analogue) history of the water elevation.

Wave buoys have proved to be reliable and accurate, and have the advantage over pressure recorders in that they give a more direct reading of the water surface elevation. A disadvantage is that they do not detect long-period waves. Typically, wave buoys should not be considered for monitoring waves of period in excess of 20–25 s.

Wave buoys are vulnerable to damage by collision with passing vessels, cannot be deployed in the surf zone, and problems have been encountered with the mooring systems. For these reasons, it is recommended that, where possible, the receiving station is located so that the buoy is within sight (albeit with the aid of binoculars).

In some localities, radio interference can spoil the telemetry signal, leading to missing or corrupted data. If this is considered likely, then a telemetry trial should be undertaken prior to deployment of the buoy to determine the best location for the receiving station, given the expected distance to the buoy transmitter.

Pressure recorders

There is a demand for pressure recorders in applications where long-period waves are anticipated and must be monitored, and when it is required to monitor waves and tides simultaneously. A further advantage is that the instruments can be deployed further inshore than wave buoys.

The recorders are located below the surface of the sea and record the water pressure as a wave passes overhead. The pressure signal is either logged by a self-contained cassette or solid state recorder, or is transmitted to shore via a cable. In the latter case, problems have been encountered where the cable passes through the surf zone.

The main disadvantage with pressure recorders is that they do not monitor waves directly. The procedure for converting pressures to wave parameters is complex because pressures due to shorter-period waves attenuate more rapidly with depth than do those due to longer-period ones. Moreover, the depth of water is continuously changing with the tide. For this reason, the analysis of pressure readings and conversion to wave heights should normally be undertaken by the instrument manufacturer or an agent specializing in such work.

Because of the attenuation problem, it is preferable to locate the instrument at a level just below the troughs of waves on the lowest tide. This will generally entail securing the unit to a fixed pile or similar structure. This is often impractical and it is necessary to deploy the unit at or near the seabed using a purpose-built support frame.

Wave staffs and other devices

Various types of wave staffs have been used for recording waves. They employ an electronic means of sensing the surface elevation of the waves. The essential feature of wave staffs is that they must be attached to a rigid structure, but with adequate clearance to avoid interference effects. They tend to be prone to damage from boats and contamination from debris, seaweed, etc. One advantage is that their calibration can be readily checked by reference to visual markers on the staff or by raising and lowering the devices relative to calm water.

Other methods of measuring waves, but which are rarely used in seawall applications, include 'inverted echo-sounders' and 'downward-looking' devices. Inverted echo-sounders are located on the seabed but require a substantial umbilical cable to supply power to the device and to return signals to the recording station. They avoid the pressure-attentuation problems associated with pressure recorders, but are susceptible to data corruption due to signal reflection from subsurface debris, fish, etc. 'Downward-looking' devices use radar or infra-red signals to detect water elevation. Like wave staffs, they must be secured to a rigid structure and are therefore more useful in offshore applications than for seawalls. Alternative systems using clifftop deployment have been examined. Such methods are unlikely to be economically viable for the seawall designer, but this may change in the future.

4.4.4 Analysis of wave records

Modern recorded wave data are normally in digitized form on a computer disk, whereas older records may be on charts. With the advent of low-cost computing using PCs, new systems taking data from wave buoys are incorporating data processing in real time, the computer being used to log raw data and carry out initial analysis. This arrangement is ideal, as it enables the operator to monitor conditions and detect any malfunction. Such facilities may not always be available, however, and there may be a need to undertake the calculations manually, or at least to understand the principles of the available software.

Waves are not recorded continuously throughout the deployment period as this would generate unmanageable quantities of data. The normal practice is to record waves every 3 h for a 20-min duration. Each intermittent record is considered to represent the conditions over the 3 h centred on the time of the observation. If this is considered to be too coarse and more detailed information is required for storm events, an additional mode of operation can be incorporated, whereby the recording is continuous while the wave height exceeds a pre-set threshold value.

When the results of wave monitoring are extrapolated to predict extreme events then account must be taken of the intermittent nature of the recordings. Long-term statistics of wave analysis (extreme events) are dealt with in Section 4.4.7. This section is concerned with the short-term statistics of wave analysis and, more specifically, the computation of the fundamental parameters significant wave height H_s and mean zero crossing period T_z. Other parameters may be derived from the analysis, the most important probably being H_{max}.

The main methods of analysis are wave counting, spectral, and Tucker–Draper, as described below.

Wave counting

The basic wave parameters can be established by determining the distribution of wave heights in a record by measuring the individual waves. The zero crossing period (T_z) is determined from a count of the number of times (N_z) that the wave trace crosses the mean water level in an upward or downward direction (Figure 4.4). By measuring the heights of the individual waves (crest to trough), each defined by a crossing of the mean water level, and by ranking the values so obtained, the significant wave height H_s can be calculated directly.

Given that in a 20-min record there might be typically 250 waves, the procedure described above is necessarily slow unless carried out by computer.

Spectral analysis

Digitized data will usually be processed by spectral analysis, and computer software is readily available from specialist companies for this purpose. Spectra provide a visual indication of the energy distribution and can help to identify particular features in the wave activity. For example, a spectrum with two peaks indicates the presence of two strong wave components of different frequencies, perhaps locally generated sea waves and swell. The 'spectrum' (Figure 4.5) is a plot of the spectral density $S_{(f)}$ against the wave frequency f ($f = 1/T$, where T is the wave period). The spectral density $S_{(f)}$ represents the wave energy per unit of frequency. The total energy E is given in the spectrum by the area beneath the plot.

The shape of the spectrum depends upon the balance of energy in the sea. In the case of the JONSWAP spectrum (sea not fully developed) the concentration of energy in certain frequencies (due to high wind speed or limited fetches) is taken into account. A special case of JONSWAP is the Pierson–Moskowitz (PM) spectrum, which represents fully developed seas. Properties of the spectrum enable various wave parameters to be determined.

The PM spectrum does facilitate certain simplifications in the mathematical treatment of the spectrum, in particular:

$$H_s = 4.0\sqrt{E}$$

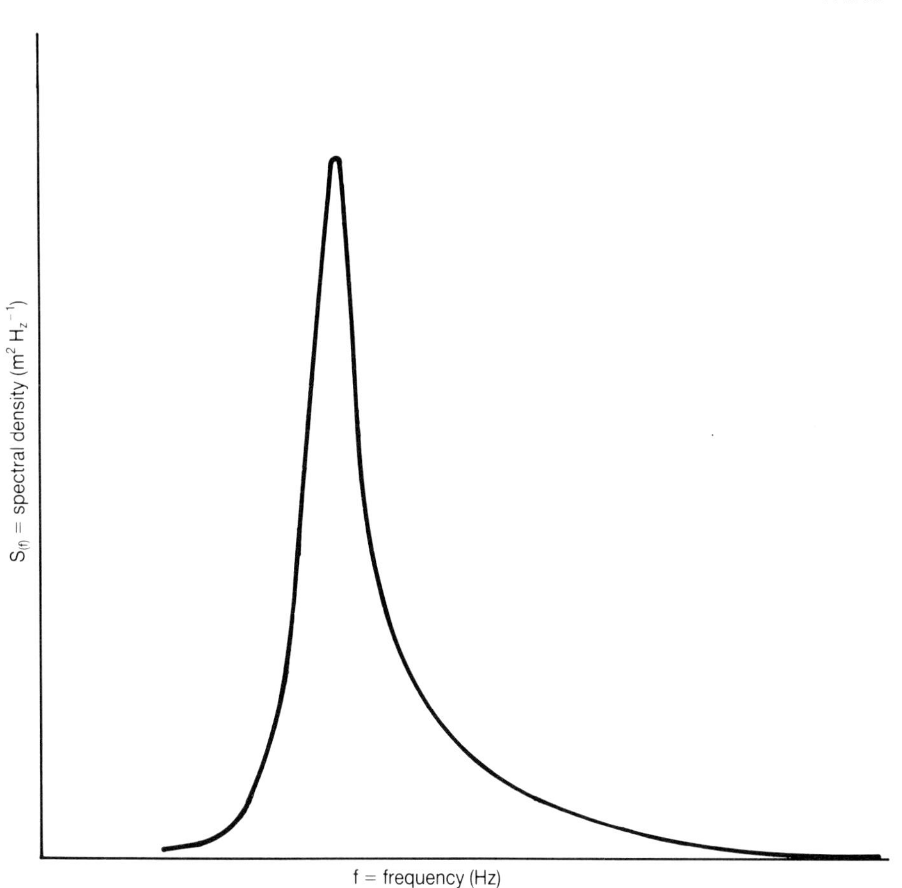

Figure 4.5 Typical wave spectrum

and zero crossing period of T_z is related to T_p by the equation

$$T_p = 1.4T_z$$

Many more relationships may be utilized for PM or JONSWAP spectra.

Tucker–Draper method

The method is described in two papers by Tucker[17] and Draper[18]. Basically, the method takes advantage of the statistical distribution of wave heights found in nature, enabling the parameters of interest to be evaluated manually from a limited number of measurements on a record. If computer analysis is not available, this is recommended as the fastest manual technique.

4.4.5 Predicting waves from wave data

The synthesis of the wave data from wind records is referred to as wave 'hindcasting'. It is a way of estimating the wave conditions which would have resulted given the wind speed, fetch (distance over which the wind blows), water depth over the fetch, and wind duration. The scope of a hindcast study can vary enormously. On the one hand, a simple and quick exercise can be undertaken using prepared wave forecasting charts. This is particularly useful in the initial stages of a project. Alternatively, computer models can determine, with much greater thoroughness, wave conditions at a single point or over a wide area. The choice of hindcast method will depend on the nature of the project and the availability of other data. This section outlines the underlying principles, together within the data requirements for undertaking a hindcast study.

The magnitude of waves generated by a given wind speed can be limited either by the fetch length or by the wind duration (and, to a lesser degree, water depth). Hand analysis will, more often than not, be undertaken using tabulations of wind frequency (i.e. occurrence of wind by speed and direction). This method gives no information on the duration of the wind condition, and this can lead to some uncertainties in the results, especially where very long fetches are concerned. The problem can be overcome by computer analysis. Because very large quantities of data can be processed by computer it is possible to hindcast waves from 'hour-by-hour' wind records, and hence the duration of any specific condition is implicit to the analysis[23].

Methods for hindcasting waves from wind and fetch data can be considered in two categories:

- Those which predict a wave height and period from which a typical wave spectrum can be inferred and the principal methods are the SMB (Sverdup, Monk and Bretschneider[19]) and the Darbyshire–Draper.[20]
- Those which describe the wave spectrum directly, and the most commonly used types are the PM (Pierson–Moskowitz[16]) spectrum and JONSWAP (Joint North Sea Wave Project[15]).

The basic data required for any kind of wave hindcast are wind (speed and direction), fetch and depth. Calibration data are desirable and should be used if available.

Wind data

Potential sources of wind data are discussed in Section 4.3.2. Often published wind data relate to average hourly wind speeds, or gusts. Procedures have been developed to take account of different durations. An example is given in the *Shore Protection Manual*[14].

Four hindcasting methods

SMB method

This method uses empirical expressions derived from comprehensive observations at locations in the North Pacific, North Atlantic and Great Lakes. The expressions, which are reproduced in the *Shore Protection Manual*[14], yield values of significant wave height H_s and corresponding significant wave period (T_s). The expressions are expanded as a series of graphs corresponding to deep water conditions and to a range of finite water depths.

Darbyshire–Draper method

The Darbyshire–Draper method is based on observations around the UK coast and is considered to be valid only for these areas. Produced as a set of design curves, the method facilitates the prediction of the maximum wave height occurring in a 10-min duration. This is said to be approximately equal to 1.6 H_s.

PM spectrum

The PM spectrum is essentially a special case of the JONSWAP spectrum although it is simpler and was devised before JONSWAP. Because it assumes fully developed seas, the PM formulation is defined purely in terms of the wind speed.

JONSWAP spectrum

JONSWAP uses a formula derived from observations in the southern North Sea during the Joint North Sea Wave Project. It is applicable to sites facing semi-enclosed bodies of water such as the North Sea, the English Channel and the Irish Sea.

The December 1986 amendment of BS 6349 Part 1[1] introduced the graphical presentation of JONSWAP to supersede the SMB version. The graph, which gives H_s and T_p, cannot be used to derive the spectrum, for which the JONSWAP formulae must be referred to.

Fetch and depth

Information on basic fetch and water depth can be obtained from Admiralty and other charts. Small-scale charts with sufficient coverage to include boundary coastlines will be required in addition to those covering the area of interest in more detail. Fetch length depends upon the exact direction chosen from a given point. It is necessary to average the different lengths in order to arrive at a representative fetch for a specified arc of wind wave attack. This has been a matter of some conjecture: BS 6349 adopted the same approach as the *Shore Protection Manual* (prior to 1984) whereby an 'effective fetch' was calculated from a series of radial fetch lengths for irregular coastlines. For narrow-fetch conditions (i.e. those limited in width, e.g. by estuary boundaries) a reduction factor was proposed. This was superseded by the amendment of December 1986 which states that 'the fetch used in wave forecasting techniques should ideally be restricted to one within which the wind speed does not vary by more than 2.5 m/s from the mean speed and the wind direction does not vary by more than 30°'. The 1984 version of the *Shore Protection Manual* also rejected the concept of effective fetch for narrow-fetch conditions and in the same edition modified its methods for evaluating fetches for irregular coastlines. The revised methods of evaluating fetch lengths, referred to above, accompanied changes in the proposed methods of predicting waves in the respective publications. The designer should use the most up-to-date information, but more importantly, he should apply the procedures according to one reference only. Engineering judgement will be as important as strict adherence to formalized procedures.

Calibration data

Calibration may take the form of a limited amount of instrumentally recorded wave data. The corresponding synthetic wave data can be hindcast for the same period. Comparison between the measured and the synthesized data provides a basis for adjusting certain parameters within the hindcast procedure in order to improve the accuracy of the results. It is particularly appropriate in the computer hindcasting methods when such trimming can allow the production of long-term directional wave statistics.

4.4.6 Shallow water effects

As waves travel towards the shore they are modified by shallow water, i.e. water of a depth less than one half of the wavelength. However, waves tend not to be modified significantly until they enter water depths of less than one quarter or even one tenth of the wave length. The effects are not amenable to manual analysis in a number of cases, as discussed below. Computational models are necessary for a thorough assessment. These are discussed in Appendix B. The various shallow water effects are as follows.

Refraction by shallow depths

As waves enter shallow water they slow down. If wave crests are not parallel to contours, i.e. if their approach contours obliquely, they 'bend' as a direct result of the slowing, being focused onto shallow areas that protrude from the shore (Figures 4.6 and 4.7). This focusing increases wave heights locally so that, often, headlands suffer a more severe wave activity than adjacent bays. Because of their longer wave lengths, refraction effects are greater with longer-period than with shorter-period waves in the same depth of water.

The general effect of wave refraction is:

- To bend wave rays (orthogonals) so that they become more perpendicular to the coastline;
- To change the distance between rays.

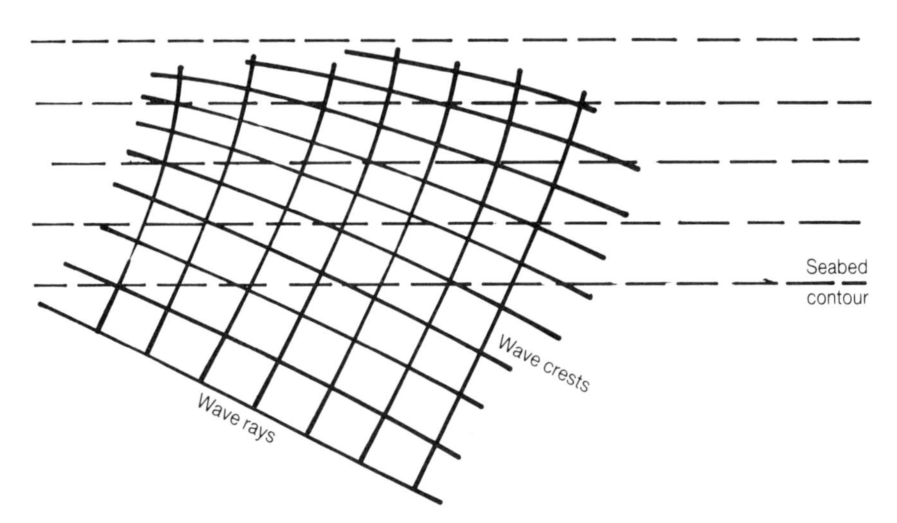

Figure 4.6 Wave rays and crests approaching a regular shoreline

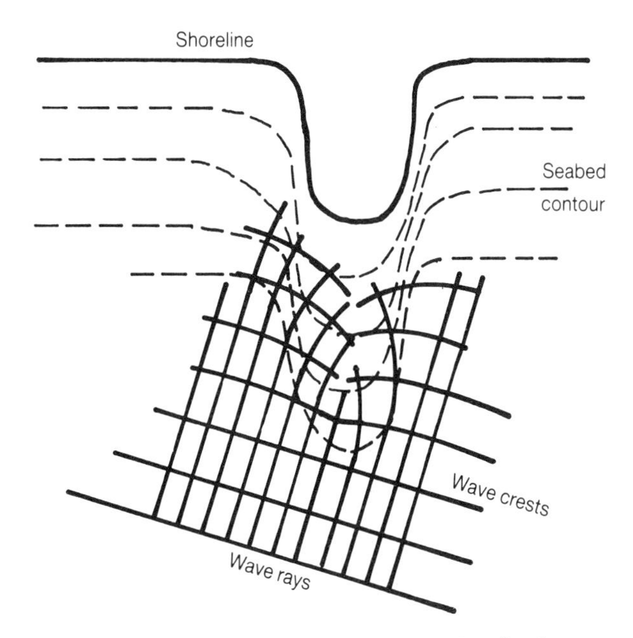

Figure 4.7 Wave rays and crests focusing on headland

On coasts which approximate reasonably well to the idealized case of straight and parallel seabed contours, hand calculation of refraction (by depth) can be carried out[14] for individual (regular) waves. If contours are irregular then relatively simple computer models can be used (Appendix B) which can also be employed to calculate transformation of wave spectra. Where contours are very irregular, diffraction becomes important because of the severe focusing due to refraction.

Refraction by currents

In areas where there are reasonably strong currents or tidal streams these may refract waves. The effects are largest where there is a large spatial change in current speed or direction, and where wave periods are short (the opposite to the case with depth refraction). Because of the complexity of current refraction, analysis is best carried out by computer.

Shoaling

When waves slow down because of shallow water or currents the form of the wave is modified. This leads to a change in wave height. Because shoaling is caused by change in velocity it is inextricably linked with refraction, and both are best evaluated together.

Diffraction

Diffraction refers to the phenomenon when wave energy travels in a direction different from that of the wave rays. The most widely known examples of diffraction are the spreading of waves into the shadow areas behind breakwaters. Diffraction also occurs when wave rays are strongly focused as a result of refraction. In this latter case the effect of diffraction is to smooth out the spatial changes of wave height caused by focusing.

In simple cases diffraction around breakwaters can be estimated manually from standard graphs[1]. The *Shore Protection Manual*[14] gives a technique for assessing diffraction around offshore breakwaters. Diffraction associated with focusing, insofar as it occurs in situations where there is complex refraction, is best analysed, along with refraction, in a numerical model.

Bed friction

In shallow water wave energy can be lost through friction at the seabed with consequent reduction in wave heights. The rate of loss is a function of water depth, wave height, wave length and the nature of the seabed. The effects of bed friction are greatest in extensive shallow areas and least where the foreshore slopes steeply into deep water. Friction losses in certain cases can be estimated manually using graphs in the *Shore Protection Manual*. It is frequently advisable to include for bed friction in numerical models of wave refraction (Appendix B).

Wave breaking

When, as is often the case, seawalls are fronted by shallow water, the wave height reaching the wall is limited by breaking, in that waves higher than a critical value will break. Derivation of the maximum breaking wave that can reach a seawall is given in the *Shore Protection Manual* although this is based on regular waves. This gives maximum breaking wave height in terms of water depth, foreshore slope and wave period (see Figure 4.8).

Alternatively, H_b for irregular waves can be derived from the expression by Vincent[24].

$$H_b = \frac{1.17(\alpha g d)^{\frac{1}{2}}}{\pi} T_p$$

where d = water depth and α = the Phillips constant in the JONSWAP formula[15], often taken as 0.0081 for a fully developed sea (from Hasselman *et al*[15].).

The value of H_b derived from this expression should be compared with the inshore significant wave height predicted without consideration to breaking, to assess the significance of breaking. If breaking is significant, higher waves within the spectrum

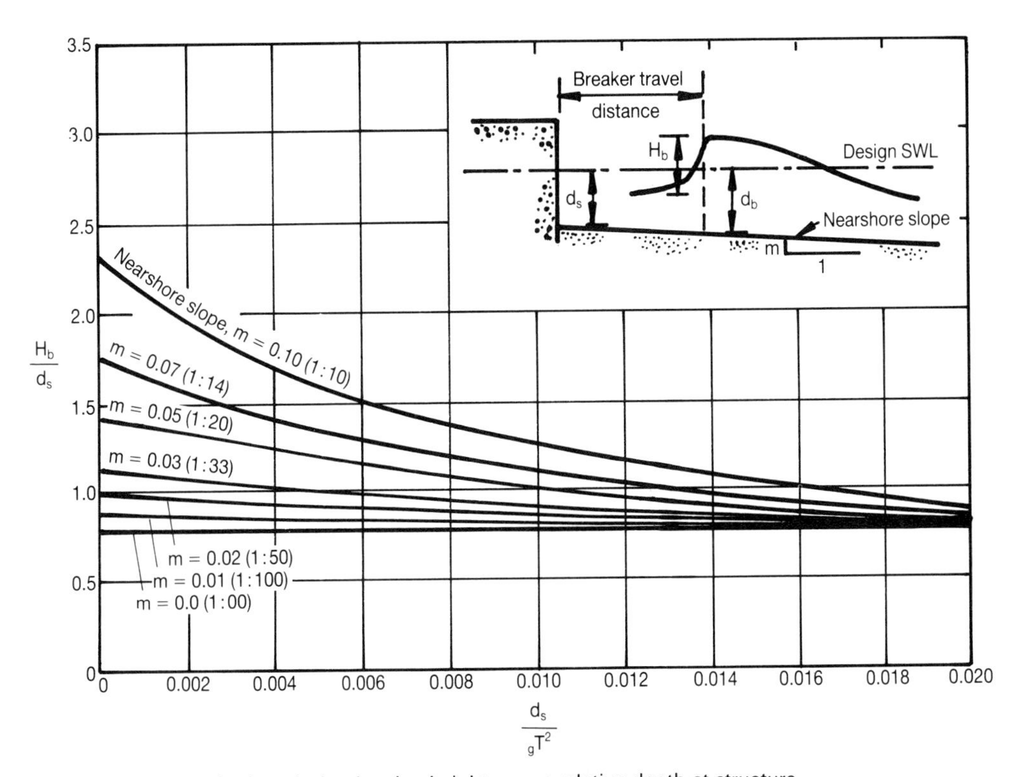

Figure 4.8 Dimensionless design breaker height versus relative depth at structure

are more likely to be destroyed than smaller ones, so use of the normal relationships between H_{max}, $H_{1/100}$, etc. and H_s might be expected to be conservative.

Neither of the above two references presents methods which are universally applicable. It is recommended that they be used with caution and, if necessary, a physical model should be employed.

Finally, where waves break offshore, over banks or bars, this should be allowed for. In such circumstances it has been found that the maximum significant wave height inshore of the banks is approximately 50–55% of the depth of water over them. Wave energy losses due to breaking can be incorporated into many numerical models of shallow water waves, although the techniques are not fully proven.

Wind

Where the shallow water extends some distance from the shore, such that it constitutes a significant fetch for the generation of waves, then wind gain of energy should be allowed for in the analysis of shallow water effects. Computer models can include this aspect.

Shallow water effects are many and complex. Scale effects and the size of the area covered preclude complete physical models. The phenomena are too complex as yet for the engineer to be absolutely confident of results from numerical models, although they are invaluable tools (see Southgate[25]). Such models should therefore be backed up with field data with which to calibrate them (see Appendix B).

4.4.7 Extreme events

Extreme wave conditions which are chosen for design purposes are usually specified by their return periods. These should be predicted using the derived offshore conditions on the basis of statistical extrapolation techniques and subsequently transferred inshore.

Once an acceptable set of wave data has been established, a probability distribution needs to be fitted to it. To do this, the wave data are collected into bands of significant wave height. The frequencies of occurrence of significant wave heights within each band are then calculated. These values can be combined to give the frequency of occurrence of significant wave heights greater than any particular value. Graphs of these frequencies of occurrence are known as exceedance curves. When wave data are presented in this form they have usually been found to fit a standard statistical distribution function with reasonable accuracy. Two of the most commonly used distributions are the Weibull function and the Fisher–Tippett I function, shown below, although other distributions such as Gumbel and Log-normal can also be used, as suggested by the Flood Studies Report[10].

- *Weibull function*

  $P(x) = \exp[-(x-\alpha)/\beta]$

- *Fisher–Tippett I function*

  $P(x) = 1-\exp[-\exp'-(x-\gamma)/\delta]]$

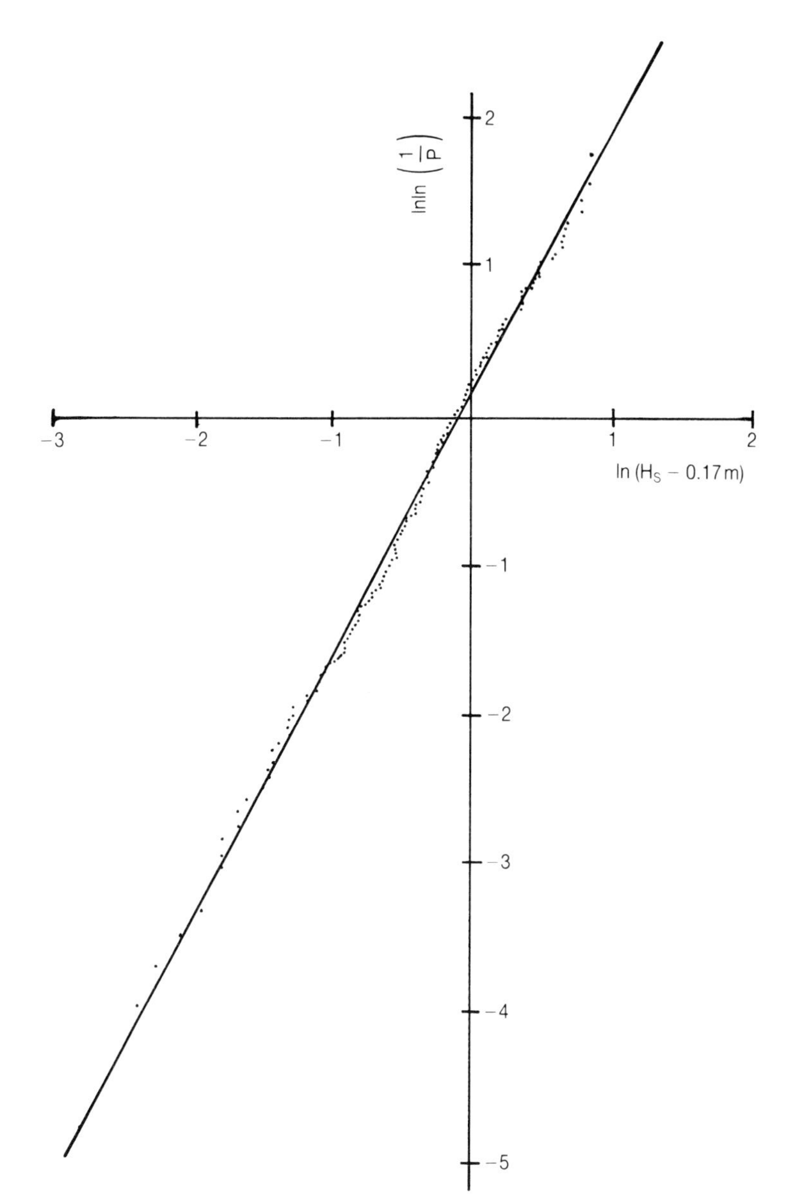

Figure 4.9 Weibull distribution of H_3 184 points (same as Figure 4.10)

where $P(x)$ is the probability of a wave length being greater than x, and α, β, γ and δ are parameters determined by fitting with the data. In the Weibull distribution a plot of $\log_e (1/P)$ against $\log_e(x-\alpha)$ will give a straight line, while in the Fisher–Tippett I distribution a plot of $-\log_e[\log_e(1-P)]$ against x will give a straight line.

Generally, wave data should be plotted using the Weibull, Fisher–Tippett I and, if necessary, other distributions, and the one which gives the best fit should be adopted, best fit being assessed visually and on the basis of the correlation coefficient. The best-fit distribution should be used to estimate extreme significant wave heights required for design. Figures 4.9 and 4.10 show, respectively, Weibull and Fisher–Tippett I distributions fitted to the same set of hindcast wave data. In this example, both distributions appear to give an equally good fit to the data. Normally, when

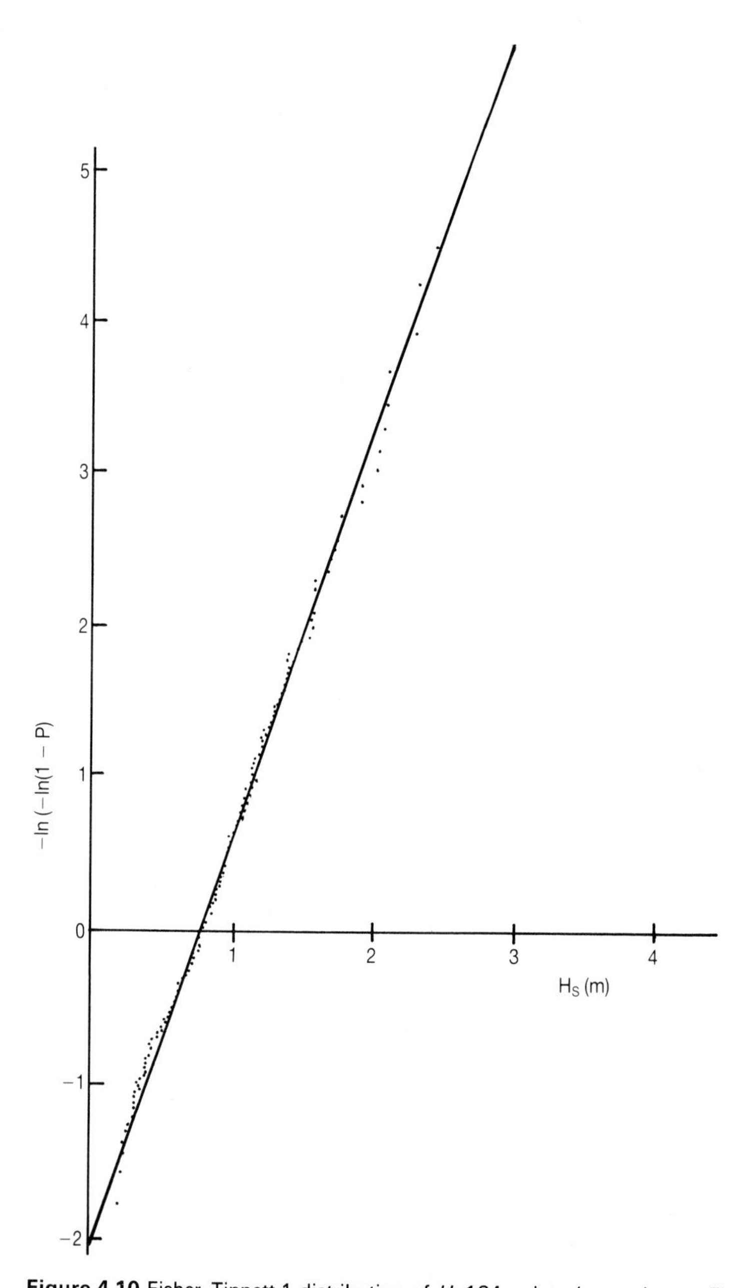

Figure 4.10 Fisher–Tippett 1 distribution of H_3 184 points (same data as Figure 4.9)

these distributions are extrapolated to find extreme significant wave heights, the Weibull distribution will give higher waves than the Fisher–Tippett I distribution. The distributions should be judged case by case, but the one giving the higher significant wave heights (usually Weibull) will be the more conservative.

In this method, extreme significant wave heights corresponding to severe storm events are determined. They can then be transferred inshore. Assuming that a Rayleigh distribution holds for extreme sea states, other wave height parameters corresponding to the extreme significant wave height can be determined. Extreme wave periods can be predicted in a similar manner. Often, the wave period, spectrum and storm duration corresponding to a particular extreme wave height are required. These quantities are difficult to predict, and some very broad simplifying assumptions have to be made. For instance, in predicting the wave period it is assumed that the wave steepness (ratio of wave height to wavelength) is the same in extreme storms as in the measured storms. In predicting the full wave spectrum the same spectral shape (in terms of dimensionless parameters) as measured storms is assumed. Storm durations can be estimated if the measured wave data show a correlation between the storm duration and maximum wave height, which can then be extrapolated.

The problem of predicting extreme waves which will occur at the same time as a high water level is somewhat more complex. This topic is discussed in more detail in the next section.

4.5 Joint probabilities of waves and water levels

Wave run-up elevations or overtopping discharges from wave action at a seawall depend on both the still water level and the wave conditions. In most situations, this means that the same run-up or wave overtopping can be caused by high water levels coupled with modest wave action, or by severe wave action occurring at lower water levels, or by various intermediate combinations. In order to determine how frequently waves will overtop the seawall it is therefore necessary to identify all the possible combinations of waves and water levels which can cause the wave overtopping, and then to sum up the frequencies of occurrence of all those combinations. For this purpose, it is necessary to know the joint probability of given wave conditions occurring simultaneously with a given water level.

Methods of determining joint probabilities of waves and water levels are still the subject of continuing research, and no standard methods have yet evolved. However, this section gives brief descriptions of various methods which have been used with differing degrees of success.

4.5.1 Dependence of waves and water levels

Joint probabilities of occurrence of waves and water levels are relatively straightforward to determine when waves and water levels are either fully dependent on each other or are fully independent. However, in most practical cases the occurrence of given wave conditions is neither fully dependent nor fully independent of water level.

Figure 4.11 illustrates that waves are caused mainly by meteorological forces, whereas total water levels are the result of a combination of astronomical and meteorological forces. The degree of dependence will therefore vary considerably from site to site. The worst situation will occur at locations satisfying the following conditions:

- Relatively low tidal range;
- Relatively large surge height;
- Surges typically accompanied by strong onshore winds;
- Wave conditions limited by available water depth.

Under these conditions the seawall would have to be designed to withstand both the highest water level and the largest waves acting simultaneously.

4.5.2 Data requirements

The most accurate method of determining the joint probabilities of occurrence of waves and water levels is by examining long-term simultaneous records of the various parameters. These records would preferably cover at least ten years, with measurements at hourly intervals, although three-hourly intervals (the normal standard for wave records) or at every high water would be acceptable. However, simultaneous records are rarely available, mainly because there are very few locations where wave measurements have been carried out for periods longer than about a year. Almost always, therefore, the wave conditions have to be hindcast from wind data which fortunately are more readily available (see Section 4.4.5).

When long-term records of water levels and wind conditions (or, more rarely, wave conditions) can be obtained they should be in the form of an hourly time series of records of:

- Water levels – recorded water level;
- Waves – height, period, direction, spectral shape;
- Winds – speed, direction, duration.

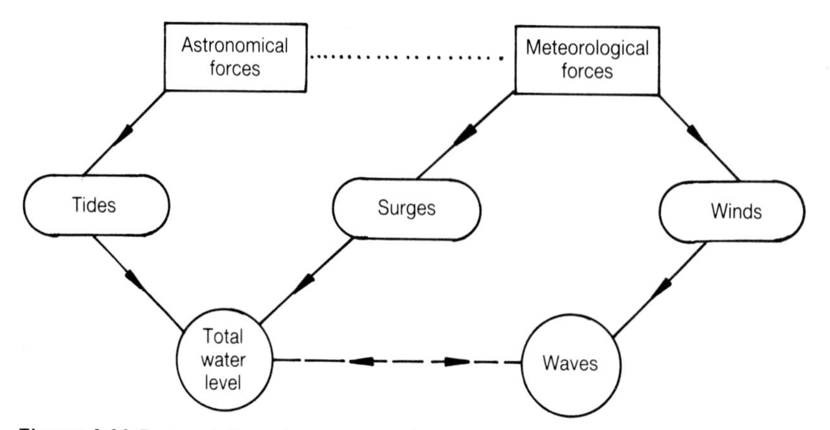

Figure 4.11 Factors influencing waves and water levels

Examples of the dependence of waves and water levels

(a) Surges in the Severn Estuary are caused by deep depressions moving rapidly across the Atlantic towards the British Isles and making their landfall in Northern Ireland or further north. In the Severn Estuary these depressions cause winds which are broadly westerly, approximately aligned with the main axis of the estuary. Along coastlines facing west (for example, near Weston-super-Mare) large surges are therefore likely to be accompanied by large waves. However, the surges are quite small compared with the tidal range, so the degree of dependence between waves and total water level is likely to be quite weak.

(b) Surges in the Outer Thames Estuary are caused by deep depressions moving rapidly down the North Sea from north-east Scotland to the Low Countries. In the southern North Sea these depressions cause north to north-westerly winds, which blow across the width of the estuary. Along the northern banks of the estuary (for example, near Southend) there will therefore be virtually no wave action during large surges. The surges here are quite large compared with the tidal range, so the degree of dependence between waves and water levels will be fairly strong, but with a negative correlation. In other words, at this location extreme water levels are very unlikely to be accompanied by large waves.

The exact requirement will depend largely on the purpose of the joint probability calculation. In many instances some of the wave parameters can be omitted because their effects on the output parameter under consideration (e.g. overtopping) are either unknown or are insignificant.

Discussion of required wave parameters

Wave height, H — This information is always required.

Wave period, T — Often wave steepness (wave height/wave length) at a particular site tends towards a constant value under storm conditions. The wave period is then directly related to wave height. Provided sufficient data are available to establish a typical steepness value, long-term records of wave period are not necessary.

Wave direction, θ — At shallow water sites, wave refraction will cause most storm waves to arrive at the coastline from an almost constant direction. At these sites long-term records of wave direction would not be necessary.

Spectral shape — For most hydrodynamic processes at a seawall the precise effects of spectral shape are unknown. Long-term records of spectral shape are rarely used.

4.5.3 Analysis of long-term records

The methods of analysis of the data will depend on:

- The type of information;
- The purpose of the joint probability calculations.

As mentioned earlier, research on this topic is still continuing and new methods are constantly being developed. The descriptions which follow are procedures to be used for good data sets. Those which are required for lesser data sets are shown in Section 4.5.4.

When good data on winds and water levels are available the first requirement is to assemble long sequences (say, ten years) of simultaneous values of water level and wave parameters at the particular site. Frequently the available information may be for nearby rather than at the site itself and some adjustments may be needed.

Once a long-term simultaneous data set of water levels and wave conditions has been assembled, the opportunities for further analysis are considerable. First, the data can be scanned to determine how frequently a given value of one of the parameters, such as wave height or water level, is equalled in the duration of the data set. Second, they can be examined to see how frequently given values of pairs of parameters occur. Finally, they can be studied for the occurrence of given values of groups of three or more parameters. This is clearly not straightforward but is often very useful, especially when the requirement is to extrapolate to extremes. It is discussed further in Section 4.5.5.

4.5.4 Synthesis from limited records

When a long-term simultaneous data set cannot be assembled the first step is to derive from the available data the probability density function for each of the main parameters (i.e. to establish the expression describing how frequently, for example, a given wave height or water level occurs). For the analysis to proceed further, a certain degree of dependence between the various individual parameters has to be assumed or deduced. At the simplest level, these assumptions may take the form:

- Waves and water levels are either fully independent or fully dependent;
- Wave heights and periods are fully dependent;
- All waves arrive at the seawall at the worst possible direction.

As noted in Section 4.5.3, neither of the wave and water level assumptions are likely to be correct, but the results obtained by repeating the calculations for both these assumptions will give the two limits within which the 'true' answer will lie. At that stage the engineer should judge whether at his particular site the waves and water levels are more likely to be fully independent or fully dependent, and bias the estimated results accordingly.

At a slightly more sophisticated level, the assumptions about waves and water levels can be replaced by:

- Wave heights and surges are either fully independent or fully dependent (positive correlation) or mutually exclusive (negative correlation);
- Surges and predicted tides are fully independent.

Since waves and surges are largely covered by meteorological events whereas tides are generated by astronomical forces, this second set of assumptions is rather more logical. However, more information is required on water levels, including a breakdown of the recorded levels into the two components of predicted tide and surge residual.

Translation of information from nearby records

(a) Water levels

These may be adjusted by one of two methods as follows:

- Assume that surges behave in the same way as predicted tides. Use the standard procedures for transferring predicted tide levels from a standard port to a secondary port; (See Admiralty Tide Tables.[5])
- Separate out the surge and predicted tide components. Adjust the predicted tide using standard procedures. Either assume that the surge height is unchanged between the two locations or if there are sufficient data use an empirical correction factor. Recombine the adjusted predicted tide and surge height.

(b) Wave data

Wave data will probably need considerable analysis before they can be used for joint probability calculations. They are unlikely to include information on wave direction, or to be of more than one year's duration. In order to extend the data set and introduce direction it should be combined with the available wind data.

Typically, the following steps should be performed:

- Collect mean hourly windspeeds and directions for the period of the wave data set (Section 4.3.3);
- Hindcast wave conditions at the recording site for the same period (Section 4.4.5). In some cases wave refraction calculations may also have to be carried out;
- Calibrate the wave hindcasting technique by comparing the calculated with the recorded wave conditions; and
- After calibration, calculate wave conditions at the required locations, using wind data obtained for the entire period of the water level data set.

A long-term data set of wave height, periods and directions will thus have been assembled for the particular site. This can then be combined with the long-term water level data set by matching the times of each record.

Discussion of useful pairs of parameters to examine

Wave height/wave period: this can be plotted to produce a scatter diagram often used in wave data analysis and gives guidance on the wave periods most likely to accompany large wave heights.

Wave height/wave direction gives guidance on the most likely direction of large waves.

Wave height/surge residual will give some indication of any interdependence between waves and surges at the particular site (see Table 4.2).

Wave height/water level indicates whether there is any correlation between these two parameters (see Table 4.3).

Surge residual/predicted tide level: at some sites large surges tend not to occur at the same time as high water levels, and this tabulation indicates whether this is so at the particular site.

Table 4.2 Joint occurrence of hourly wave heights and surge residuals, Dover

			Surge residual (m)						
		Totals	*-1.2*	*-0.8*	*-0.4*	*0*	*+0.4*	*+0.8*	*+1.2 +1.6*
	Totals	65 222	23	644	34 459	28 494	1466	129	7
Significant wave height (m)	3.5								
		4	0	0	3	1	0	0	0
	3.0								
		114	3	14	66	24	7	0	0
	2.5								
		887	7	77	428	334	39	2	0
	2.0								
		2857	4	136	1284	1301	123	9	0
	1.5								
		8417	8	194	4261	3734	217	3	0
	1.0								
		24 804	1	138	14 278	9995	355	33	4
	0.5								
		28 139	0	85	14 139	13 105	725	82	3

Notes: All wave directions. Water depth 7.7 m at mean tide level. Record duration 1 February 1971 to 30 November 1979.

Table 4.3 Joint occurrence of hourly water levels and wave heights, Dover 1971–1979

Significant wave height (m)	Totals	Still water level (tide and surge) (metres above MSL) -4.0 – -3.0	-3.0 – -2.0	-2.0 – -1.0	-1.0 – 0.0	0.0 – 1.0	1.0 – 2.0	2.0 – 3.0	3.0 – 4.0	4.0 – 5.0
Totals	65 222	565	9489	13 261	9470	9106	12 414	10 036	879	2
3.5 – 3.0	4	0	0	0	0	0	1	3	0	0
3.0 – 2.5	114	0	9	12	17	17	29	28	2	0
2.5 – 2.0	887	4	87	135	133	159	220	139	10	0
2.0 – 1.5	2857	23	304	522	383	443	664	487	31	0
1.5 – 1.0	8417	53	956	1539	1160	1241	1928	1451	89	0
1.0 – 0.5	24 804	231	3812	5212	3666	3410	4606	3597	270	0
≤ 0.5	28 139	254	4321	5841	4111	3836	4966	4331	477	2

An example of outline calculations for non-simultaneous data sets

Assumptions

(a) Tides and surges are independent.
(b) Waves and surges are fully dependent (i.e. large waves occur simultaneously with large surges).

Procedure

1. From the available data, establish the probability density functions (pdfs) for total water level, predicted tide level, recorded surge residuals, and wave height.

2. Select the required total water level. Identify all possible combinations of predicted tide and surge residual (positive or negative) which can jointly cause the required total level. Calculate the joint probability of occurrence of each combination by multiplying together the individual probabilities of the surge and tide.

3. For each combination identified above, estimate the most likely wave height. This is obtained from the pdf for wave heights by setting the probability equal to the surge height probability (full dependence). The likelihood of the given total water level being accompanied by this particular wave height is then simply the joint probability of occurrence of the particular tide/surge combination.

4. Repeat steps 2 and 3 for different water levels. By summation, derive the joint probabilities of given water levels and given wave heights being equalled or exceeded. By further summation over all wave heights, the resulting probabilities for total water level should agree reasonably well with those derived directly from the measured total levels. If they do not, then the assumption that tides and surges are independent is incorrect.

The degree of sophistication of the joint probability calculations, or guidance on the most appropriate assumptions to make, can be improved if some simultaneous data are available, even if this is not sufficiently extensive or detailed for a full and straightforward analysis.

It will be evident that these techniques unavoidably involve subjective judgement. It is recommended that the engineer seek specialist advice before undertaking such a study, since the consequences of underestimation of water levels can be serious.

4.5.5 Extrapolation to extremes

Simultaneous data sets of waves and water levels, whether obtained directly from measurements or synthesized from other data, will typically be about 10–20 years'

An example of the estimation of extreme run-up elevations (single-parameter method)

Assumptions

(a) All waves arrive at the seawall in the same direction.
(b) All waves have approximately the same steepness.
(c) $R_2 = 2H_s$, where $R_2 = 2\%$ run-up elevation above still water level.
(d) Frequencies of occurrence of given water level/wave height combinations are as indicated in Table 4.3.

Procedure

1. For all water level/wave height combinations calculate the wave run-up elevation above datum.
2. Identify all combinations which give the same run-up level. In Table 4.3 this gives a set of diagonal 'contour' lines (Table 4.4).
3. By summing along each diagonal, calculate the number of occurrences of each run-up elevation.
4. Fit a standard probability density function to the run-up occurrences and extrapolate as necessary (Figure 4.12).

duration. It will therefore not be possible to deduce directly the extreme conditions corresponding to return periods of, say, 50 or 100 years. For this purpose, some form of probability density function has to be fitted to the data and then extrapolated to the required extreme event. For a single parameter this is quite straightforward using standard techniques, whereas for two or more parameters occurring simultaneously the necessary calculations are much more complex. If possible, therefore, the parameters should be grouped together to form a single new parameter, preferably the required output parameter (e.g. run-up elevation, overtopping discharge, wave forces, longshore power, etc.). However, there are some occasions when conversion to a single parameter is not possible. In this case, extreme values of the input parameters have to be estimated and the extreme value of the output parameters calculated from these extremes.

Single-parameter extrapolation

For this method every possible combination of the various input parameters is replaced by a single value of output parameter. This requires that the output parameter can be represented as an empirical or theoretical function of the input parameters (typically, water level, wave height, period and direction). If a simultaneous data set has been assembled this is a relatively straightforward though perhaps rather tedious process, especially if three or more input parameters are involved. However, to illustrate the principles of this method a simple example involving only two parameters is given.

The example uses only two input parameters, but in principle the same method can

Table 4.4 Example contours of equal wave run-up

Significant wave height (m)	*Totals*	Still water level (tide and surge) (metres above MSL): −4.0 to −3.0	−3.0 to −2.0	−2.0 to −1.0	−1.0 to 0.0	0.0 to 1.0	1.0 to 2.0	2.0 to 3.0	3.0 to 4.0	4.0 to 5.0
Totals	65 222	565	9489	13 261	9470	9106	12 414	10 036	879	2
3.5–3.0	4	0	0	0	0	0	1	3	0	0
3.0–2.5	114	0	9	12	17	17	29	28	2	0
2.5–2.0	887	4	87	135	133	159	220	139	10	0
2.0–1.5	2857	23	304	522	383	443	664	487	31	0
1.5–1.0	8417	53	956	1539	1160	1241	1928	1451	89	0
1.0–0.5	24 804	231	3812	5212	3666	3410	4606	3597	270	0
0.5	28 139	254	4321	5841	4111	3836	4966	4331	477	2

Wave run-up (metres above MSL): -3.0, -2.0, -1.0, 0.0, 1.0, 2.0, 3.0, 4.0, 5.0, 6.0, 7.0, 8.0, 9.0, 10.0, 11.0

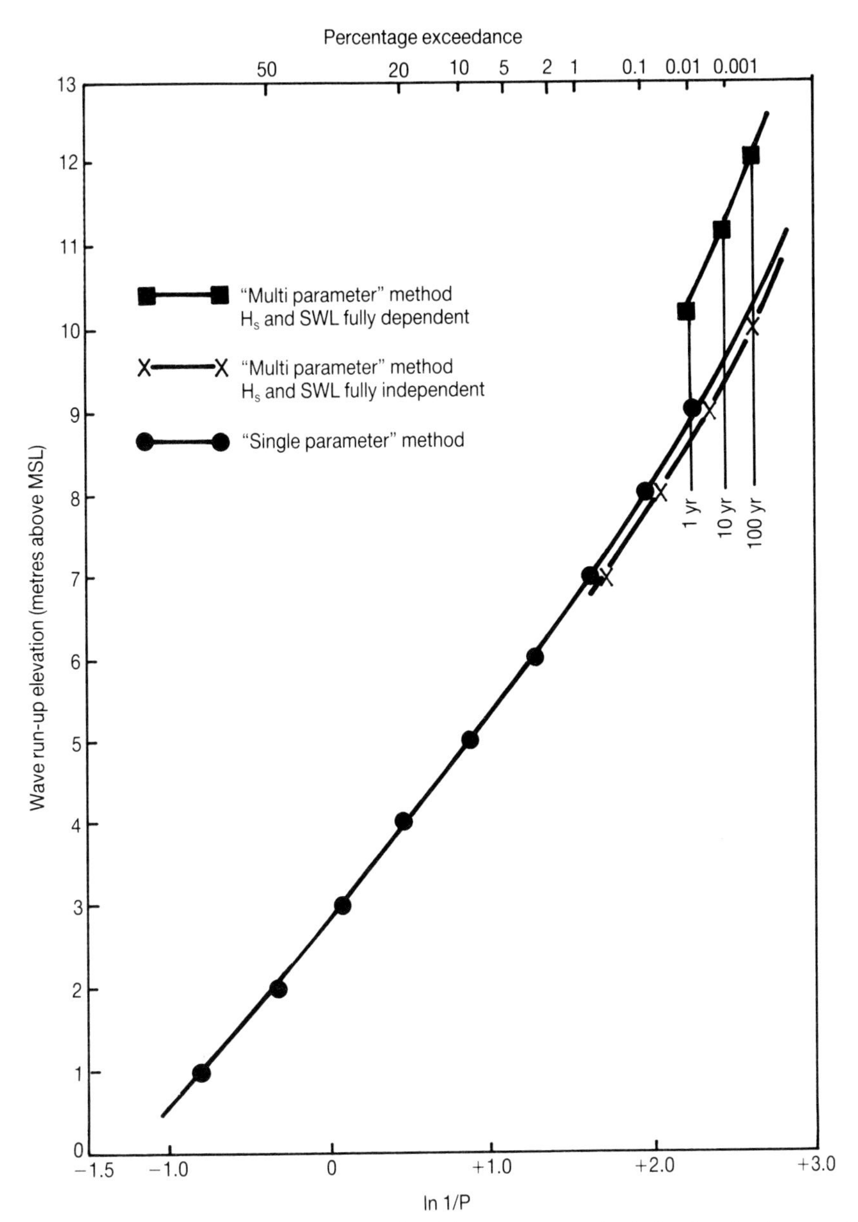

Figure 4.12 Comparison of single- and multi-parameter methods for the simple case of two input variables

An example of partial correlation of input parameters

Given

Data set which appears to show that large surge residuals have a tendency to be accompanied by large waves, but that this is not always the case.

Outline procedure

1. For a given surge residual, determine the pdf for wave heights and note the coefficients of the distribution.
2. Repeat for different surge residuals.
3. Prepare a graph showing the variation of these distribution coefficients with surge residual height. If there is in fact no significant correlation, then the coefficients will probably show scatter without any noticeable trend.
4. Extrapolate the graph to estimate the distribution coefficients for extreme surges and thus derive the pdf for extreme surges.
5. Use the extrapolated pdf to estimate the likelihood of the extreme wave height occurring simultaneously with the extreme surge.

be applied to groups of three or more parameters. For example, suppose that the wave steepness and the wave direction were not constant. Wave run-up above still water level would then be a function of wave height, period and direction. In this case it would probably be necessary to take each entry in the simultaneous data set in turn and evaluate the run-up elevation for each. The new synthesized wave run-up data set is then sorted to give the frequencies of occurrence of given values of run-up elevation.

Multi-parameter extrapolation

Conversion to a single output parameter is sometimes not possible, either because:

- A simultaneous data set is not available; or
- The behaviour of the seawall during extreme events is totally different from that under normal conditions.

In these cases multi-parameter extrapolations have to be carried out. First, the required extreme value of each individual input parameter is calculated. The next stage is to determine the likelihood of the extreme values of two or more of the input parameters, such as wave height and water level, occurring simultaneously.

For this it is necessary either to assume or to deduce a correlation between pairs of input parameters. Some of the common assumptions which are made were discussed

An example of the estimation of extreme run-up elevations (multi-parameter method)

Assumptions
(a)–(c) As in the previous run-up example.
(d) Waves and water levels are either fully dependent or fully independent.
(e) The frequencies of occurrence of given water levels and given wave heights are as given in the top row and first column, respectively, of Table 4.3.

Outline procedure
1. Fit pdf's to water level and wave height, respectively.

2. Identify all water level/wave height combinations which can lead to extreme run-up elevations.

3. For each combination calculate the joint probability of occurrence either by:

- Multiplying together the individual probability (fully independent case);
- Considering only those combinations where the waves and water levels have the same probability of occurrence (fully dependent case) and take this probability of occurrence as the joint probability.

4. In the fully independent case, sum the joint probabilities of all possible combinations to give the probability of occurrence of the required run-up elevation.

5. Plot the results as shown in Figure 4.12. Since the assumptions (d) (i.e. whether the two parameters are fully dependent or fully independent) represent the two extreme situations, the results bracket those obtained by the single-parameter method, as expected. In this particular case, the single-parameter method (involving no assumptions about wave height/water level dependence) gives results very similar to the fully independent assumption. An experienced coastal engineer looking at the possible causes of large surges in the Straits of Dover would probably come to the same conclusion.

in Section 4.5.4. However, when there are good-quality data available the degree of correlation between pairs of input parameters can often be deduced directly, although some extrapolation will always still be necessary. In most cases any correlation derived from the data will be partial.

Once the degree of correlation between various input parameters has been established, either by deduction or by assumption, the next stage is to identify all possible combinations of parameters which can cause the extreme joint event. By summing the probabilities of occurrence of each possible combination the probability of occurrence of each joint event can be obtained.

In some instances, multi-parameter extrapolations can be complex, especially if the various parameters are neither fully dependent or fully independent but are partially correlated. For example, wind speed and wind direction may be partly related to the surge residual, whereas the wind duration may be almost independent of surges, and the surge residual may be almost independent of predicted tide level. To estimate the likelihood of a given extreme total level (tide plus surge) occurring simultaneously with a given extreme wave height therefore requires a summation of probabilities over five partially correlated parameters, for each of which the probability density function has been extrapolated to extremes. This illustrates quite clearly that the biggest drawback of this method compared to the single-parameter method is the possibility of large errors in the final result, as the errors in each of the individual extrapolations accumulate through the calculation. If it is not possible to avoid the method of multi-parameter extrapolation, then the calculations should be repeated for different inter-parameter correlations to determine the sensitivity of the final result. Since the calculations are often very complex, this will almost always require that the calculations be performed by computer.

4.6 Topographic surveys

Good topographical data are required, as for all civil engineering works, to assist in defining the extent of the works, accesses, contractors' working areas, etc. In addition to these functions, the data are also needed for coastal projects as basic data for analysis.

In the latter case the data may cover:

- General ground levels in the hinterland to assess possible extent of flooding (see Chapter 8);
- Description of the coastal slope (see Section 4.8);
- Description of beach and coastline (see Section 4.9).

4.6.1 Data sources

The latest versions of Ordnance Survey maps (SUSIs – Supply of Unpublished Survey Information) should be obtained as the first step. These are available at scales of 1:1250 (urban areas) and 1:2500 (rural areas). Further useful data may be obtained from existing topographical surveys, and in this respect the local district council, county council, National Rivers Authority, etc. should be contacted. Drainage authority surveys of manhole cover levels can be particularly useful in giving general level data. All available data should be collated and deficiencies in coverage identified. The engineer should check on-site (by levelling) the validity of these old surveys. This will indicate the extent of additional survey work that will be required.

4.6.2 Surveying

Clearly, the requirements of the survey will vary from site to site. On land the survey data required will be similar to those for general works of civil engineering and could include:

- Locations of roads, pavements, buildings, etc.;
- Locations of services, manholes, outfalls, etc.;
- Points of environmental significance, e.g. trees and other features constituting constraints on the works.

The survey should cover features of likely interest to the engineer such as slips, springs and outcrops.

On the beach and foreshore it is likely that more new survey work will be required. This could include:

- Detailed surveys of the extent, profile and nature of beach structures, seawalls, groynes, slipways, breakwaters, etc.;
- Beach surveys.

Beach surveys would be concerned with the profile, line and shape of the beach itself. If the beach is granular it will be mobile and is likely to vary with time both in the short term (day by day), medium term (month by month or year by year) or in the long term. The changes can also be very large (more than 2 m fall overnight). The importance of these data and their use is discussed in Section 4.9. It should be noted that:

- The beach should, as a matter of good management, be surveyed at least twice a year;
- Surveys immediately after storms or other extreme events can give useful data on severe beach drawdown;
- The coverage should be of sufficient density to describe the beach (i.e. long straight beaches will require less dense coverage than ones with close groynes);
- For any individual location the beach surveys under consideration should extend several kilometres along the coast beyond the works in either direction;
- the data should be adequate to define the beach location, level and profile out sufficiently beyond low water to form a link with hydrographic surveys.

4.6.3 Beach profiles

Since beaches slope down towards the sea the logical method of surveying (using conventional topographic techniques) is to take profiles at right angles to the shore. These should extend landwards to the limit of the beach, which may be a seawall or permanent vegetation and as far seawards as practicable, but at least far enough to overlap with hydrographic survey work. To allow repeat surveys, alignment and the point of zero chainage must be accurately fixed and recoverable. The value of past beach profiles is all too often reduced because their precise position is no longer known. In line with good survey practice, sufficient levels should be taken along the profile to give a good description of the beach shape.

In selecting the spacing of beach profiles along the shore the ideals with respect to gaining a full description of the beach should be weighed against consideration of cost. While long lengths of straight or gently curving beaches can be adequately covered by profiles at, say, 100 to 400 m centres, an irregular beach (perhaps with groynes) is not so simple. In the immediate area of works to be constructed a fully detailed survey will be required (perhaps two or three profiles in each groyne bay), if only as a baseline survey for the construction contract. For annual monitoring of the overall behaviour of the beach, however, one should choose representative groyne bays. These could be of the order of every 100-600 m along the coast (but chosen to be representative). Within each chosen bay, the shape of the beach could be defined adequately by three profiles.

4.6.4 Photography

Aerial photogrammetry is a valid alternative to conventional topographical survey techniques as a means of obtaining beach profiles. It becomes more cost-effective on longer lengths of coast and in areas that are not easily accessible. Recent developments in the use of oblique photography offer further cost savings, and in certain areas can be used in comparative analyses of erosion and accretion to determine beach profiles. Conditional on suitable ground control being established, beach profiles can be derived. Advantages over conventional surveying techniques are:

- They allow greater flexibility in deriving the profiles: once the photographs are taken, as many profiles as required can be derived at any time in the future;
- They give a good overall picture of the beach which is, in itself, very useful in visually assessing coastal changes.

They are, of course, limited to that portion of the beach not covered by the tide at the time of the photograph.

4.7 Hydrographic surveys

In order to assist in understanding and, if possible, quantifying the various aspects of the coastal regime, hydrographic surveying should be undertaken not just as an immediate precursor to a scheme of works but as routine monitoring on a regular long-term basis. The surveying should include:

- Seabed soundings;
- Current measurements;
- Seabed samples;
- Water samples;

- Wave recordings (see Section 4.4.3);
- Tide records (see Section 4.2.2).

The extent to which these items should be undertaken as part of a monitoring programme or for individual projects is discussed below.

4.7.1 Seabed soundings

Before commissioning a soundings survey, all existing data should be examined. Much survey work is undertaken by the Admiralty who are responsible for navigational charts around the UK. Depending on the relevance to navigation, and in particular their proximity to shipping routes, some areas of the seabed are surveyed regularly by the Admiralty, some only infrequently and often not this century. Nonetheless, before embarking on a soundings survey the engineer should contact the Hydrographer of the Navy, Taunton, regarding the date and extent of hydrographic surveys in his area. If useful data are available, the Hydrographer will be able to supply copies of local 'Collector Charts' which show all the soundings data used in the preparation of the published chart. The published chart only contains, for simplicity, a distillation of these data for navigational purposes. The engineer should also contact other local authorities regarding possible surveys.

If the engineer does not have his own hydrographic survey team, equipment and boat, it is unlikely to be worthwhile carrying out regular soundings surveys for monitoring alone, unless there are areas inshore (perhaps sandbanks or meandering channels) that show rapid and/or major changes with time. Soundings surveys are undoubtedly required as basic data for individual projects. In this case they should be used to:

- Extend beach profiles out to, say, at least 4 m below Chart Datum, to extend coverage of the active beach;
- Give the bathymetry in the area of the proposed works and so assist in defining wave climate and other coastal processes.

In extending beach profiles the extent of the work will be governed by the spacing. In considering the bathymetry the amount of work required should be carefully evaluated both in terms of its extent in plan and of the density of sounding lines. Along the shore the survey should at least cover the area of the works. Its extent offshore should take into account:

- The slope of the bed (there is no point going seawards of the edge of deep water);
- The likely impact of the seabed bathymetry on coastal processes at the shore (e.g. offshore banks may govern the inshore wave climate and should therefore be carefully surveyed).

The spacing of soundings lines should be considered with a view to the size of bed features that need to be defined, but a reasonable line spacing could be of the order of

25-100 m. Cross lines should also be surveyed to check for errors. Specifications for soundings surveys are given in reference 2. Techniques for soundings surveys are discussed in BS 6349, Part 1[1].

4.7.2 Current measurements

During the initial assessment of existing coastal processes the relevance of currents (tidal, fluvial or other steady or semi-steady flows, as distinct from orbital currents within wave action) will have been established. If they are important to the assessment of coastal processes, and no existing data defining the current regime can be found, then current measurements will be necessary. These will take the form of either current metering or float tracking.

Essentially, there are two types of current meter; direct reading and recording. Care should be taken in using current meters in locations exposed to all but the most mild wave climates, particularly in shallow waters. The constantly reversing orbital currents within wave action, if of the same order as the steady currents, will distort current speed and direction readings. If this is the case, vector averaging current meters will be required. Current meters of both types are discussed in BS 6349[1].

Current meters only provide data at one point at a time. Floats can be used to give a more general description of flow patterns in an area, although they suffer in windy conditions and can easily be lost if more than one float is being tracked at a time in sea conditions that are not calm. For further descriptions of float-tracking techniques see BS 6349[1].

4.7.3 Seabed samples (including beach samples)

Seabed samples should be obtained both from the beach and the offshore area which is the subject of study. The extent of beach samples required is discussed in Section 4.9.7.

When taking samples, the location should be recorded as accurately as feasible, e.g. by twin-sextant fixes or an electronic positioning system, and the samples retrieved by a purpose-made sampler. The bed level at the location should be noted. Proprietary samplers are available that facilitate the retrieval of bed samples with minimum loss of fines. The samples should be at least 1 kg (as Table 1 of BS 5930)[39], should be tested for particle size distribution and visually classified (in accordance with BS 1377: 1975)[38].

4.7.4 Measurement of suspended solids

These are required to provide data on sediment transport. Techniques are outlined in BS 6349[1]. Measurements can conveniently be taken at the same time as current metering and at the same locations. This allows sediment flux to be assessed by knowing the quantity of material in suspension and the speed and direction in which it is travelling. The amount of material in suspension is very much a function of wave activity, particularly in the surf zone. At the very least, the level of wave action should be noted during sampling. Due to the inherent difficulties in measuring within the surf zone, it is recommended that the engineer use experienced specialist organizations for this work.

4.8 Geotechnical investigations

Geotechnical investigations should begin with a desk study where all the existing data are reviewed, lead on to a thorough site reconnaissance, and culminate in one or more phases of ground investigation. This, in turn, will lead to the derivation of engineering parameters from *in-situ* and laboratory tests for use in design.

The scope of the investigation should be wide enough to cover the coastal cliffs and foreshore strata, so that an assessment of their stability can be made. Similarly, certain areas remote from the site should be included when borrow pits for suitable fill materials need to be located. Where the investigations include existing structures, reference should be made to Section 4.11.

The general procedures and methods to be used when carrying out geotechnical investigations are given in BS 5930[39] and by Weltman and Head[37]. Further information which is relevant to seawalls is given in Section 6 of BS 6349[1].

4.8.1 Geology of site

The starting point for any geotechnical investigation is a background knowledge of the geology of the site. An appreciation of the site geology will assist in the planning of the ground investigation (Section 4.8.4) and aid the interpretation of the results from the fieldwork.

The UK coastline reveals a wide variety of geological strata, which are reflected in many coastal forms. A great deal can therefore be deduced from the physical nature of the coast. This deduction is best carried out by specialists, preferably with local knowledge. The engineer should therefore consult local universities and colleges as well as, in the UK, the British Geological Survey.

4.8.2 Existing historical and geotechnical data

Much existing data will probably have been gathered during the desk study as part of the project planning phase (see Section 3.1). Sources of information are indicated in Appendix B of BS 5930, in BS 6349[1], and by Dumbleton and West[34]. Those which are particularly relevant to seawalls include:

- Current and old Ordnance Survey maps;
- Geological maps and memoirs;
- Recent and past aerial photographs;
- Local libraries and museums;
- Local authority records;
- Previous ground investigations;

- Recorded movement of existing structures;
- Recorded ground movements, landslips, etc.

Ground conditions encountered during the construction of adjacent works (where documented) can often be of considerable value, as more of the ground strata may have been exposed and inspected than might happen during normal ground-investigation work.

4.8.3 Site reconnaissance

A thorough visual examination of the site should be made once all the relevant historical and geotechnical data have been assembled. Where these indicate that the site geology and geomorphology are anything other than straightforward, the assistance of an experienced engineering geologist should be sought.

General notes on site reconnaissance are given in Appendix C of BS 5930[39]. Aspects which are particularly relevant to seawalls are:

- Nature and characteristics of any exposed strata, whether on the foreshore or in the coastal cliff;
- Nature and characteristics of the beach material;
- Susceptibility of the foreshore strata to erosion;
- Evidence of springs, natural drainage and groundwater flow;
- Evidence of movement in existing seawalls.

Where there are cliffs on a receding coastline, care should be taken to distinguish landslipped material and mudslide debris from *in-situ* material.

4.8.4 Ground investigation

The standard methods of ground investigation consist of trial pits, boreholes, and various *in-situ* testing techniques. In each case the main aim should be to establish the overall soil profile, or soil and rock profile, and the groundwater conditions that exist across the site.

It is important that the whole phase of ground investigation be adequately supervised by a competent geotechnical engineer or engineering geologist. Unless the ground conditions are particularly well known or straightforward, this should be full-time supervision. In this way a full engineering description of each stratum can be obtained at the time the material is recovered from the ground. When *in-situ* testing is being done, supervision is equally important to ensure that the work is carried out with due care.

Ideally, the ground investigation should be conducted as an operation of discovery, utilizing a flexible step-by-step approach. It may often be possible, for example, to carry out a limited amount of investigation using machine-dug trial pits during the course of the site reconnaissance. Based on the results of this work, it will then be possible to plan the main phase of the ground investigation using the most appropriate and cost-effective methods.

The extent and depth of the ground investigation will be determined by the geology of the site and the nature of the proposed seawall construction. Where weak compressible materials are encountered, investigations should be taken deep enough to allow an estimate of consolidation settlements to be made. If bearing piles are thought to be a possibility, the investigation should be continued until a suitable bearing stratum has been reached and shown to be of adequate thickness.

In certain cases a detailed description of each stratum underlying the beach, together with their depth and thickness, will be sufficient for designing the works. More usually, it will also be necessary to assess the engineering properties of the materials encountered. This is done by sampling the ground and carrying out laboratory tests, or by using a range of *in-situ* tests.

Sampling the ground

There are various methods available for recovering samples from the ground for subsequent classification and testing. The general-purpose driven tube sampler is widely used for obtaining 100 mm diameter samples. In soft cohesive soils, a piston sampler must be used if class 1 samples are to be obtained. This quality of sample is required when determining the strength, deformation and consolidation characteristics of the soil.

In soft soils it is also possible to use a continuous soil sampler, which is jacked into the ground from the surface. This enables a complete profile of the ground to be obtained and will ensure that no thin layers of silt or sand are missed. The sample quality of the recovered soil is often class 1, and therefore suitable for strength and other testing. The method is commonly used in conjunction with cone penetration testing (see below).

Groundwater

Groundwater has a dominant influence on the construction and future performance of seawalls. Consequently the investigation should aim to provide a comprehensive picture of the groundwater conditions at the site. Piezometers and standpipes should be installed in boreholes when an accurate knowledge of pore water pressures is required. Readings should be continued for at least a year, so that variation can be monitored. Observations of groundwater levels during boring operations should be made but treated with caution, as they rarely represent equilibrium conditions.

In-situ measurements of soil permeability can be made when an assessment of future groundwater seepage may be required. Any permeable stratum found that may have an influence on the performance of the seawall should be penetrated to its full depth.

In-situ testing

Various techniques are available for assessing the profile and properties of the ground *in-situ*. Sample disturbance effects are thereby minimized, and in many cases it enables parameters to be measured which could not be determined using conventional methods of ground investigation. In each case the raw data will require interpretation before reliable engineering parameters are obtained. The methods of *in-situ* testing commonly used during ground investigations for seawalls include the following:

- Standard penetration test;
- Vane test;
- Cone penetration test.

The standard penetration test is carried out in the bottom of boreholes and is primarily used to assess the relative density of granular materials. This, in turn, is used to estimate the strength and compressibility of the soil by means of standard correlations. This test is also utilized in stiff clays and soft rocks, where similar correlations exist. The method of test is described in BS 1377[38].

Cone penetration testing, where a conical probe is jacked slowly into the ground and the resistance to penetration measured, has become much more widely used in the UK in recent years. It provides a rapid means of determining the soil profile, evaluating the strength and deformation characteristics of the soils, and interpolating ground conditions between boreholes. Penetrometers can broadly be classified as either mechanical or electrical, and various types of rig are available for their installation. They are generally used in conjunction with conventional boreholes to enable the interpretation of the strata to be checked and allow correlations with laboratory-measured parameters to be made. The methods and interpretation currently in use for penetration testing are given by Meigh[36], who includes a comprehensive list of references covering the extensive literature on this subject.

A recent development of the penetrometer is the piezocone, which incorporates a porous tip in the standard cone to measure pore pressures. This gives greater accuracy when profiling the soil (for example, when identifying thin sand horizons in a cohesive soil) and assists in the interpretation of engineering soil parameters. It can also enable an assessment of effective stress shear strength parameters to be made. The technique is still under development and its use is summarized by Meigh.

Cone penetrometers are not able to penetrate dense gravel or cemented soil layers. Where these occur within the soil profile, they will result in refusal of the cone. If these materials are encountered at or near the ground surface they can be penetrated by the use of pre-boring.

Foreshore working

When working above the high water mark, ground investigations can be carried out in the normal way, using the techniques most appropriate in the circumstances. On the foreshore, where there is a limited tidal window, conditions often favour the use of trial pits. Providing the soil profile at depth is known, this approach is often quite satisfactory. When digging trial pits it is important that an experienced geotechnical engineer or engineering geologist is available to supervise the investigation and make a comprehensive log of the strata exposed.

Access to the foreshore for ground investigation work is often a major problem.

Programming the works to coincide with either spring or neap tides should be considered. Spring tides will allow deeper excavations to be carried out in the dry without the need for pumping. However, access which may be available throughout the tidal cycle during neap tides might be cut off at high water during springs.

Deep trial pits in loose shingle will involve quite large excavations. Where beach levels fluctuate considerably it may be worth carrying out the excavations in the winter. During this time beach levels are usually lower and disruption to tourist interests will be less.

When conditions on the foreshore are favourable it may be possible to carry out cone penetration testing (see above) using a specialist rig. Under certain circumstances boreholes may be required on the foreshore. A calm weather window will be required, and substantial staging will have to be erected, capable of supporting the drilling rig at all states of the tide.

Existing structures

The standard methods of ground investigation can also be used when assessing the condition and stability of an existing seawall. In certain cases it may be helpful to use rotary core drilling down through an existing structure in order to assess its internal condition and determine the founding level. This subject is covered more fully in Section 4.11.

4.8.5 Geotechnical parameters

On completion of the ground investigation, soil samples will be transported to the laboratory, where a range of standard classification tests should be carried out. These include determinations of moisture content, Atterberg limits, particle size distribution and specific gravity. Chemical analyses of soil and water samples should also be undertaken. These tests are described in BS 1377[38].

Other geotechnical parameters may be measured to suit the specific requirements of the seawall design. Typical examples and their areas of application are given below:

- Undrained shear strength (total stresses) – Bearing capacity, Earth pressures (short-term), Slope stability (short-term)
- Drained shear strength – Slope stability (long-term), Earth pressures (long-term)
- Consolidation parameters – Settlement prediction (amount and rate)
- Compaction properties – Embankment construction

A schedule of standard laboratory tests is given in Table 4 of BS 5930[39].

4.8.6 Cliff slope stability

Where the coastline contains receding cliffs, which will have suffered coastal landslides in the past, a considerable proportion of the total geotechnical effort should be directed towards investigating their past and present instability. This is the necessary starting point for designing suitable cliff-stabilization works to ensure the future overall stability of the scheme (see Section 6.2.1). In general, the approach to be followed is similar to that already outlined in the earlier parts of this chapter.

A thorough review of all sources of historical material should be carried out. Local authorities, libraries, museums, historical societies and newspapers often supply valuable information. Photographic material of all kinds can help to provide a historical profile of the site. This includes vertical, oblique, and infra-red aerial photographs, press photographs, and postcards. Previous stabilization works which may have been carried out should also be identified at this stage.

A review of research into landslides in the UK has been compiled for the Department of the Environment[34]. This includes regional reviews and atlases listing landslide data. Two volumes are included on landslide investigation techniques and remedial measures, and a further two on causes and mechanisms of landslides. Separate volumes deal with landslide hazard zoning and planning.

During the site reconnaissance phase it is helpful to record on a large-scale map all the salient geomorphological features observed. These will include streams, scarps, mudflows, surface irregularities and tension cracks. The nature of the vegetation can provide clues to past movements (for example, tilted or bent trees, or variations in vegetation between original ground surface and old failure surfaces).

In carrying out the ground investigation phase it is particularly important to proceed slowly using a step-by-step approach. Shallow sub-surface investigations should be made first, typically using trial pits and trenches. Previous slip surfaces can be identified in the sides of trial pits and block samples that include a discontinuity taken for subsequent laboratory testing. At this stage surface slope monitoring can be started using simple techniques such as surveying movement pegs.

Deeper sub-surface investigations can then be carried out, usually by drilling boreholes. These will be used to determine the soil profile, to identify slip surfaces, and to install instrumentation. Where the overall geology is obscured by landslips, one or more deep boreholes from the top of the cliff may be advisable. Various techniques can be used for identifying slip surfaces, which are reviewed by Hutchinson[35]. Instruments which are commonly installed are inclinometers to monitor future ground movements and piezometers to measure pore pressures in the different strata within the slope. Some piezometer tips should be located at or just above slip surfaces to enable appropriate back analyses to be carried out.

Laboratory testing should be done in the usual way, although particular attention should be paid to the determination of residual shear strength parameters. These can be measured for an existing slip surface by carrying out a drained shear box test, with the discontinuity carefully aligned along the joint between the upper and lower halves of the shear box. Peak and residual shear strengths can be measured on intact samples using the ring shear apparatus. Stability analyses can then be performed as described in Section 6.2.1.

4.8.7 Foreshore strata stability

Where the foreshore strata consist of clays or soft rocks, exposure by temporary or permanent removal of beach material will lead to their erosion. Some assessment of the rate of erosion and lowering of the strata will be required in order to assist in the design of the wall toe (Section 5.5). The most damaging case is where there is a thin layer of beach material which becomes mobile under wave and current action, thus wearing down the underlying strata by abrasion.

The rate at which the foreshore strata are likely to erode is difficult to assess. It is broadly a function of the nature of the strata and the coastal processes (Section 4.9). Factors which are particularly relevant are:

- Strata type;
- Beach cover;
- Wave and current action.

The rate of lowering will clearly be influenced by the softness of the material. Where the strata are heavily laminated, with horizontal or near-horizontal bedding planes, harder strata will be lost by the erosion of softer underlying material once the face of the strata has been exposed.

Temporary works and the movement of plant during construction may have a one-off accelerating effect on the rate of foreshore lowering. This can be mitigated to some extent by employing careful construction methods. These effects should, however, be taken into account when designing the wall.

4.8.8 Identification of suitable fill material

Where the construction of an embankment-type seawall is being considered, investigations will need to be carried out to assess the properties and suitability of the locally available materials. This may involve investigating local borrow pits. Generally, the investigations required will be those described in Sections 4.8.1–4.8.5.

4.9 Coastal processes

Following the initial assessment and appreciation of coastal processes, data should have been collected to supplement those already available from monitoring and other sources (visual observations, previous reports, etc.). Depending on the nature of the coastal regime and problems to be solved, data will be required on waves, water levels, currents, seabed levels and sediments, beach levels, coastal erosion and coastal works. This section deals with the need for and application of those data in order to obtain an understanding of the coastal regime as a basis for assessing:

- Future changes in beach levels as design parameters;
- The impact of the proposed works on the coastal regime;
- The impact of the coastal regime on the proposed works.

4.9.1 Long-term and widespread changes

For any given site the engineer should, as a first step in assessing the coastal processes, investigate reports prepared by the geographical or geological departments of local colleges of further and higher education. In assessing the coastal processes the engineer should not confine the assessment to the discrete area adjacent to the new seawall. Much more widespread changes will be relevant. These tend to be longer-term, and the overall philosophy of the investigation should be one of working from the general to the particular, i.e. from long to short-term and widespread to local. In this way, the engineer can give a sound understanding of the processes at his site in the context of what is happening on a wider scale. The following is a list of long-term changes that can be expected to be of significance in the UK.

Geological erosion

Much of the surface rock at the coast, especially in the south and east, is sedimentary and is not resistant to erosion. Since the retreat of the ice cap after the last Ice Age (some 5000–10 000 years ago) wave action in the newly formed seas has continued to cause widespread erosion.

Sea level rise

As discussed in Section 4.2.4, mean sea level is rising gradually relative to much of the British coast. Although the rate may only be a few millimetres per year, such vertical changes can lead to much larger landward movements of the water line and increased wave action at the shore. Clearly, this will become much more significant if some of the recent, higher, predictions of sea level rise prove correct. Work by Bruun[27] and Barth *et al.*[28] expands this aspect.

Starvation of the beach

Many coastal erosion problems around the UK result from a dearth of suitable beach material. In some instances the material on a beach reached the area several thousand years ago and has scarcely been added to since. A good example is the shingle beach at Slapton Bay in Devon. In many other areas the supply of new material is tenuous. Only a few rivers in the UK produce any significant amounts of beach material. This is particularly so in lowland areas. Other sources are from cliff erosion (although this is now often having to be prevented to protect property), from the slow erosion of the seabed in shallow water, and from shell debris.

Loss of material to offshore banks as the result of wave and current action adds to the problem, although this loss may only be temporary in some circumstances. As sea level rises relative to the land, the percentage of time that waves can mobilize on offshore banks slowly decreases. This means that such banks are even less likely to contribute or return material to the beaches in the future.

Finally, even the hard quartzite shingle and sand particles on beaches slowly abrade, producing a slow decrease in beach volume.

General discussion of coastal processes

The sea is constantly moving under the action of tides, producing currents and changes in water level. Superimposed on this is wave action. As a wave travels towards the shore and the water shallows, the wave is modified to the point where it breaks and produces locally high velocities and turbulence.

All materials which make up the coast and coastal seabed will be erodible or transportable to a greater or lesser degree.

The interaction between the sea and shore therefore forms a complex system of mechanisms and processes. The action of waves and currents change the form of the seabed, which in turn modifies the waves and currents. As a result, a coastline that is truly stable is rare. The system of mechanisms is also influenced by rainfall, river flows and wind. The principal processes at work in the coastal regime include:

- The steepening of a beach (comprising granular materials) by swell waves, caused by a predominantly onshore drift of materials within the surf zone;
- The flattening of a beach by storm waves, caused by a predominantly offshore drift in the surf zone and deposition to seaward of it;
- The agitation of seabed material by wave action, which brings it into suspension, so allowing the material to be transported by relatively small currents;
- The transport of beach material along the shore, which results from waves arriving at an angle to the coast and, possibly, by tidal action;
- The transport of littoral material from sections where waves or currents are high to areas that are more sheltered, or into deep water;
- The rise and fall of sea level with the tide, with changes in barometric pressure and wind, which exposes different parts of the shore to attack;
- The movement of offshore banks, as a result of tidal currents, which can in turn modify tidal currents and wave propagation;
- The removal of beach material away from the shore by wave-generated currents (rip currents);
- The aeolian transport of sand onshore from the beaches, possibly to form dunes which remain as a source of beach material in storms;
- The erosion of cliffs by the combined effects of waves, weathering and slope failure, which supplies material to the littoral zone;
- The loss of beach material by abrasion, the subsequent fines being lost to more sheltered areas.

The above list is not exhaustive but serves to illustrate the types of processes at work. More detailed and thorough discussion can be found in textbooks on geomorphology such as Pethick[26] and the *Shore Protection Manual*[14].

Climatological effects

The wind and hence the wave climate are not constant from decade to decade. A change in the prevalence of winds from a certain direction can alter the normal pattern of wave-induced movement of beach material, perhaps reversing the traditional nett direction of movement over many decades. An example is provided in the present nett north-westward drift of shingle on Chesil Beach at West Bay near Bridport, UK. Had this been a long-term trend, over centuries the beach would have disappeared (or never have been formed) since there is no significant source of beach material along the coast to the south-east. An increase in wind strength may similarly cause a long-term change in the beach profile.

One feature of all the above processes is that they act over wide areas, and this can be helpful in their detection. For example, the effects of global warming will be felt worldwide. Thus if a long-term process is affecting one beach it is very likely it will be also changing a similar beach nearby.

It is also worth remembering that, although such mechanisms act over many years, this does not rule out rapid changes in the coast. Cliff erosion in hard rock areas such as Cornwall can be virtually insignificant; in comparison, clay cliffs can erode and retreat at 1–2 m a year as a result of these processes.

4.9.2 Short-term changes

In contrast to long-term processes, the engineer also has to be aware of a variety of more rapidly acting mechanisms, which may or may not produce permanent beach changes. Some examples follow.

Storm action

A single severe storm event, creating large waves and perhaps coupled with a high tidal level, may produce more substantial changes in a beach in one or two days than many months or even years of more normal conditions. In some cases, the damage caused may be irreversible. In most situations, however, beaches will recover naturally, although this may take many months or even years.

Seasonal effects

Most beaches around the UK coast exhibit seasonal variations in their profile. Typically, in winter beach levels are lower than in summer. Material is drawn down by large waves to produce a flatter beach profile. In summer, material from below mean sea level is usually transported landward by more constructive wave action, resulting in a steeper beach. This general response is variable, depending on the weather. A stormy period during the summer may reverse the normal behaviour, as will a mild winter. For a seawall design, the tendency for the beach to be lower and flatter during stormy weather is an important consideration on both structural and hydraulic grounds.

Human interference

All the examples above have involved responses of beaches to natural processes. Generally speaking, human interference on the coast produces rather rapid beach changes. Examples include the construction of groynes or harbour arms which interfere with the movement of beach material along a coast and the dredging of a deep channel close inshore. Activities such as mining beach material for aggregate, or cliff stabilization, may take longer to produce beach changes generally, although they will often cause localized problems quite rapidly. Figures 4.13 and 4.14 shows how a beach at Hengistbury Head in Dorset responded to the construction of a long groyne in the 1930s. It is important to note that changes occurred rapidly at first, and then slowed as the beach reached a more stable configuration.

4.9.3 Historical surveys and analysis

It must be stressed that, while modelling techniques have advanced to the point where attempts can be made to forecast future coastal changes, the complexity of the coastal regime is such that a basic understanding of it should still start with an assessment of past changes. Indeed, the ability of numerical or physical models to reproduce these changes is a fundamental part of validating them.

The sources of historical data and means of comparison are discussed in Section 3.1. The preliminary comparison should be extended to produce a history of the movement of the high and low water lines, not only in the vicinity of the proposed works but for some distance either side as well. On open coastlines, this comparison should extend up to 5 km away, at least in the form of representative sections. If cliffs are present, their edge position should also be compared. On more irregular coastlines, perhaps with major headlands, the comparison may not need to extend so far, although spot checks up to 5 km away are useful.

In many cases this comparison procedure will have been carried out by previous research workers, often geologists, geomorphologists and geographers. Finding relevant literature is a useful supplement to (but not a replacement for) the comparison of shoreline positions.

The low water line is often not as reliable an indicator of beach changes as the high water mark. This is partly because the beach slope at low water is much flatter than on the upper beach. As a result, minor changes in beach level, perhaps as a result of a storm or seasonal effects, will produce a large horizontal movement of the low water line.

Particular attention should be paid during this exercise to any rapid, localized changes in beach position which might indicate interference with the natural regime. New structures, or reclamations, should also be looked for. Useful supplementary evidence, especially of changes in the last 20 years or so, may often be obtained from aerial photographs (see Section 3.1.2).

The analysis should conclude with upper and lower estimates of:

- The rate of recession of the cliff edge, or advance of the vegetation line on any accreting frontage;

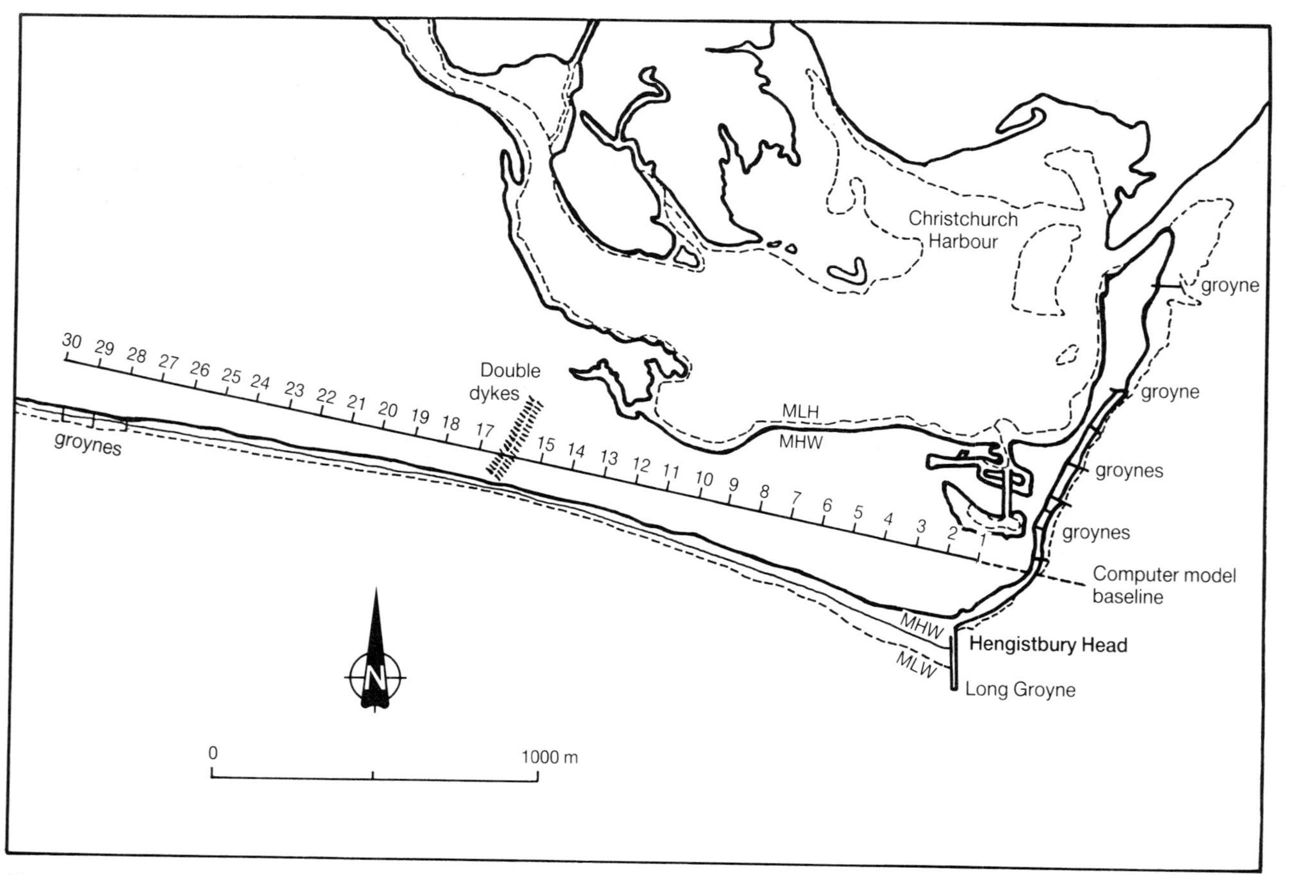

Figure 4.13 Development of beach at Hengistbury Head, UK

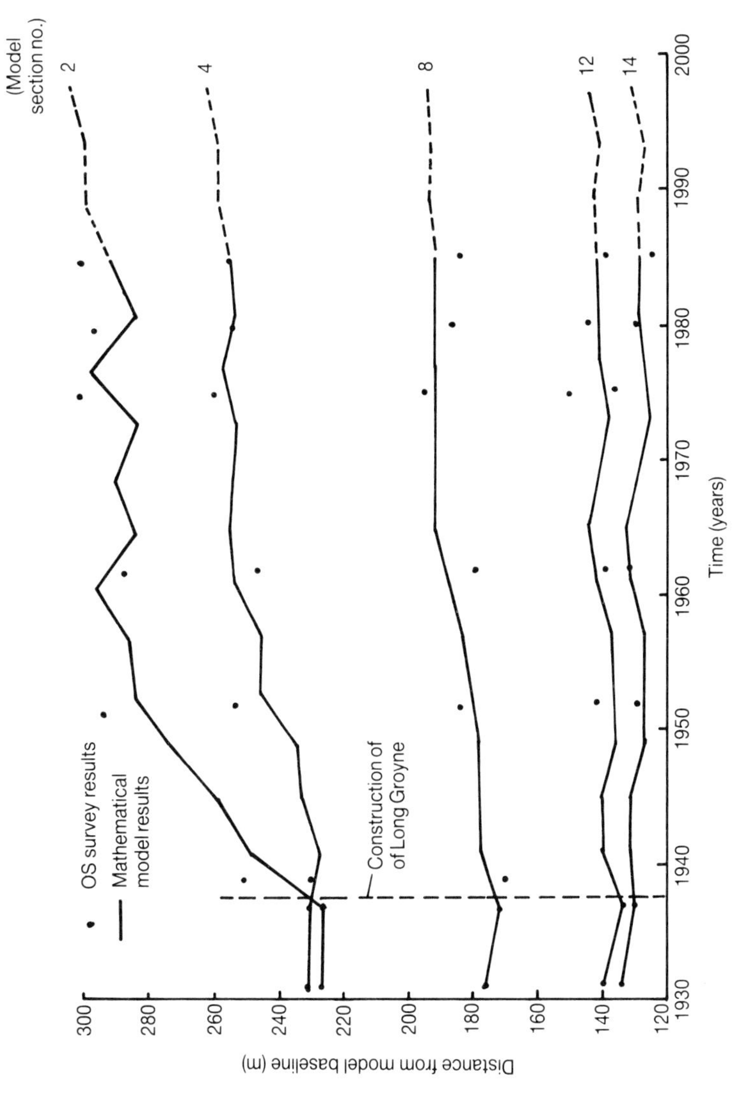

Figure 4.14 Recorded and predicted coastline changes following construction of Long Groyne at Hengistbury Head

- The rate of movement of the high water mark;
- The net change in the volume of beach material on the frontage.

4.9.4 Existing beach profiles

There are substantial lengths of coastline (notably in the south and east of England) where district councils or drainage authorities have been recording beach profiles over a number of years (Section 4.6.2). Depending on their frequency in time and along the coast, these give a very valuable guide to the engineer regarding general trends, emphasizing the great value of monitoring.

Analysis of beach profile data can yield information on:

- Seasonal variation in the profile of the beach (i.e. how far it is drawn down in winter);
- Response of the beach (i.e. how far it is drawn down) in storms;
- Trends of erosion or accretion;
- Equilibrium beach profiles.

Clearly, the reliability of the analysis of beach profile data will be a function of how often and for how long the profiles have been recorded and how accurately they have been surveyed. Isolated profiles can be misleading if taken at an untypical time. Further, short-term (seasonal and storm-related) changes may mask more subtle long-term trends, although the latter may be equally as important in the design of a structure to last, say, 50 years. Again, this emphasizes the advantage of monitoring, allowing the establishment of a long-term data set, rather than short-term intensive surveys related to a project.

If a reasonable duration of profiling is available (say, at least five years and at least twice yearly) the data are best computerized and analysed using simple statistics to give trends and confidence limits. Such a technique also allows ready storage of profile data.

This analysis, together with historical data, could alone form the basis for estimating the future development of a coast at a site of interest. Often this is all that is required to demonstrate the need for coastal defence works. What it will not do is to predict fully what might happen to the beaches following the construction of a seawall, since its presence will alter the nature of beach behaviour identified from historical data (see Sections 5.2.1 and 5.3.2).

The prediction of beach changes after the construction of a seawall is dealt with in Section 4.9.7.

4.9.5 Field observations of sediment processes

In parallel with the investigations into historical data and beach profiles, an essential part of any investigation into sediment transport on a beach is a survey of its existing characteristics. The recovery of beach and seabed samples are discussed in Section 4.7.3, and these give information on the potential transportability of the material.

Samples should be taken in and alongshore from the area of the works, preferably at positions of beach profiles.

The number of profiles subject to sampling should be assessed in the light of the variation in the nature of the beach along the study coastline. At each profile, sufficient samples should be taken to allow the variation in particle size down the beach to be assessed. The extent of testing can be minimized by an initial visual assessment of the samples and a careful visual inspection of the beach.

Seabed samples, possibly supplemented by side scan or a diver's survey, should be used to examine the extent of seabed movement. Specialist experience is often necessary to gain maximum value from these observations, but information that can be useful includes the following:

1. Extent of rippling of a sandy seabed is an indicator of the extent of the seabed subject to transport. The direction of the ripples indicates direction of transport. The ripples are, of course, only representative of the latest conditions to act on them, which may not be typical.
2. Extensive seabed vegetation can indicate stability, i.e. lack of change in seabed levels.
3. Plotting on a plan the location of the various samples and their particle sizes. This indicates possible sources and sinks for beach material. Bare rock shows a lack of deposition but does not necessarily mean lack of transport. Large quantities of beach material can be carried across rock platform without significant deposition.

It is also useful to check the depth of the potentially erodible or mobile sediment layer on the beach. If it is less than a metre, then the prescence of an impenetrable substratum of rock or clay may influence the movement of sediment. In this respect, borehole information may be useful.

The presence of a clay or rock stratum indicates a possible lowest limit of past beach level. Providing the rock is effectively inerodible, it also shows the lowest possible future beach level. However, many rocks are by no means inerodible; e.g. chalk and stiff clays can easily be eroded by several metres over a period of five to ten years.

Depending on the magnitude of currents, current measurements are basic data necessary for an assessment of transport, supplemented by measurements of suspended solids (Sections 4.7.2 and 4.7.4). Tidal currents are important in the transport of sediment. Quite low currents (i.e. below the threshold for normal sediment transport) can transport sediment which has been brought into suspension by the oscillatory agitation of waves. Waves themselves generate longshore currents and rip currents. Measurements of these are of considerable use on long beaches where substantial currents build up along the shore. A full understanding of these is best based on a numerical model validated by site measurement (Appendix B).

4.9.6 Sediment budget

Having gathered the basic data, it is not a simple matter to evaluate the workings of the coastal regime at the site of a proposed wall. A useful philosophy of approach is the 'sand budget cell', as discussed initially in Section 3.2.2. The basic logic is that, if the beach is lowering or receding, then losses must exceed supply. If erosion has commenced where there previously was none, either losses must have increased or supply reduced. Possible causes of erosion, based on this concept, are discussed below.

Longshore drift

Consideration of all the factors in Figure 3.1 can highlight problem areas, and Sections 4.9.3–4.9.5 provide information to assist in this process. At the same time, however, the engineer should attempt to quantify the magnitude of longshore and cross-shore drift. To some extent, these can be determined from site and historical measurements. For example, the construction of a harbour breakwater which blocks longshore transport can provide the best data on the rate of drift by calculating the quantity accumulating on the updrift tide in a known number of years before bypassing commences. This will give the mean annual drift. This will be net drift, i.e. on a coastline aligned east/west it will be the difference between the westwards gross drift and the eastwards gross drift.The gross values often are of an order of magnitude larger than the net drift (reflecting a wide angular spread of wave attack). Small changes in gross values can therefore lead to relatively large changes or reversals in net drift. It is important, therefore, to have a simple means of correlating wave conditions with longshore transport. This allows the tables of percentage occurrence of wave heights by direction to be extended to give an estimate of longshore transport rates (Section 4.4).

Various formulae exist for estimating longshore transport. Great care should be used when employing them since they normally apply to long straight beaches without groynes. This is often far from reality. In general, there is more reliable work for sandy beaches than there is for shingle. The most widely used is the *Shore Protection Manual*[14] formula, in this case

$$I_s = K\,P_s$$

where I_s = immersed weight longshore transport rate,
P_s = longshore component of wave energy flux at breaking (based on the significant wave height),
K = proportionality factor.

For methods of deriving the longshore energy flux the reader should refer to the *Shore Protection Manual*, where guidance on the appropriate value of K is given. Normally, this is taken as 0.4 for sand, but various researchers have studied it and have assessed it as ranging from 0.1 to 2.0. This wide range reflects the difficulty of measuring drift rates, the simplicity of the equation and the complexity of sediment transport (no account is taken of particle size or density). Using $K=0.4$ can give a good first estimate of sand transport, however, which will be an upper limit if the beach is not long, straight and wholly sand. Little information is available for gravel beaches but K values of the order of 0.02 have been estimated in work by Hydraulics Research Ltd.

More rigorous analyses of longshore transport have been developed, and these allow the effect of currents to be included. However, bearing in mind the complexities of sediment transport and the rapidly advancing state of numerical modelling, it is recommended that specialists be consulted for all major schemes and all but the simplest situations.

Onshore/offshore transport (cross-shore transport)

Little in the way of analytical techniques exist for the engineer to assess cross-shore transport. It is best to rely on site observations and records and, if cross-shore transport is likely to be significant, he should consult specialists who may well need to employ numerical or physical models. However, an assessment of equilibrium beach profiles, as compared with those that exist, can give a good indication of whether offshore losses are a chronic problem. Techniques are being developed for the evaluation of shingle beach profiles. The best for sand beaches are those presented by Swart[29,32]. The techniques, however, cannot cater for the direct impact of seawalls, and quantification of offshore losses in this case will require recourse to a physical model.

Calculation of the input and output drift rates as indicated will give a good general picture of the local balance or otherwise in the sediment budget. For example, it may well show that:

- Sediment transport into the cell at one end is less than that out at the other, due to a variation in wave climate along the shore – a cause of erosion;
- Sediment is being lost offshore since water depths immediately offshore are deep and thus the beach slope is too steep to reach equilibrium in a storm – a cause of erosion;
- The sediment budget is balanced by coast erosion at the site: prevention of this with a seawall may transfer the problem elsewhere and/or intensify the erosion in front of the new wall.

In the light of these results, the engineer may well need to reconsider whether a seawall is the best solution or if some other measures may be more suitable (see Section 2.2).

4.9.7 Estimates of the impact of a seawall

Sections 4.9.1–4.9.6 are aimed at an understanding of existing coastal processes. This will, in establishing trends of change and an understanding of them, give an idea of how the beach and coast may change in the future. Clearly, this will be an integral part of deciding whether a seawall is needed, is appropriate and whether it should be accompanied by other works such as beach nourishment, groynes or an offshore breakwater. However, such an assessment of what will happen in the future must allow for the fact that the very presence of a seawall will alter the coastal regime to some extent. This is unavoidable. If waves are to be resisted by a seawall they will also be modified and thus, to some extent, so will the coastal processes (Section 5.3.2). Furthermore, if the seawall prevents erosion then supply of material to the beach will be reduced. These changes should be borne in mind in the environmental assessment (Section 3.1).

In trying to assess the impact of a seawall the engineer should always be aware of the complexities of coastal processes and the fact that the coast is almost always in a state of change. In most cases, even with the most sophisticated investigations, it is not possible accurately to predict future changes. A good policy therefore in planning seawalls or works to them is to minimize likely problems by reducing the impact of the works.

This is discussed in Section 5.2.1, with regard to the position of a structure, but, in summary, the engineer should:

- Keep the seawall as far landward as possible;
- Keep the alignment of the seawall as smooth as possible;
- Minimize reflection of waves from the seawall (i.e. dissipate energy at the wall or ensure that it is fronted by a beach).

Having ensured that the impact is minimized, the engineer should then attempt to assess what that impact will be. At best, analytical techniques (i.e. without recourse to models) will be simplistic but can nonetheless be useful. If the seawall prevents erosion then the material previously supplied to the littoral zone will need to be provided from elsewhere (e.g. beach nourishment) or additional erosion will ensue. This is likely to be concentrated initially in front of the wall. The seabed will fall until it naturally stabilizes or until hard bed material is encountered. Thereafter the extent of erosion may spread alongshore progressively. The depth at which the erosion will terminate (in the absence of a hard stratum) cannot confidently be predicted without models, but knowledge of the deficiency in supply of material can greatly assist in a qualitative assessment.

Many of the problems of seawalls are the result of wave reflections (Section 5.3.2). On readily erodible foreshores the increase in wave activity in front of the wall, as a result of reflections, will, at the least, redistribute the beach, causing toe scour. The depth of this scour cannot be predicted analytically and requires physical models. There are indications that reflections from the wall can lead to a local increase in longshore drift, but there is no consensus on the extent of this or even if it exists. Prediction of the magnitude of this change therefore requires model studies. Specialist advice should be sought on the most appropriate models to be used (Appendix B). It can be said, however, that reflection-related scour problems will tend to be more severe with more reflective walls (Section 5.4).

The above has considered the impact of the wall on the beach. To establish design minimum beach levels this impact should be added to the changes that could occur even without the wall, i.e. on the basis of the analysis in Sections 4.9.4 and 4.9.6.

These changes include:

- Cyclical changes;
- Progressive changes;
- Further potential changes.

Examples of changes to be assessed in determining beach levels

Cyclical changes
- Beach movement due to drift reversal;
- Changes in beach profile due to seasonal factors or storm events;
- Programme of beach recharge.

Progressive changes
- Continuing loss of beach material;
- Gradual loss of exposed strata on foreshore;
- Progressive lowering of underlying strata when beach covering is intermittently removed;
- Change in beach profile due to the seawall itself.

Further potential changes
- Interference with supply of beach material from updrift;
- Failure of groynes;
- Failure to continue with beach recharge;
- Change in beach profile arising from secular rise in sea level.

An additional option open to the engineer in optimizing the design of a seawall is the use of a pilot scheme. Where novel forms of construction offer potential for cost savings or improved design, it may well be that the full performance cannot be anticipated in advance. The pilot scheme should still be subject to the best available design procedures, but subsequent monitoring of its performance may well allow future phases of construction to be better designed (see Section 2.3).

Further aspects of the impact of a seawall that should be considered are:

- On an eroding coast (in the long term) a seawall can soon be well seaward of the natural high water line: as a result, particularly at the updrift end, it may act as a groyne;
- Many coasts exhibit a slow cyclical variation (e.g. spits in front of estuary mouths which tend to grow then erode, 'nesses' which migrate), and problems occur when a particular shoreline configuration is 'frozen' by building a wall;
- A seawall can disrupt the interchange of sand between beach and dunes (where such a mechanism previously existed).

4.10 Construction and maintenance

Design for construction and maintenance is considered in Section 6.8 and requires data on:

- Access;
- Tidal rise and fall (Section 4.2);
- Foreshore levels and changes to them (Sections 4.6, 4.7 and 4.9);
- Wave action (Section 4.4);
- Environmental requirements (with respect to amenity, geology, boating and shipping – Section 3.3);
- The availability of useful materials, perhaps on-site;
- Working areas (Section 4.6 and 3.3);
- Services.

To a large extent these data will be gathered in the process of gaining design data. There will be a need, however, to obtain more data specific to the needs of design for construction and maintenance. This section discusses those aspects of data not covered in Sections 3.3 and 4.2–4.8 or in which greater detail is needed. These are:

- Access;
- Environmental requirements;
- Availability of materials;
- Working areas;
- Services.

Much useful data can be obtained from discussion with the interested parties involved with the project. These range from local authority officers or committee members and central government to members of the public in their role as users or frontagers. The results of enquiry from these sources may identify further sources of special value, e.g. local interest societies and trade associations.

In general terms, the usage of areas adjacent to a proposed existing seawall will influence construction, and data are required on inshore shipping or boating movement, foreshore leisure activities, and the use of the adjacent hinterland for industry, leisure or other environmental interests. In planning the types of construction to be adopted, the nature of the clients' organizations and its capability for ongoing inspection and maintenance may be relevant and should be investigated. The constraints imposed by financing are discussed in Chapter 8.

4.10.1 Access

The requirements for information on access are concerned with:

- The needs of occupiers or users to be provided with adequate access during construction and on completion of the works;

- The need for access by those constructing the works;
- The need for access for maintenance.

Procedures involved in obtaining the right to use an access either permanently or temporarily during construction is dependent on ownership and use of the land. The engineer should hold initial discussions with local planning and highway departments as well as with the owners of the land to determine conditions on which use will be permitted. Negotiations for access can become protracted: problems and permissions should be addressed early to avoid delays to the works.

4.10.2 Environmental requirements

Section 3.3 discusses the areas of possible impact of the seawall on others and when gathering the data required for an environmental assessment the investigation should include matters relating to construction. These include traffic, noise (Section 3.3.3), disturbance to flora and fauna (Section 3.3.2), and existing uses of the shore (Section 3.3.4). These requirements may impose constraints on time of day or the time of year when work can be carried out or method of working for construction and maintenance.

4.10.3 Availability of materials

When access is difficult, use of materials available on-site (perhaps clay for an embankment or rock for a revetment) can be very attractive. Maintenance may well be easier if local materials are used. Their cheapness can more than offset their lower quality, while using 'native' materials can be environmentally beneficial. Geotechnical and other data should be gathered for the local materials from local authorities or by site investigation (see Section 4.8). Guidance on their performance in the sea may be obtained from inspection of natural or older features (perhaps cliffs in the case of rock or old flood banks in the case of clay).

On an accreting beach it may prove feasible to use some of the beach material as aggregate. Sufficient samples should be taken to allow suitability to be assessed.

The engineer will require data from local suppliers and will usually need to determine the locally available types of materials. Quality is just as relevant as quantity and enquiries should indicate both so far as this is possible. In particular, the rock produced by local quarries, its type, strength, resistance to abrasion, flakiness and the sizes in which it can be quarried should be studied. The numbers and qualities of ready-mix concrete plants, the type of aggregates used, and whether they are prepared to use better, abrasion-resistant, aggregates may be relevant. If so, the designer will need to obtain data on a source of suitable aggregate. During the enquiries, the opportunity to incorporate the by-products of other industries, such as fly ash from power stations or waste overburden from quarries, should not be overlooked.

4.10.4 Working areas

Relevant data, particularly on land ownership, will need to be gathered. The working areas are very likely to incorporate areas of the foreshore, whose ownership is often not clear. In the UK the Crown normally owns the seabed to seaward of low water and sometimes to seaward of high water. Early discussion with the local district council should give initial guidance on land ownership and rights.

4.10.5 Services

Data from the local authority and statutory undertakers of existing services should be obtained by contacting all relevant local and national agencies. In addition, visual inspection and local discussion will be required to determine the location of any private services such as outfalls.

4.11 Existing structures

It is anticipated that the majority of future seawall works in the UK are likely to involve existing seawalls, whether the works be replacement or rehabilitation. Where an existing wall is substantial, its removal is likely to be costly and may incur a risk to property protection. Therefore there are potential cost savings to be made by incorporating the wall into the new design. In order to do so, it is desirable to obtain an adequate assessment of its structural soundness and stability, hydraulic performance and the residual life as part of the new structure.

Design work associated with existing walls is considered in Section 5.7. This section deals with acquisition of the necessary data. The data necessary to assess an existing wall or the reasons for its failure are similar to those for a new wall, and so are, to a large extent, covered by Sections 4.2–4.9. The requirements differ, however, insofar as it is important to assess:

- The details of the wall as it was constructed;
- The past performance of the wall;
- The degree to which the wall has changed (deteriorated) since its construction;
- The degree to which the conditions (beach levels, wave climate, seabed levels) have changed since the wall's construction.

The aim of data gathering should be to provide sufficient information to:

- Prepare a representative cross section of the wall, including soil strata and strengths, both when it was constructed and in its present state (or its state just before it failed);
- Define the loads on the structure (waves, soils, live loads) when it was constructed and in its present state (or its state on failure).

This will allow a thorough analysis of the structure as discussed in Section 5.7. Where full details cannot be obtained sensible maximum and minimum values may have to be attributed for subsequent use in sensitivity analyses.

4.11.1 Details of seawall as it was constructed

Design or as-built drawings may be available from the coast protection or land drainage authority, or from consulting engineers' records (see also Section 3.1.4). Further useful data can be obtained as discussed in Section 3.1.2. When examining original drawings, care should be taken to establish the extent to which they are a true record of what was actually built. Techniques of site investigation which can be used to prove the validity of drawings, or to establish the nature of the wall if drawings are not available, include:

- A detailed visual inspection of the wall;
- Trial pits – in front of or behind the wall;
- Topographical survey cross sections;
- Internal investigations to assess the structure composition.

Corings can be of value (see Section 4.8). There are specialist techniques for non-destructive testing of walls (e.g. sonic systems and ground-probing radar) and specialists should be consulted as to their appropriateness.

When carrying out these investigations the engineer should bear in mind the extent to which the investigation work itself might affect the safety of the structure. The location of trial pits in front of a wall should be sited to cause minimum disturbance.

Trial pits and corings provide information on the structure at the actual location of the trial pit or probe and some interpolation is required. It is not always possible therefore fully to establish the condition of a structure from such investigations. Allowance should be made for additional investigations during the course of any subsequent work on the structure (see Section 5.7).

4.11.2 Past performance of the seawall

When isolated severe events have caused damage to the wall or led to substantial overtopping a study of the conditions at the time can be invaluable in assessing the performance of the wall. This is discussed in Sections 3.1.5 and 3.2.1 but, as further data are recorded for the project, these should be used to build up a full description of the particular event. As an extension of the list given in Section 3.1.5, the data should include:

- Predicted tide level;
- Recorded sea level;
- Wave climate in the period leading up to, during and following the event (Section 4.4.5), taking account of shallow water effects (see Section 4.4.6);

- Estimates of overtopping quantities (if appropriate) and records of flooding;
- Estimates of beach levels at the time (Section 4.9).

The above represents a fairly intensive exercise in respect of analysis of wave climate and beach levels. It can, however, provide data essential for a good design, insofar as they can give a sound understanding of how the wall functions, what its deficiencies are, and of how it failed if that was the case. Less intensive exercises can also be of use in understanding the performance of a wall if, for example, a wall is periodically overtopped. Collation of data on winds (direction as well as speed), beach levels, waves and water levels can serve to indicate the combination of conditions which cause problems. Such an exercise is far easier if the wall and coast are properly monitored. Monitoring of the wall itself, e.g. routine levelling at standard locations, is also of value where the problem is one of overall stability.

4.11.3 Changes in the wall since construction

As in Section 4.11.1, this should start with a visual inspection, supplemented by measurements of the thickness of timber and steel members, rounding of rock armour and abrasion loss on concrete faces, all useful and easily obtainable. The thickness of steel sheet piling can be measured with an ultrasonic gauge. Preferably, the visual inspection should take place at low water when beach levels are low, which will limit the need for trial pits. The engineer should seek and note signs of cracking, movement and holes or undermining which might lead to loss of fill. If the latter is evident, remote video records down a cored hole can give useful information on the scale of the problem.

4.11.4 Change in conditions since wall construction

The marine environment at the wall may well have changed since the wall was constructed. Changes can include:

- Long-term changes in sea level (see Section 4.9.1);
- Land subsidence, perhaps the result of mining;
- Falling beach levels (Section 4.9);
- Meteorological changes.

In mining areas the engineer can benefit from discussion with the relevant mining company, who may well give guidance on the degree of subsidence in the past and future. There is evidence that in certain parts of the world the climate is changing (see Section 4.9.1).

The above points refer to matters related to coastal processes, i.e. the seaward side of the wall. Distress in the wall may well be caused by movement of the coastal slope, particularly in the case of walls to protect high ground from erosion. Soil and coastal slope conditions are covered in Section 4.8. The engineer should, in the case of existing walls, check additionally for works which may have caused a deterioration in slope stability. Points to look for are:

- Drainage pipes discharging onto the slope or near it;
- Changes to the drainage characteristics of the slopes and land behind (e.g. impermeable paving, grading of land);
- New construction (roads, houses, land filling or grading) which may have led to an increase in loading or vibration.

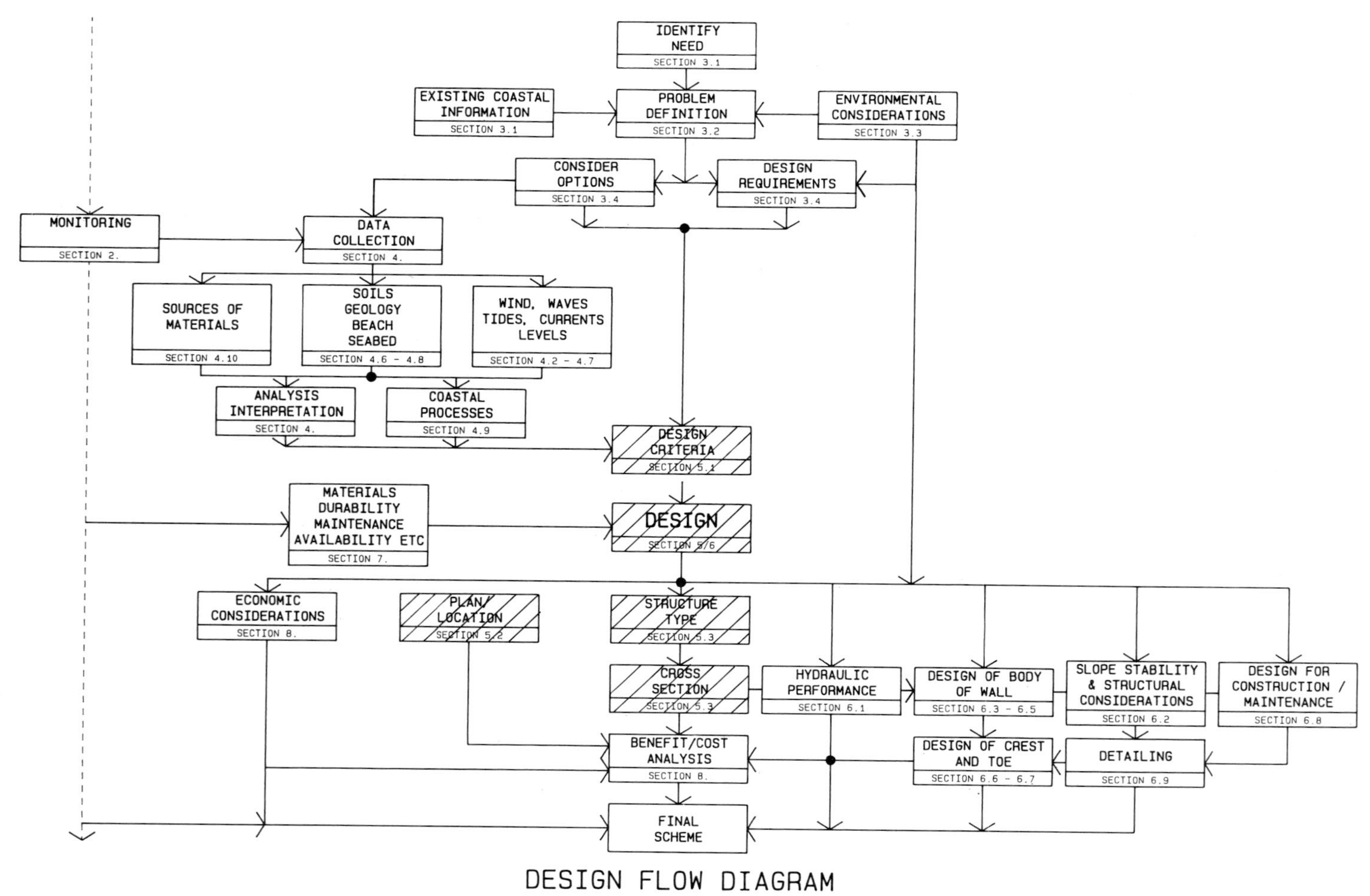

DESIGN FLOW DIAGRAM

5 Seawall structure – overall concept and types

In the preliminary stages of a project, existing information will be collated, analysed and used to define the functional requirements of the seawall, as discussed in Chapter 3 and covering:

- Cost/economics;
- Environmental assessment;
- Structural performance; and
- Principal function.

This is the basis for the initial design and provides the framework for data acquisition discussed in Chapter 4.

The collation and analysis of the enhanced data provide a basis for review of possible options and an outline design. This chapter gives guidance for the review by discussing the concept and types of seawall which might be used. Detailed design considerations follow in Chapters 6 and 7 with financial and economic material in Chapter 8. A key functional requirement is the environmental performance of the wall. These aspects are not dealt with separately in these chapters, so reference should be made to the various sub-sections of Section 3.3 as appropriate, to ensure that the preferred option satisfies all the functional requirements as far as this is possible.

In this chapter the various topics are sub-divided to encourage a logical procedure leading to selection of suitable options. Section 5.1 deals with design philosophy. Sections 5.2 and 5.3 go on to consider the location of the wall in terms of its plan layout and cross section. Sections 5.4–5.6 discuss the various options available for the body, toe and crest of the wall, whereas Section 5.7 highlights those design aspects which are appropriate to works to existing walls.

Satisfying each of the design criteria in full may not be possible, so the design is often a compromise where the relative importance of each of the factors is evaluated. The satisfaction of one factor may well influence others so that, of necessity, the design proceeds iteratively.

At this point it is necessary to review the primary functions of a seawall, which may be one or more of the following:

1. To protect a shoreline from the effects of erosion;

2. To protect land and property from damage by wave attack;
3. To prevent or alleviate flooding of low-lying land.

The functions stated in (1) and (2) are quite properly described as 'coast protection', but it must be pointed out that it is only the land behind the wall that is protected and not the coast in general. Such a wall, if sited on a naturally eroding coastline, will not prevent or stop the overall process of erosion and may, in certain instances, aggravate the situation. The exact effect of such a structure on the erosion process is difficult to determine (Section 4.9.8). Initially it may appear to have been halted or reversed but for safety, the designer must consider the possibility that it will continue or worsen. This may necessitate additional beach-control works such as the use of groyne systems as an integral part of the seawall design (Chapter 2).

In the case of a wall whose main function is to prevent or alleviate flooding the size of the structure and its very existence on the coastline requires that the design takes full account not only of the flooding aspect but also the effects on the relevant coastal processes.

5.1 Design philosophy

A prerequisite for determining design criteria is the selection of the overall design standards, i.e. the required life of the seawall and the acceptable risk of being overwhelmed by exceptional waves or tides.

5.1.1 Life of the seawall

In different aspects of the design process there are a number of various 'lives'. For clarity, in this book the following are defined:

- *Structure (serviceable, or working) life.* The length of time that the structure *actually* lasts and is capable of functioning.
- *Component life.* The life of a particular component of the structure, i.e. the length of time which it lasts before requiring replacement.
- *Design life.* The minimum length of time the component structure or scheme is *designed* to last.

Clearly, when the component life is substantially less than the design life, maintenance plays an important role in the eventual structure life.

The choice of design life requires careful consideration and regard for the marine environment in which it will function. The use of a long design life may result in a very costly scheme. A shorter design life may be predetermined by expected changes in the use of the land protected or may show financial advantage even after provision is made for future replacement. It is usual for the design life chosen to be the economic optimum solution by which the functional requirements can be met. The choice is often strongly influenced by the availability of inexpensive local materials of limited durability. It may be found that the shorter design life leads to a cost-effective scheme with provision for future replacement (see Chapter 8).

Equally, the design life of an overall scheme need not necessarily be the same as that for a component part. For example, a sea-defence scheme may be designed to a design life of 50 years in the full knowledge that certain parts will require replacement every ten years. In this case the design life of the structure, which is important in cost benefit terms (Chapter 8), is normally taken as the life of the major component of the structure (perhaps a reinforced concrete wall or rubble slope).

The Code of Practice for Maritime Structures[1] gives recommended minimum design life for shore-protection works and breakwaters as 60 years and for sea-defence works as 100 years. Based on data in CIRIA Technical Note No. 125,[2] the amount of refurbishment necessary on considerably younger structures suggests that these criteria have not been easily met, often as a result of design shortcomings. Table 5.1 is extracted from TN 125 and shows the range of design lives that are normal in the UK, based on responses to a survey. Clearly, there is a substantial difference as compared with the values presented by the code of practice. The engineer should consider carefully the design lives that are realistically attainable both practically and cost-effectively, taking due note of such aspects as abrasion and corrosion.

Design life is different from the return period for design conditions. The latter relates to the risk of design conditions being exceeded (see Section 5.1.2). A sea-defence wall with a life of 30 years may, for instance, be required to resist overtopping by a one in 100-year tide.

5.1.2 Risk of design criteria exceedance

Phenomena such as winds, waves, tides and surges are fundamental design factors. Extreme values of these are, therefore, essential design criteria. However, there are frequently no absolute maximum values of these (although there are exceptions, such

Table 5.1 Typical design life and level of protection (from CIRIA Technical Note No. 125)

Type of use of seawall structure	*Design life (years)*	*Level of protection (return period of event in years including any correlation)*
Temporary and short-term measures	1–20	5–50
Majority of coast protection or sea defence walls	30–70	50–100
Occasional works subject to specific greater risk	30–70	100
Special structures of high capital cost and/or high risk (including conventional power stations and barrier works)	—	Up to 1000
Nuclear power stations	—	10 000 and greater

Risk and return period: examples

A seawall with a design life of 50 years is to be built to protect developed land from flooding.

It may be considered that, because of the nature of the development which is to be protected, overtopping due to an excessively high water level would be very serious. An acceptable risk of exceedance may therefore be selected as 10% in the life of the seawall.

In this case, to establish the appropriate return period,

$$T_R = \frac{1}{n} \times \frac{1}{1-(1-R)^{1/\mathrm{Ln}}}$$

$$= \frac{1}{714} \times \frac{1}{1-(1-0.1)^{1/(50 \times 714)}}$$

$$= 475 \text{ years}$$

As a second example, one considers a seawall built to a design life of 50 years against a design wave condition with a return period of 100 years (which is often the case, according to CIRIA Technical Note 125).

Risk of exceedance

$$= 1 - \left(1 - \frac{1}{100 \times 2920}\right)^{50 \times 2920} = 0.39$$

i.e. by the time the structure reaches the end of its design life there is a 39% chance that design conditions will already have been exceeded.

Note: it is assumed in analysis that a wave condition lasts three hours (see Section 4.4),

$$n = \frac{365 \times 24}{3} = 2920$$

as when wave height is depth limited). In circumstances when there is no realistic maximum, the solutiion is to choose extreme values which are very rare. It follows, therefore, that there is a finite chance that the design conditions will be exceeded during the life of the wall. For convenience, this probability of exceedance is normally characterized by 'Return Period' (T_R). An event with a return period of N years is likely to be exceeded, on average, once in N years. The most appropriate return period should be chosen in consideration of the consequences of exceedance (e.g.

overtopping and consequent flooding). Sections 8.4 and 8.5 deal with the economic assessment of the consequences of exceedance.

As mentioned in the previous section, the return period selected for the various design criteria should not be confused with design life. For example, if the return period of any extreme event is set the same as the design life, then there is a 63% chance that the extreme event will be exceeded before the end of the design life:

$$R = 1 - \left(1 - \frac{1}{nT_R}\right)^{Ln}$$

$$\text{or } T_R = \frac{1}{n} \times \frac{1}{1 - (1 - R)^{1/Ln}}$$

where R = risk, L = design life, and n = number of events per year (e.g. considering extreme high waters, $n = 714$ = number of tides/year).

The return period need not be the same for all aspects of design since the consequences of exceedance may differ. For example, it may be less serious for a seawall to be overtopped (short-term damage) than for the body of the wall to be destroyed (possibly catastrophic).

5.1.3 Probabilistic design

The design of seawalls is to an extent (although not fully) 'probabilistic' as opposed to 'deterministic'. It is probabilisitic to the degree that wave, currents and water levels are evaluated probabilistically, with a statistical risk of exceedance. These factors are then applied deterministically, i.e. by determining the strengths, size of members, etc. that are required to resist or accommodate these factors. Full probabilistic design entails applying probability distributions to all the properties of the wall (e.g. strengths of materials, thickness of armour layers) as well as to the loads. It is costly and requires a very thorough understanding of the workings of the wall, although it leads to a more rigorous, reliable and efficient design. Advances in research into the working of seawalls and in computational techniques are making probabilistic design less costly. However, at present it is only for the more major schemes that full probabilistic design is feasible.

5.1.4 Design criteria

Consideration of the functional requirements will allow design criteria to be determined under the four major headings shown in Figure 3.4. In the boxed example, the criteria are not all independent. For instance, the return period of the design wave would be very much a function of the economic requirement to achieve maximum net benefit, as discussed in Section 5.1.3. Equally, not all the criteria are compatible with each other. The need to avoid visual intrusion may run counter to the need to restrict overtopping in extreme conditions. There is a necessity to achieve the best compromise in a number of areas of the design. This is discussed further in Sections 5.2–5.7.

For example, the following design criteria may be derived for a seawall to replace existing sea defences on an amenity beach:

Cost/economics

- Capital cost limited by pre-set annual expenditure budget;
- Minimal maintenance available;
- Design solution to be chosen on the basis of maximum economic benefit.

Environmental impact

- Works are on tourist beach so construction must be outside holiday season;
- Pedestrian access to and along the beach to be preserved throughout construction and subsequently;
- Any structures must not extend to above a certain level to preserve views from nearby houses and amenity areas;
- Geological outcrops in nearby cliff to remain exposed;
- The appearance of the wall should be appropriate to an amenity beach;
- Existing beach to be preserved and longshore transport not to be stopped.

Structural performance

- Wall to reduce overtopping to given level under wave and water level conditions appropriate to given return period;
- Wall to be stable under design wave and water level conditions, known beach variations and imposed soil loads;
- Wall to be designed for minimal maintenance;
- Maximum life in the light of construction, maintenance and disruption problems.

These criteria should be derived from initial design and data acquisition (Chapters 3 and 4) and the knowledge that the principal functions of the wall are to alleviate while not harming an existing amenity beach.

The main purpose of a seawall is to prevent erosion or alleviate flooding, where wave action plays a major part. Those design criteria that are concerned with hydraulic performance and the consequent interaction with coastal processes are therefore perhaps the most fundamental in the selection of possible seawall options.

5.1.5 Analysis of failure

The central philosophy of approach to seawall design is to consider possible modes of failure and design against them. In the case of an existing wall which has failed it is essential to be able to identify the mode of failure, so that works to the wall can be designed to remedy the defect.

To a degree, if the seawall does not satisfy any of the functional requirements it has failed. However, this section deals specifically with the assessment of possible modes of failure in respect of the basic aspects of hydraulic, geotechnical and structural performance. When such a failure occurs it is a result of the imposed loads exceeding the capacity of the wall to withstand them (including consideration of the coastal slope and foreshore). This may be because of:

- Inadequate assessment of design loads;
- Inadequate assessment of design capacity;
- Construction problems giving actual capacity less than design capacity;
- Maintenance problems giving actual capacity less than design capacity;
- Deterioration of wall capacity with time;
- Increase in loads with time; and
- The capacity of wall being exceeded as a result of a particularly severe event (see Section 5.1.3.).

The acquisition of data for determination of design loads has already been dealt with in Chapter 4, whereas the application of those loads to assess the individual aspects of hydraulic, geotechnical and structural performance of the wall is discussed in Sections 6.1–6.7. These latter sections identify methods of designing a seawall, or a part of it, to withstand a particular mode of failure. First, however, it is necessary to identify all those modes of failure that are possible for different types of wall.

Hydraulic, structural or geotechnical failure of a wall is likely to be a sequence of local failures rather than one single failure. Such a sequence might be, for example:

- Erosion of the beach;
- Collapse of the toe;
- Settlement and fracture of the revetment;
- Erosion of the underlayer;
- Settlement of the crest;
- Overtopping of the wall;
- Damage to the backface; followed by
- Breaching of the overall seawall.

In the case of sea defences, the following main groups of failures which might lead to flooding (i.e. failure of the sea defences) can be distinguished as:

1. Flow under or through the seawall;
2. Flow over the seawall;
3. Damage to the front face leading to breaching of the seawall (the example above);
4. Geotechnical instability; or
5. Slope instability.

The above are events appropriate to sea defences. In the case of coast protection (the prevention of erosion), event (5) should be extended to include assessment of the overall stability of the coastal slope.

Figures 5.1–5.5 show general fault trees for the events. The figures should be read from the bottom upwards, and indicate the causes and effects of problems.

Fault trees such as those in Figures 5.1–5.5 should not be considered as definitive, in the sense that they demonstrate a philosophy of approach to design rather than detailed descriptions of the possible sequences of failure for each of the events. They serve to show how, if the engineer considers carefully the possible sequences of local failures leading to overall failure, he can create a diagram specific to his site which will help identify the relative importance of different elements of design. For further discussion of geotechnical aspects (Figures 5.4 and 5.5) the reader should refer to Section 6.2.

There is a similarity between the logic underlying these figures and those in Section 3.2. They are a more detailed examination of the wall itself and so are an extension of Figures 3.1 and 3.2 which outlined considerations to the basic problem to be solved.

It can be seen that in the figures a common initial failure on the fault trees is associated with low beach levels. They can lead to toe failure and also allow higher waves to reach the wall. While each design case should be analysed carefully in its own right, this result does demonstrate the importance of gaining an understanding of coastal processes and thus future beach levels (see Sections 3.1 and 4.9).

Work in CIRIA Report TN 125 supports this view of the importance of the toe. Table 5.2 shows the more common types of failure as reported in a survey of coastal authorities in the UK.

Table 5.2 Types of damage

Damage reported to seawall	*Number of occurrences*	*As percentage of all seawalls reported*
Erosion of toe	63	12.3
Partial crest failure	26	5.1
Collapse/breach	16	3.1
Removal of revetment armour	19	3.7
Abrasion	16	3.0
Wash-out of fill material behind seawall	10	1.9
Concrete disintegration	9	1.7
Structural member failure	5	1.0
Landslip	5	1.0
Corrosion	3	0.6
Outflanking	3	0.6
Uplift of armouring	3	0.6
Settlement	2	0.4
Spalling of concrete	2	0.4
Damage to promenade	4	0.8
Concrete cracking	2	0.4
Total	188	36.6

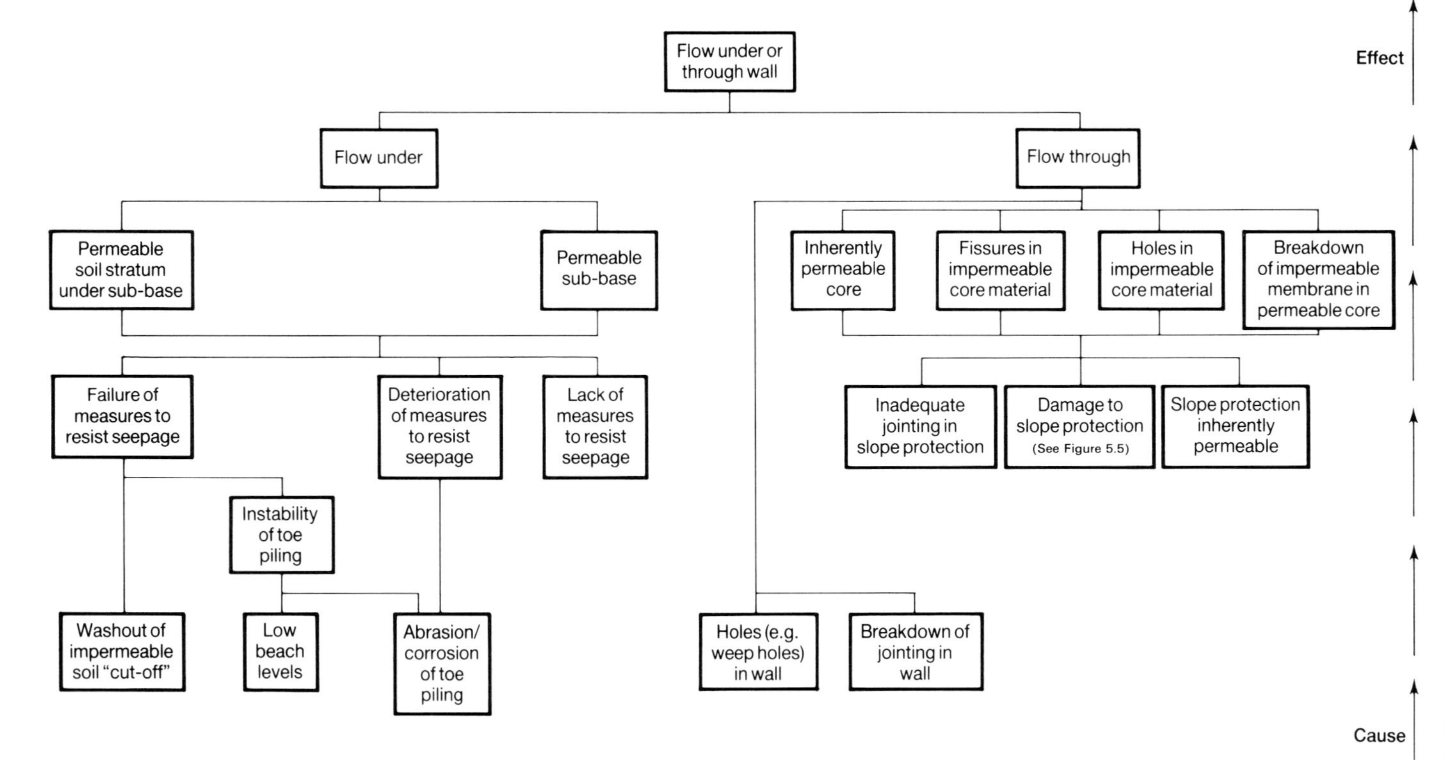

Figure 5.1 Fault tree: Events leading to flow under or through seawall

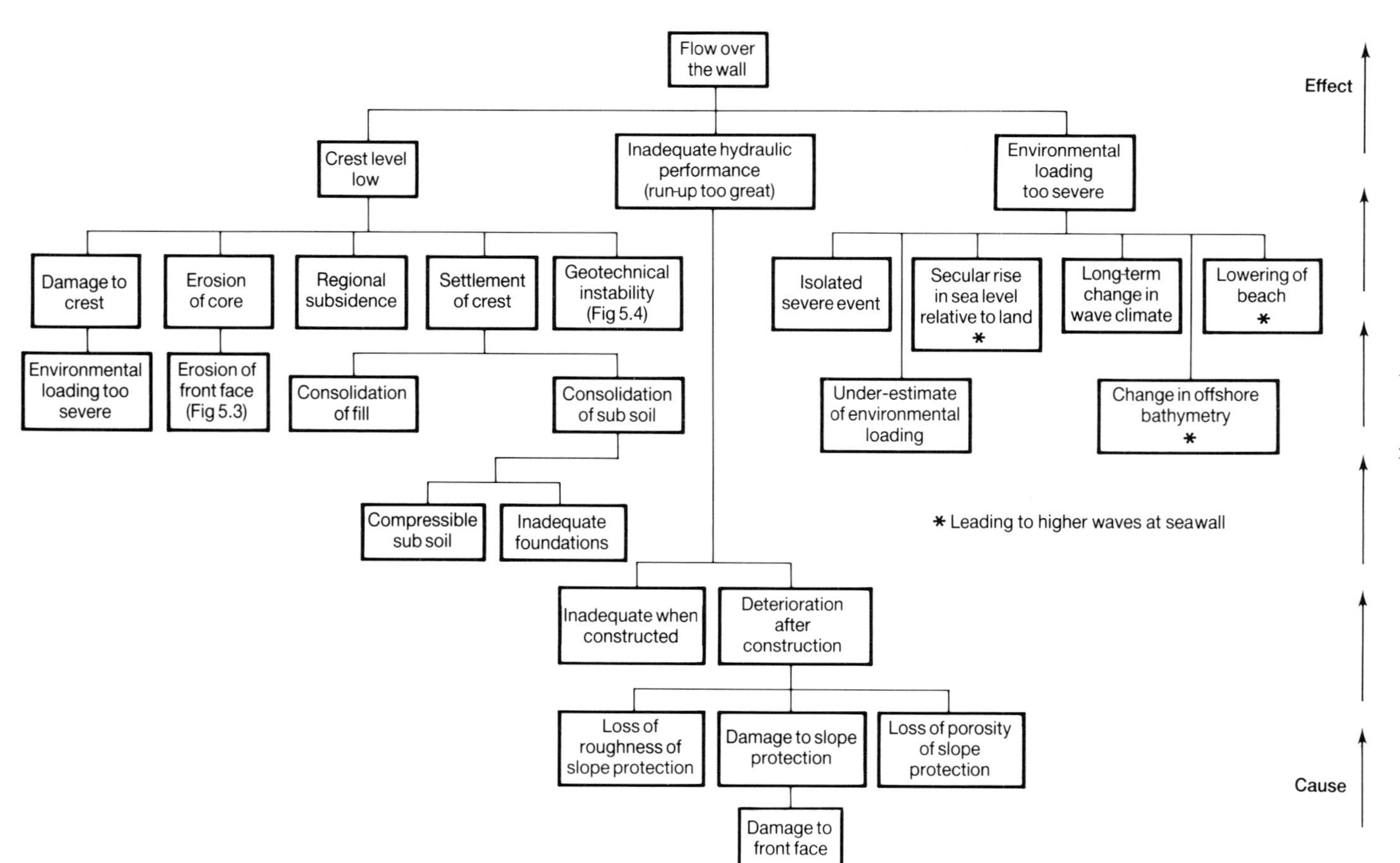

Figure 5.2 Fault tree: Events leading to flow over seawall

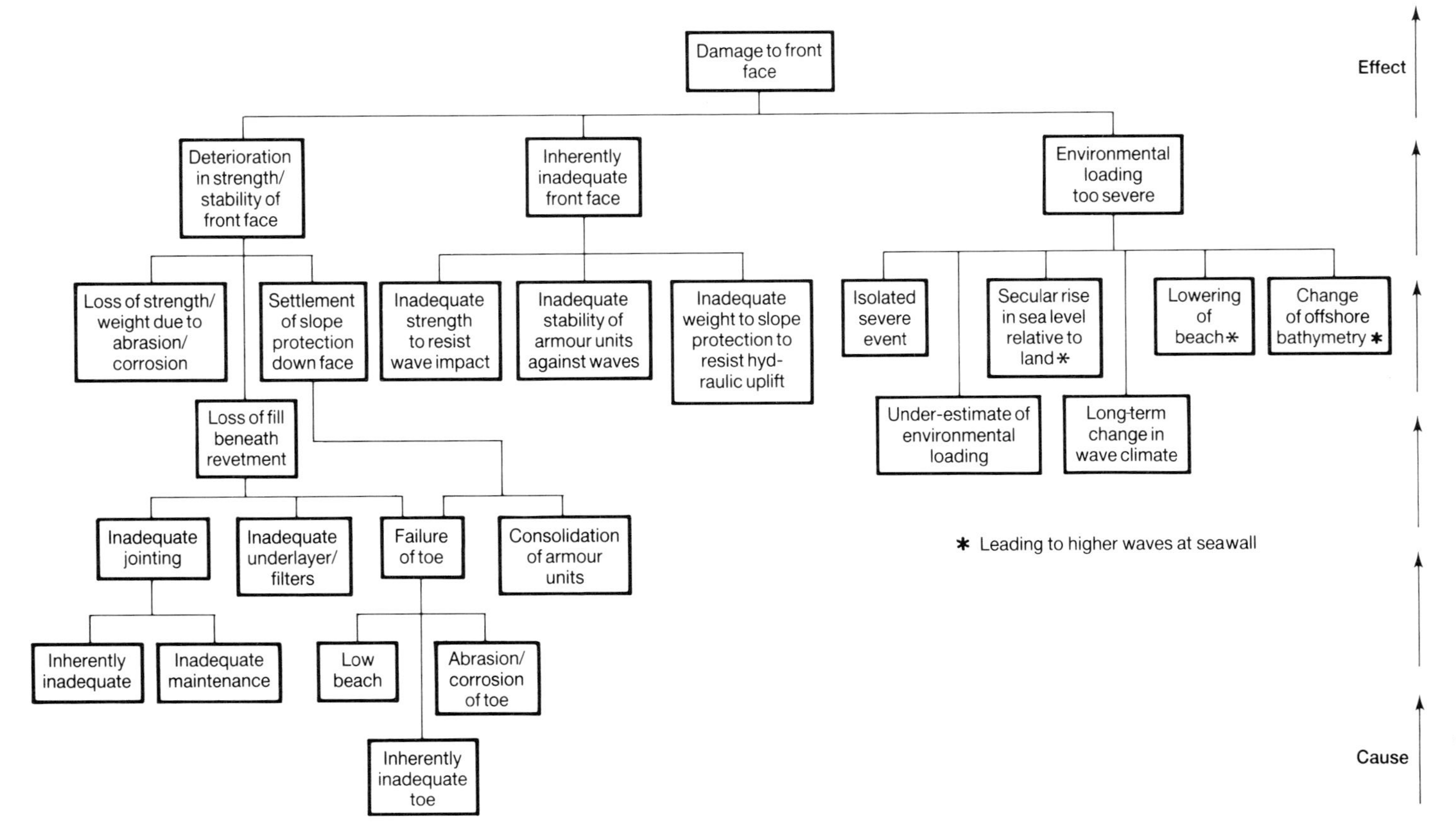

Figure 5.3 Fault tree: Events leading to damage to front face of wall

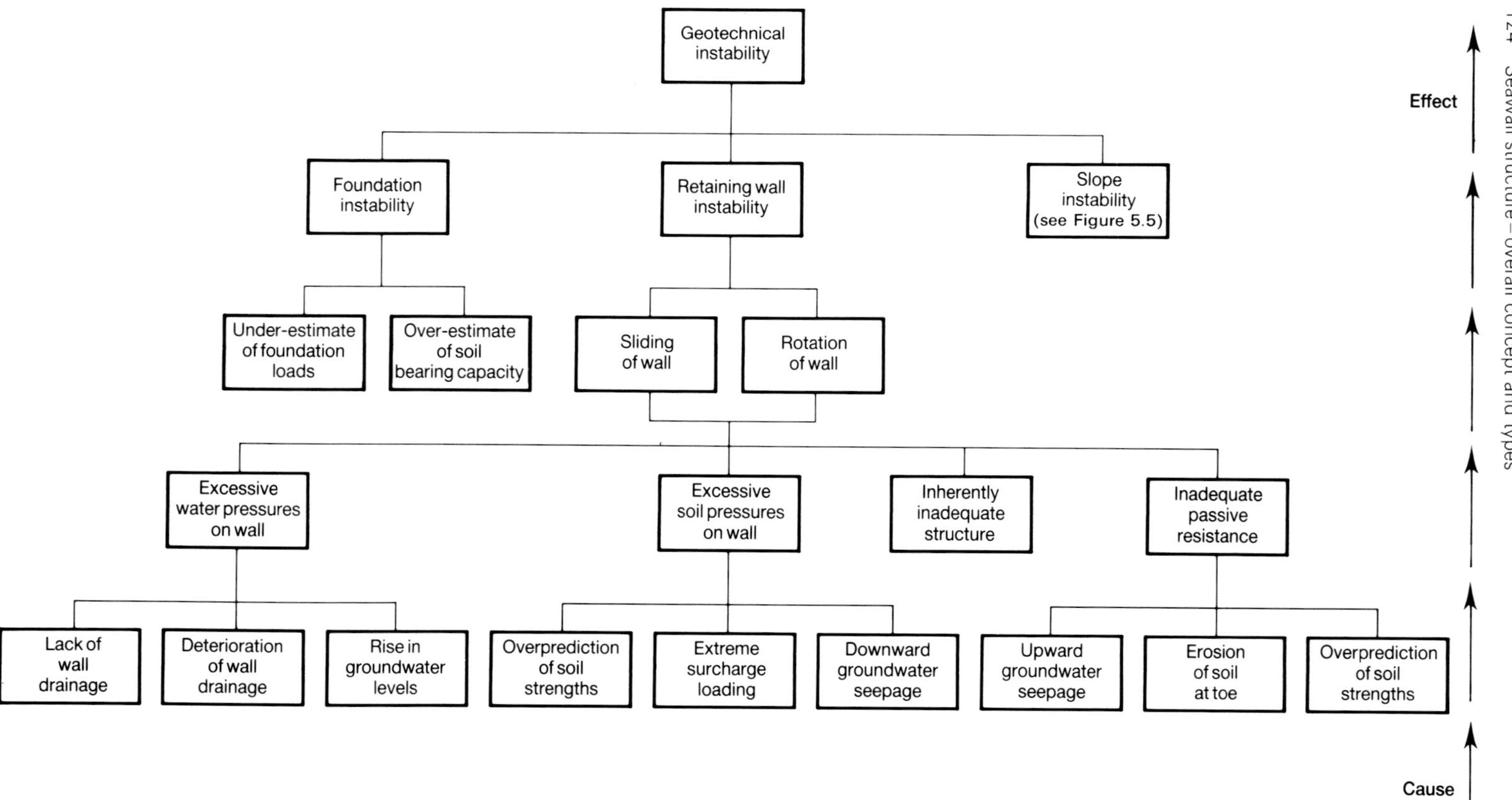

Figure 5.4 Fault tree: Events leading to geotechnical instability

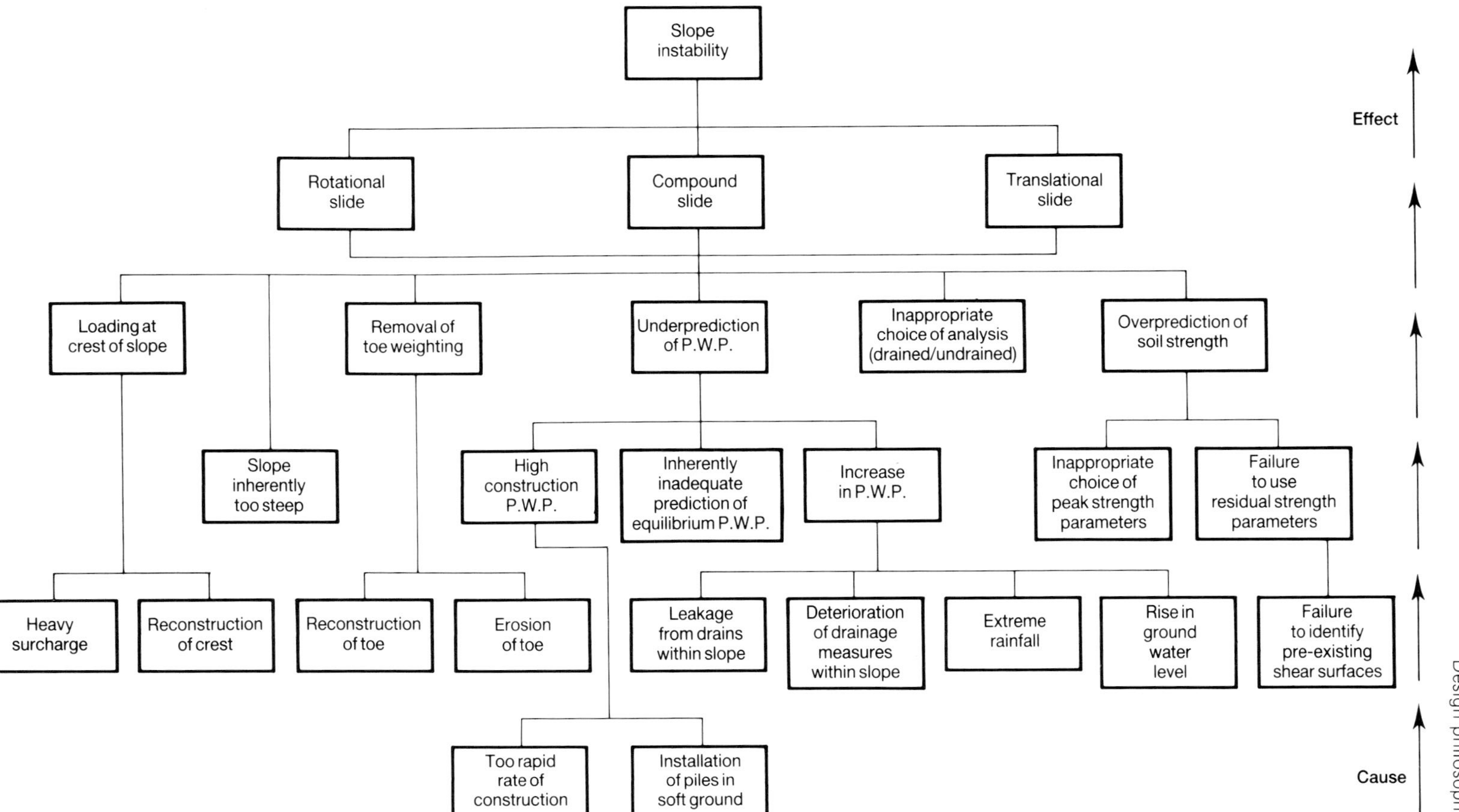

Figure 5.5 Fault tree: Events leading to slope instability

5.2 Plan layout

The hydraulic performance of a wall can often be made much more efficient by altering its plan shape. For works to an existing seawall, the potential for adjusting its alignment may be limited, although in the case of a new wall the engineer may have more scope. Given the opportunity, he should carefully weigh the possible hydraulic advantage of a smooth alignment without corners, as discussed below, against the advantages of adjusting the alignment (perhaps only slightly) to protect all areas of value and, possibly, to create a structure that is more visually pleasing.

5.2.1 Location of structure with respect to shoreline

In general terms it is desirable that the wall be located as far landward as possible to minimize both interference with the coastal regime and the hydraulic loads (wave action) on the structure. Section 4.9.7 has already indicated the difficulty in assessing the detailed impact of a new seawall on the coastal regime. In siting a new wall, therefore, two consequences should be recognized:

1. By virtue of its existence, the new wall may cut off the natural supply of material to the littoral regime, the effects of which may be felt at considerable distances from the site in question (Figure 5.6).
2. If the seawall is well landward of the normal high water mark, acting only as a 'fallback' in times of severe erosion or extreme surges, the effect on the coastal region is likely to be minimized. If, however, the wall is built further seaward, it will be in deeper water and the consequences of wave reflection and other effects on the coast are likely to be greater. Depending on its location or distance out from the shoreline, local changes or adjustment of the seabed must be allowed for as a result of changed wave conditions in front of the wall.

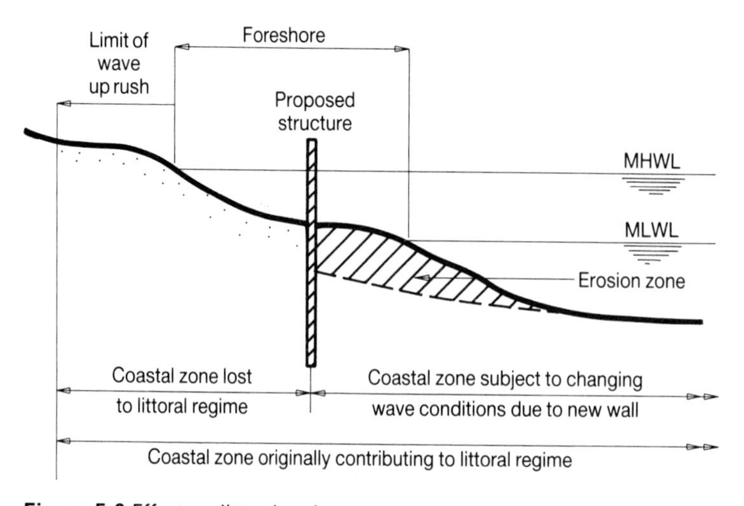

Figure 5.6 Effect on littoral regime

On a naturally eroding coastline the introduction of a seawall to prevent further landward regression will not stop the overall erosion process. The designer must therefore consider what effect this will have on the beach in front of the new structure and therefore on the design of the structure itself. It is not possible to precisely calculate such loss of beach profile (see Section 4.9.7). However, as a guide, Figure 5.7 shows the general effect of erosion. Changes in the beach profile subsequent to the construction of a seawall should be carefully monitored.

5.2.2 Plan shape and alignment

In general, the wall alignment should follow the average alignment of the beach contours. Where the new structure is a replacement for a previously collapsed or failed structure the engineer should satisfy himself as to the influence, if any, of the previous wall alignment as a contributory factor in the collapse (see Section 5.7).

Curves and re-entrant angles

Plan layouts of seawalls which embody significant concave curvatures with respect to incoming wave crests can result in a focusing of reflected wave energy in a limited area offshore with potentially detrimental effects on beach process (Figure 5.8). This phenomenon will be most marked with reflective walls (see Section 5.3). A more extreme case arises with sudden changes of direction of walls which involve re-entrant angles (Figure 5.9), and these are to be avoided if at all possible. They can cause serious concentrations of wave impact on the wall where waves are focused onto a small area.

Re-entrant angles can also result from the introduction of access steps to the beach, concrete buttresses, bastions, outfalls and other discontinuities. Consequently they should, where possible, be avoided.

In both cases the concentration of incoming wave energy will result in local wave set-up and increased overtopping. If the walls in question are vertical, or near-

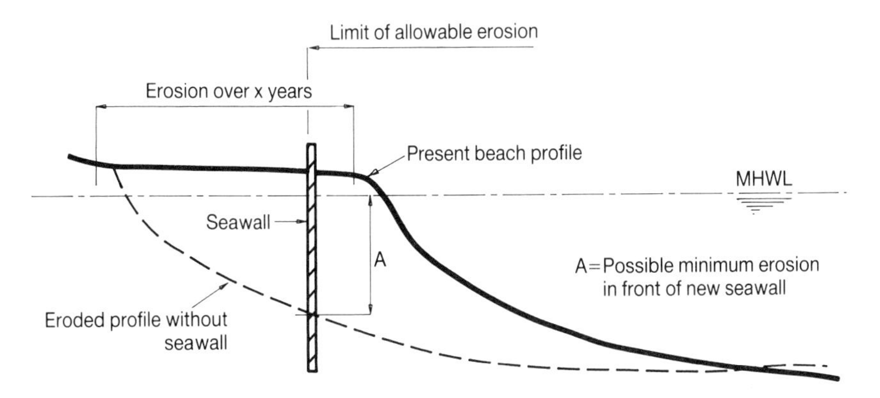

Figure 5.7 Effect of erosion

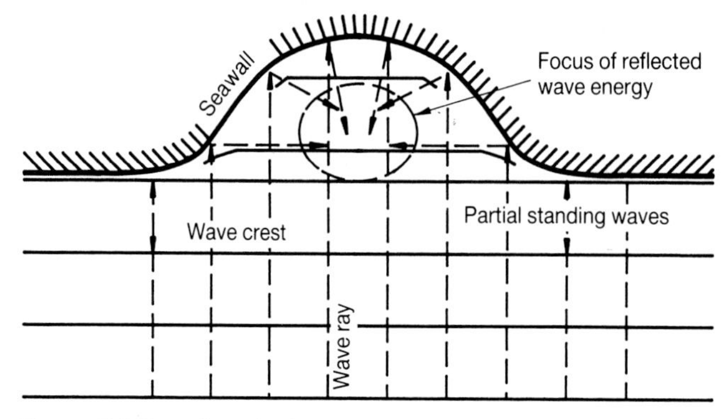

Figure 5.8 Focusing of reflected wave energy

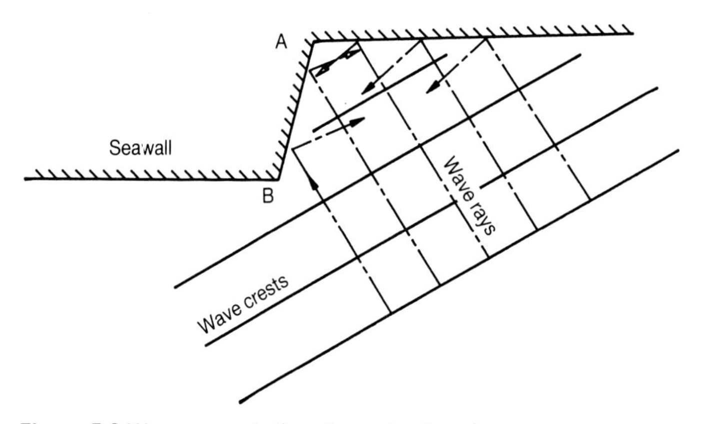

Figure 5.9 Wave concentration at re-entrant angles

vertical, large wave forces will be generated, particularly in the case of re-entrant angles, and excessive overtopping will occur with wave and spray being projected upwards to a great height. As this condition is almost always associated with onshore winds, the volume of water thrown into the air can fall with great force on the decking or promenade and can cause severe damage.

5.2.3 Major discontinuities

The siting of seawalls at major discontinuities such as rivers, breakwaters, or large outfall structures requires careful consideration. A typical situation is shown in Figure 5.10, where a major discontinuity exists by virtue of the breakwaters projecting from a coastline at a river entrance. With the littoral transport direction as shown, accretion will occur on the updrift side of the entrance (D-B) and erosion on the downdrift side (A-C), because the breakwaters form a barrier to longshore drift. Unless beach material is transported mechanically from DB to AC (sand bypassing)

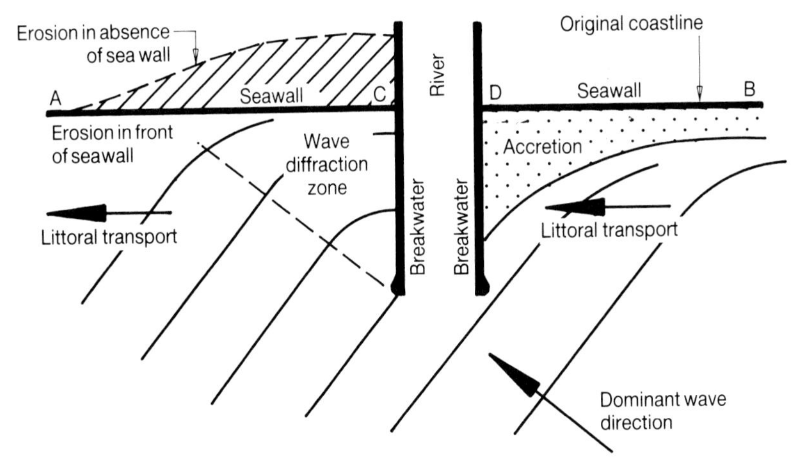

Figure 5.10 Effect of major discontinuity

the erosion will continue until the accretion builds up to the point where transport around the breakwaters is established. The location of the line of the seawall on the downdrift side should take this erosion into account, either by siting the wall some distance landward of the anticipated limit of erosion or by designing it to resist substantial toe scour.

Assessments of littoral drift rates, perhaps supplemented by mathematical modelling, can be particularly valuable in such a situation, giving a better assessment of the likely erosion rates (see Section 4.9).

5.2.4 Junctions and terminations

Some of the most difficult problems in seawall design are encountered at the junction of a seawall with an existing structure such as a breakwater or at the termination of a seawall on an unprotected coast. A common situation is shown on Figure 5.11. This represents the junction between solid coast defences and a mobile beach.

The termination to the new seawall is by means of a large bastion groyne to seawards and a sheet-piled cut-off to landward. Assuming, in this instance, that the drift is as shown, the subsequent erosion downdrift can present serious long-term problems. The bastion groyne in itself is a major blockage to longshore transport, as described in Section 5.2.3. An additional problem lies in the potential for erosion to extend behind the new wall. In this case it is catered for by the introduction of a cut-off wall. It may also require periodic nourishment, or extension of the wall downdrift along the coast (as in Section 5.2.2). The re-entrant angle formed by the cut-off wall and the beach downdrift is a source of concern. Oblique waves, from directions other than the dominant one, would cause local erosion and scour, and may further substantiate the need for a seawall of some form to be constructed downdrift of the groyne.

If the walls involve sloping rip-rap or rubble armouring, sudden sharp changes of

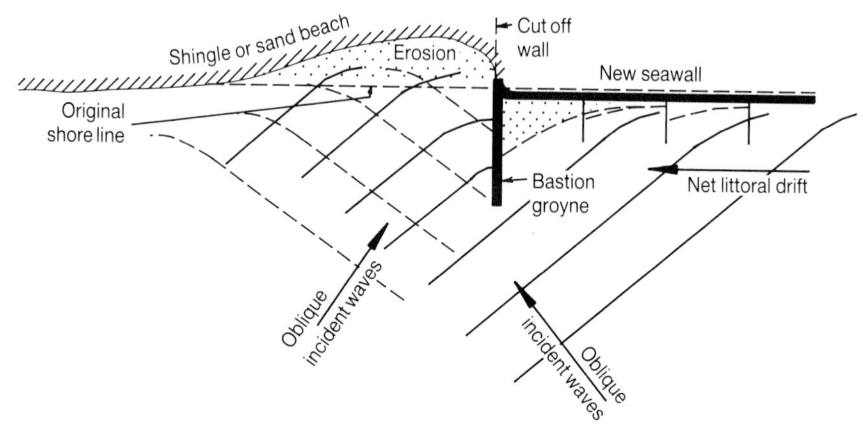

Figure 5.11 Erosion at seawall termination

direction such as this should be avoided, but if this is not possible then the corners should be rounded. The more severe wave conditions which will be experienced at A and B (Figure 5.9) may induce instability of the armour face. As there are no proved procedures for determining these wave conditions in the absence of physical hydraulic model studies, the designer should exercise engineering judgement or seek expert advice.

The introduction of curves and re-entrant angles in the plan shape of seawalls will automatically call for an assessment of the effect of oblique waves and the resulting increases in beach movement. An example of a situation which might occur is shown in Figure 5.12. In this instance all walls are subjected to oblique waves, but because of the shape, beach movement will be directed towards point B and away from point A. Depending on the length of the wall A-B and the angle of the walls with respect to the incoming waves, considerable beach movement could occur, leading to erosion or

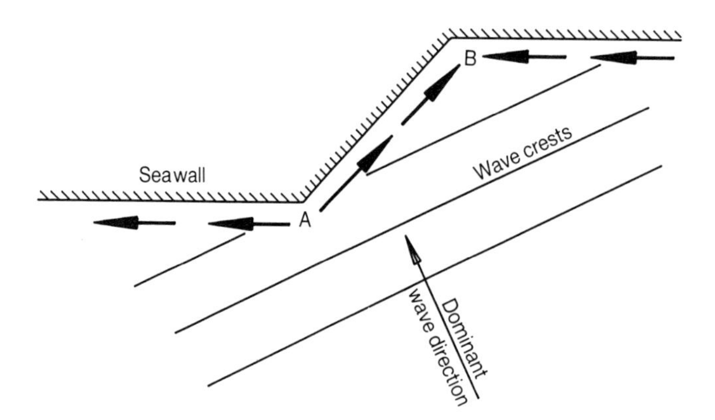

Figure 5.12 Beach movement at sudden changes of direction

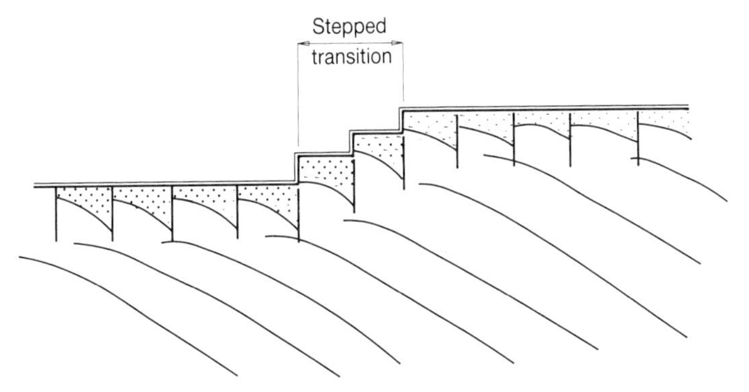

Figure 5.13 Alternative solution to changes in alignment

scour problems at A and accretion at B. The designer should therefore consider carefully the possible need to introduce measures to control such beach movement.

Where conditions allow, the transition between two sections of seawall, running parallel but offset, can be accomplished by stepping back in parallel steps equivalent in length to a multiple of the groyne spacing (Figure 5.13).

5.3 Cross section

Conditions vary greatly from site to site, and there is therefore no such thing as a standard cross section for a seawall. Each design should be considered in its own right, taking into account all the wide variety of functional requirements. This is self-evident in establishing the plan layout but is no less pertinent with respect to the cross section.

The success of the wall, whether its aim is to alleviate flooding or prevent erosion, will be fundamentally dependent on:

- Preventing wave action from reaching landward of the wall;
- Maintenance of its integrity under extreme (design) conditions of waves, beach level changes, abrasion, etc.;
- Its interaction with coastal processes.

5.3.1 Seawall classification

To allow general discussion of the various types of seawall it is convenient to classify them under four headings:

- Sloping;
- Vertical;
- Porous;
- Non-porous.

For the purpose of this book these are defined as follows:

Sloping: walls having a slope of 1 in 1 (45°) or flatter;
Vertical: walls having a slope steeper than 1 in 1 (45°);
Porous: walls whose face is permeable to wave action (e.g. a rubble slope, perforated blocks);
Non-porous: walls whose face is not permeable to wave action (e.g. *in-situ* concrete slope, steel sheet-piled wall).

The porous/non-porous classification refers only to wave action. There are materials (such as sand asphalt) that are permeable in that steady flows would pass through them but which are effectively impermeable to the rapid flows and changes in flows that occur in wave action. A sand asphalt facing on a wall would therefore be classified as non-porous.

5.3.2 Hydraulic considerations

Various aspects of hydraulic performance are dealt with in Sections 6.1–6.3. However, before making a detailed assessment the engineer should consider the hydraulic performance in more general terms, in order to assess the relative suitability of different wall types.

Bearing in mind the aspects of the basic description of a seawall ('wave action is a major consideration' – Chapter 1), an early step in the design should be the consideration of the interaction of the wall with the propagation of waves (see Figure 5.14). Waves reaching a seawall will:

- Reflect;
- Be dissipated;
- Overtop;
- Be subject to a combination of these.

In essence, the purpose of the wall is to alter the balance of these three processes, and in so doing to reduce the amount of wave action reaching the land to the rear of the wall line (i.e. overtopping or erosion) or to reduce reflections. The conservation of energy shows that in order to decrease the significance of one process then one must either:

- Increase the significance of the other two; or
- Reduce the amount of energy reaching the wall (perhaps by importing beach material or by construction in front of the wall).

An evaluation of the interaction of these three processes is central to the design of the wall.

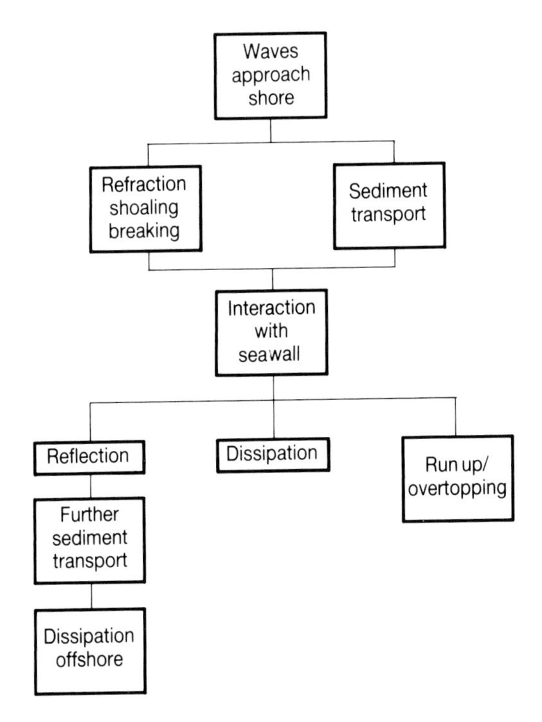

Figure 5.14 Wave behaviour at seawall

Reflections

All seawalls reflect waves, and reflections can have a significant impact on the coastal regime. The increase in reflections from the shore as the result of building a seawall will increase the amount of wave energy seaward of the wall. Waves incident on a vertical impermeable wall will be reflected almost totally giving rise to a reflected wave, approximately equal in height to the incident wave. Waves will superpose, so that where incident and reflected waves coincide, the height of the resultant wave will be almost double the original height. The wave pattern resulting from reflections can produce increase run-up of waves and a severe deterioration in boating/swimming conditions seaward of the wall.

As a result of reflections, wave action in front of the seawall will be increased, as will the sediment transport potential. This may not lead to an overall increase in sediment transport, since the increased transport in front of the wall can be counteracted by the cessation of transport behind it. It does, however, carry the risk of local scour, of a reduction of foreshore level and of undermining of the wall itself.

In general terms, rough and porous walls reflect less wave energy than smooth, and non-porous and sloping walls reflect less than vertical. This reduction in reflection is effected by increased dissipation. Wave reflection is also a function of wave steepness and length (see Section 6.1.5). Longer-period waves will tend to reflect more than those of a shorter period.

It should be noted, therefore, that if a wall is to be sufficiently far seaward to reflect waves (i.e. if it is not a 'fall-back' behind a beach) and if the seabed in front of the wall is mobile (e.g. not inerodible rock), then, in general:

- The wall should be of a form which minimizes reflections and hence the risk of scour;
- The design should include a thorough assessment of the need for beach-control measures to counteract the tendency to erosion (see Section 2.2);
- The design should involve a careful assessment of the likelihood and extent of scour that must be accommodated.

Dissipation

Waves impinging on a seawall will lose energy as a result of dissipation, primarily due to turbulence. In general terms, sloping, porous and rough walls will dissipate more energy than vertical, non-porous and smooth ones. Turbulence is induced, in the case of sloping walls, by causing the wave to break on the slope. On porous walls, such as those armoured with irregularly placed rock armour or some types of concrete armour units, turbulence results from flow within the armour layer and, if permeable, the underlayers and core. Rough walls, such as stepped seawalls, disrupt the flow of water up and down the wall. In initial considerations of dissipation, the following points should be borne in mind:

1. In general, dissipation increases as the slope flattens, but, depending on wave steepness, there tends to be no great improvement in dissipation when flattening from vertical to 1:1 (see Section 6.1.5). Flatter slopes are necessary to produce substantial dissipation in themselves.
2. In order for rough or porous walls to effect a substantial degree of dissipation the roughness/porosity element of the wall must be of significant thickness with respect to the proportions of the wave. Layers that are thin will tend to fill rapidly and become swamped by the incoming wave, allowing it to flow, uninterrupted, over the top. This should be borne in mind when considering the use of flexible armoured revetment systems based on effectively impermeable underlayers, or in roughening concrete seawalls with, for example, steps.
3. In order for the wall to perform its function it must not be fully permeable to wave action throughout its cross section. There must therefore be a decrease in permeability going from the face of the wall to its core. Internal problems of wall stability are minimized when this decrease is progressive. Discontinuities in this permeability gradient are discussed further in Section 6.3.
4. Encouraging waves to break whether by virtue of the slope of the wall or by placing a berm or apron in front of the wall will increase dissipation. The engineer should take care, however, as waves breaking on a structure can exert far greater forces than waves that do not break (see Section 6.2).

Overtopping

Overtopping has two forms: spray and green water. Spray occurs when waves break and/or hit the wall and foreshore, and is increased substantially when accompanied by onshore winds. Little can be done to eliminate spray, but walls that deflect waves upwards or produce reflections will cause more spray than those that absorb the wave through dissipation – the extreme example of the latter being a natural beach.

While the importance of spray should not be underestimated, green water overtopping leads to much greater quantities of water going over the wall. Such overtopping occurs when run-up exceeds the crest level. The elimination of it therefore requires the raising of the crest and/or reduction of run-up. Alternatively, where space and the configuration of the wall allows, the crest can be moved landward. This can, for example, be achieved by constructing a floodwall on the landward side of a promenade. Reduction of run-up can be effected by increasing dissipation, i.e. by flattening the wall slope, roughening it, making it more porous or making the wave break before it hits the structure. Alternatively, where the wall is relatively smooth, and the flow of water rushing up the wall is relatively streamlined, a throwback can be incorporated to deflect the up-rush seawards. Such a solution is often appropriate with solid vertical walls, where run-up and overtopping can otherwise be very great.

5.3.3 Structural concept

A seawall can be regarded as having elements which need to be combined to produce a coherent structure. The elements then comprise components appropriate to the function required of them. In order to examine the options for each element and the choice of suitable components, the following have been adopted for discussion (see Figure 5.15):

- Body (including the front face and core);
- Toe;
- Crest (including the back face).

Each element performs specific functions which interact with the others. These functions and the various options for the three elements are discussed in Sections 5.4–5.6.

5.3.4 Type of seawall

The classification of seawalls into four categories used in Section 5.3.1 (sloping, vertical, porous and non-porous) is also convenient when listing types of seawall. Figure 5.16 shows the more commonly used forms of seawall using this classification. The front face of the seawall determines the classification used for the body. However, the core is an equally important component of the body and is discussed in Section 5.4.1.

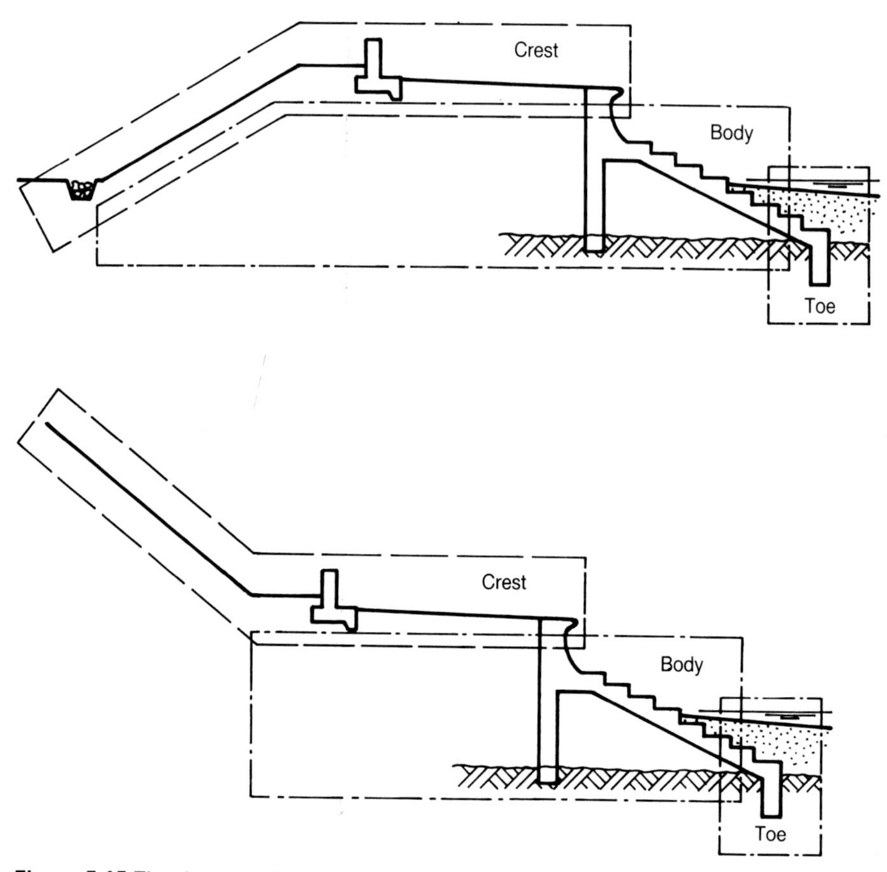

Figure 5.15 The elements of a seawall

Each seawall type will have a toe and a crest, which may merely be an extension to the main body of the wall or a different form of construction. The various toe and crest types are discussed in Sections 5.5 and 5.6, respectively. On flood defences an important element of the wall is the back face. Most of the major dyke failures in the Netherlands in 1953 were the result of back face, not front face, failure. The back face is also discussed in Section 5.6.

5.4 The body of the wall

The body is the major part of the seawall and has a great influence on its performance. In order to select the most appropriate type of construction the suitability of each type of wall structure should be assessed against the Functional Requirements, including:

- Stability against wave attack (Sections 6.3–6.5);
- Wave reflections (Section 6.1.5);
- Run-up and overtopping (Sections 6.1.3 and 6.1.4);
- Spray (Section 6.1.4);
- Aesthetics (Section 3.3);
- Durability and likely life (Section 7.2);
- Ease of construction and requirements for construction (access, working area, etc.) (Section 6.8);
- Availability of materials (Section 6.4);
- Required level and ease of maintenance (Section 6.8);
- Flexibility (ability to accommodate scour or settlement) (Section 5.4);
- Strength (ability to resist imposed loads) (Section 6.2);
- Ease of access along and across the wall (Section 6.8);
- Safety (Section 6.9);
- Cost (Section 8.5).

The above aspects are dealt with in the sections shown in parentheses. Following a discussion of the core (Section 5.4.1), Sections 5.4.2–5.4.5 give a general guide to the characteristics and use of the various different options indicated in Figure 5.16.

5.4.1 The core

The core of a seawall is often a significant proportion of the total cost. In general, when fill is required as backing to a vertical seawall or retaining wall it should be good quality, inert, free-draining granular fill such as would be used in general works of civil engineering.

The choice of fill material for a sloping seawall will be strongly influenced by both local availability and the nature of the subsoil at the site. It is inherent in the nature of many sea defences that locally available fill and foundation soils consist of marsh clays, often in association with silt or peat. Since the foundations are unsuitable for heavy loadings, flat side slopes to the core are necessary and available local clays can usually meet the design requirements. Substantial settlement in both the fill and the subsoil should be provided for in the design. Fissuring of the crest is to be expected as the top metre or so dries out unless the surface is sealed or an alternative source of fill is used near the crest. Faces exposed to wave action are likely to require revetment or armouring and the crests will require protection if overtopping is expected.

The strength and consolidation characteristics of marsh clays may limit the height of stable embankment that can be attained and substantial land usage will be required. These characteristics need to be evaluated at the initial design stage for the option to be chosen or discarded.

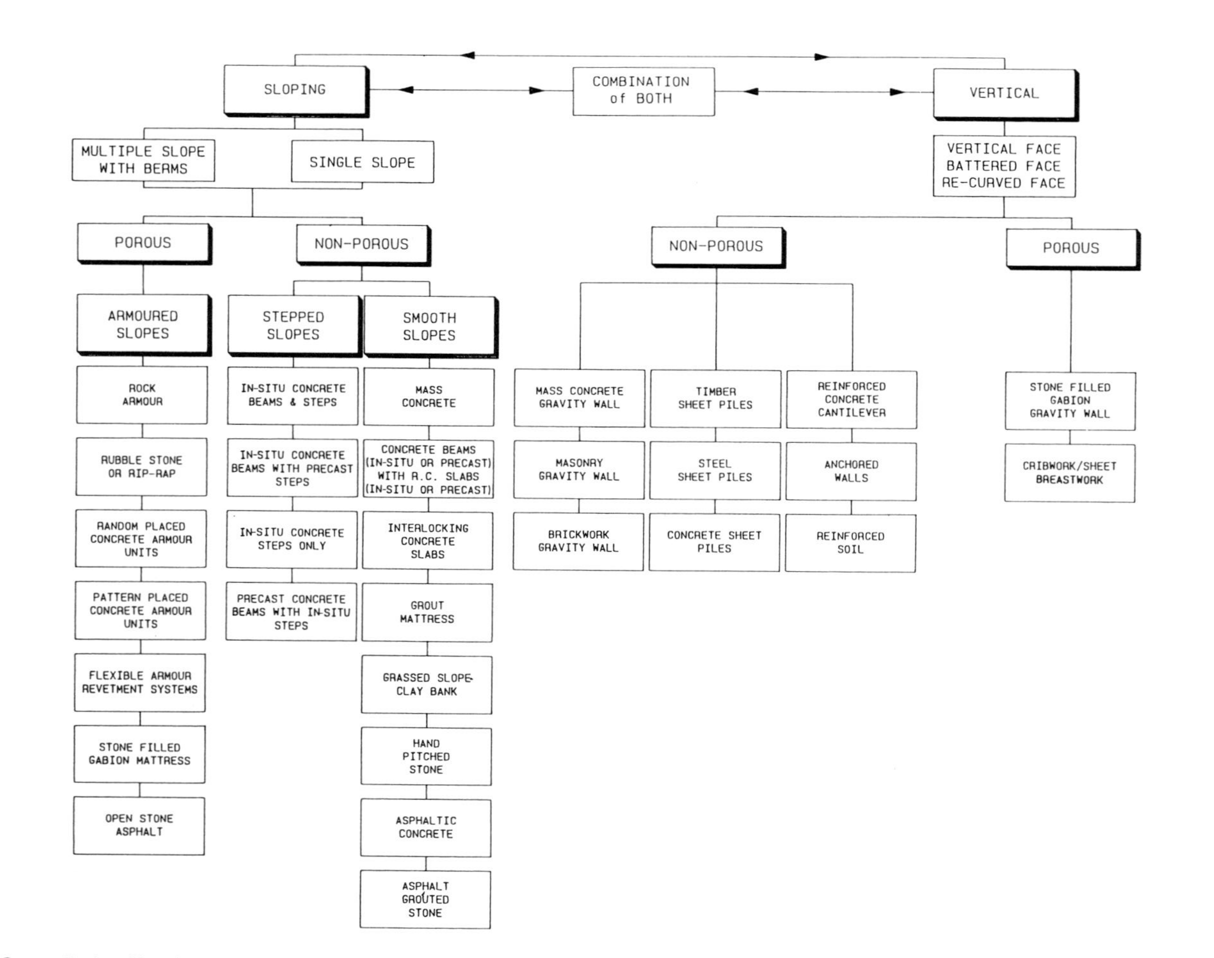

Figure 5.16 Seawall classification

5.4.2 Sloping porous walls

Rock armour (Figure 5.17 and Plate 1)

General functional characteristics of the various wall types are shown in Table 5.3. The suitability of rock armour is conditioned by the rock size required, the availability of suitable access for delivery (whether by land or sea) and suitable working area for stockpiles and heavy plant. In more severe environments requiring very large rock it can, however, present construction problems, requiring large plant and specialist expertise (Figure 5.17). The size grading required for rock armour is narrow (perhaps ±10% on stone diameter or ±30% on stone weight).

On beaches partly or wholly composed of shingle or cobbles it is essential that rock armour is as hard or harder than the material of the beaches if the rock is to be durable. Under these circumstances, consideration should be given to the relative sizes of the beach material and the interstices of the armour layer. If the interstices become blocked the layer will become hydraulically much smoother and thus more reflective.

Rock armour suffers progressively increasing damage with increasing severity of wave attack. In many cases the philosophy of design is to allow for a small degree of damage under design conditions and 5% is a commonly applied figure. In these circumstances, careful consideration should be given to the cost of bringing in plant to repair such damage.

Pedestrian access across rock armour is difficult. Providing steps across the armour can pose problems, as the introduction of a rigid element in a flexible structure will give a potential weakness.

Rip-rap (Figure 5.18)

Rip-rap is a particular type of rock armour where the size grading is much wider (say, ±50% on stone diameter). The resultant structure has attractions insofar as it uses a much greater proportion of a quarry output than does rock (armour which can produce a very high demand for narrow size ranges). It is not so appropriate to severe wave climates due to the very wide size range. When laid to slopes of 1:4 or flatter, rip-rap 'self heals', with smaller stones filling gaps resulting from wave damage. Rip-rap is particularly suitable in mild wave climates, in rocky rural areas where local rock can be used to provide a relatively cheap, durable, low-maintenance, environmentally suitable solution. In such circumstances the use of flat slopes may be acceptable (in terms of rock cost as well as space occupied), whereas this may not be the case in more heavily populated areas with less readily available rock.

Random placed concrete armour units (Figure 5.19)

For areas where rock is not readily available a large number of different types of armour units have been developed. Most of these were developed for use in breakwaters, where the depth of water and severity of wave attack are greater.

Plate 1 Rock armour at Aith, Shetland Islands, UK

Plate 2 Shed armour at Bangor, Northern Ireland

Plate 3 Seawall at mid-tide, Skegness, UK

Plate 4 Construction of stepped concrete wall at Burnham-on-Sea, UK

Plate 5 Smooth concrete slope with wave return wall at Lowestoft, UK

Plate 6 Concrete blockwork at Aberdeen, UK

Plate 7 Installation of grout mattresses at Portsmouth, UK

Plate 8 Vertical masonry wall at Ventnor, UK

Plate 9 'The foreshore is a hostile place to carry out construction work'

Table 5.3 Functional characteristics of sloping porous walls

Type of slope protection	*Range of wave climate*	*Hydraulic performance*	*Visual aspects*	*Ease of access to shore*	*Maintenance*	*Permeability to groundwater*	*Flexibility*	*Durability (assuming good materials)*
Rock armour	All	Good (depending on underlayer)	Can be non-intrusive in rural areas with local rock	Difficult (steps or ramps can give local weakness)	Requires crane	High	High	High
Rip-rap	Mild and moderate	Good	Can be non-intrusive in rural areas with local rock	Difficult (steps or ramps can give local weakness)	Vehicle access (flatter than 1:4 may 'self-heal')	High	High	High
Random placed concrete armour units	All	Medium to good (depending on underlayer)	Intrusive	Difficult (steps or ramps can give local weakness)	Can be a problem if units break	High	High	Medium to high, but less so with slender units
Pattern placed concrete armour units								
(i) Small blocks	Mild	Medium	Can be unobtrusive, particularly where vegetation	Good	Relatively easy	High, depending on the underlayer	Medium, will accommodate differential settlement to a degree	High in mild wave climate

(ii) Larger blocks	Moderate to severe	Medium to good, depending on unit	Possibly intrusive, depending on surrounding area	Difficult	Can be a problem if units break	High	Medium, will accommodate differential settlement to a degree	Medium, depending on slenderness of unit
Flexible armoured revetment systems	Normally mild	Medium (refer to manufacturer)	Can be relatively unobtrusive	Fair to good	Well designed, will be low maintenance. Can be difficult to replace individual components	High, depending on underlayer	Medium, will accept differential settlement to a degree	Medium
Stone-filled gabion mattresses	Mild	Medium to good	Can be relatively unobtrusive, particularly with use of local stone	Easy (but leads to problems of durability)	High	High, depending on underlayer	Good, will accept differential settlement	Very poor
Open stone asphalt	Mild to moderate	Medium	Subject to colour of stone: weathering reduces impact	Easy for pedestrians, depending on slope	Limited, but requires regular inspection	High	Limited	Fair

Note: Approximate ranges of wave climate are:
mild, 0–1.5/2 m wave height
moderate, 1.5/2–4 m wave height
severe, greater than 4 m wave height.

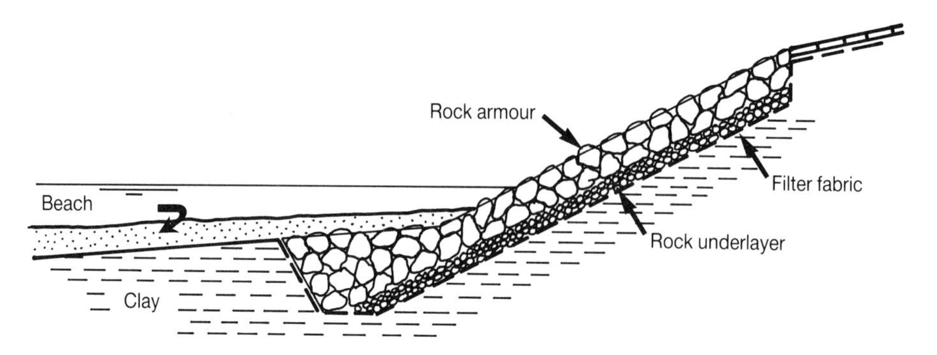

Figure 5.17 Sloping porous seawall using rock armour

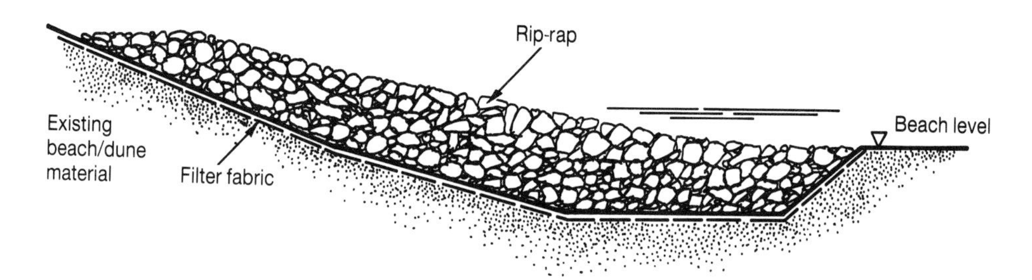

Figure 5.18 Sloping porous seawall using rip-rap

Purpose-made armour units, as distinct from naturally occuring rock, allow the production of armour units which are more stable against wave attack by virtue of interlock and shape. For a given wave climate the use of concrete units allows the weight of the units to be reduced as compared with rock.

Random armour units used in coast protection in the UK are tripods, tetrapods, stabits, cubes and dolos. Additional units, newly developed and which may be appropriate are accropodes and Antifer cubes (see Figure 5.19). Because of relatively high production costs they are often less cost-effective in mild wave climates. The stability against wave attack is characterized (in simple terms) by the stability factor (K_D) (Section 6.3.3). The higher the K_D value, the greater is the stability against wave attack. Units with a high K_D value tend to be so because of a high degree of interlock, i.e. the slender units such as dolos and, to a lesser extent, tetrapods. With the larger units in more severe wave climates the stresses induced in the units by virtue of interlock and, as a result of units rocking, can lead to breakage and sometimes catastrophic failure.

Armour units are less tolerant to damage from occasional severe storms than rock. Relying on interlock as well as self-weight for their stability (rock has little interlock), once the interlock is broken locally, more rapid damage can ensue. Random armour units are, however, often the only feasible solution in areas where rock armour is

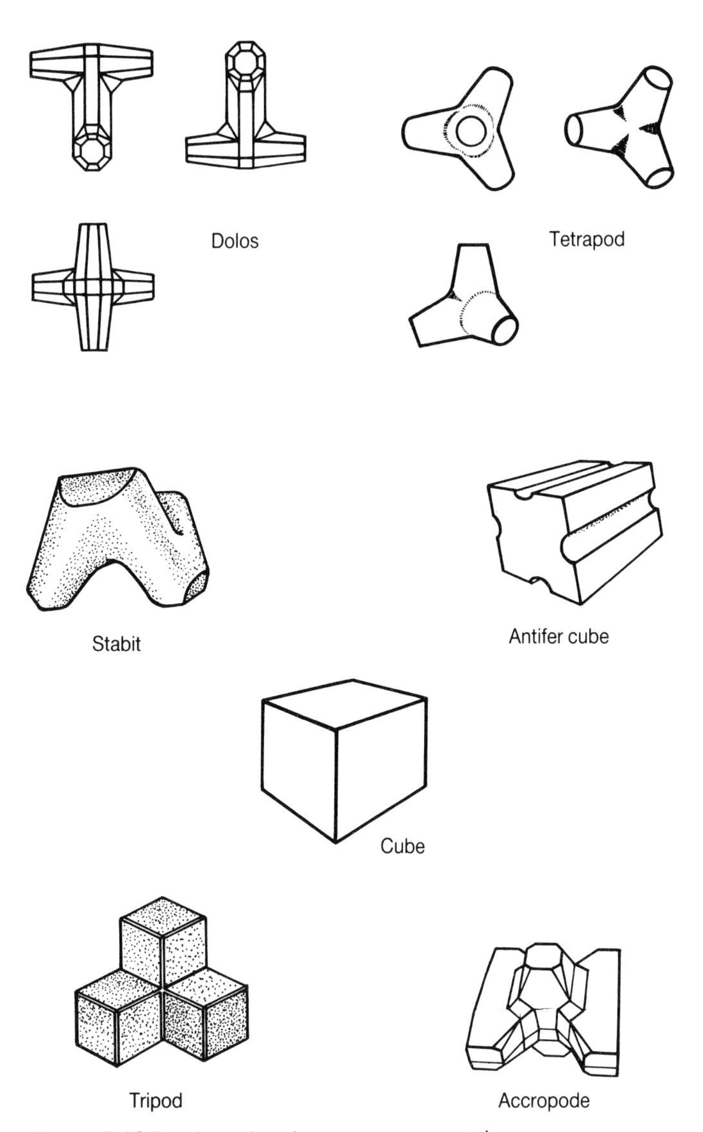

Figure 5.19 Random placed concrete armour units

costly and where locally severe wave attack requires resisting and dissipating (e.g. at the root of a breakwater or re-entrant angle in a seawall – Section 5.2).

Pattern placed concrete armour units (Figures 5.20 and 5.21, Plates 2 and 3)

Regularly laid armour units (in a single layer) are used widely in seawalls, and the category includes a wide range of precast units from small hand-placed blocks for use in protected areas such as estuaries to large complex blocks, with built-in voids for use in relatively severe wave climates.

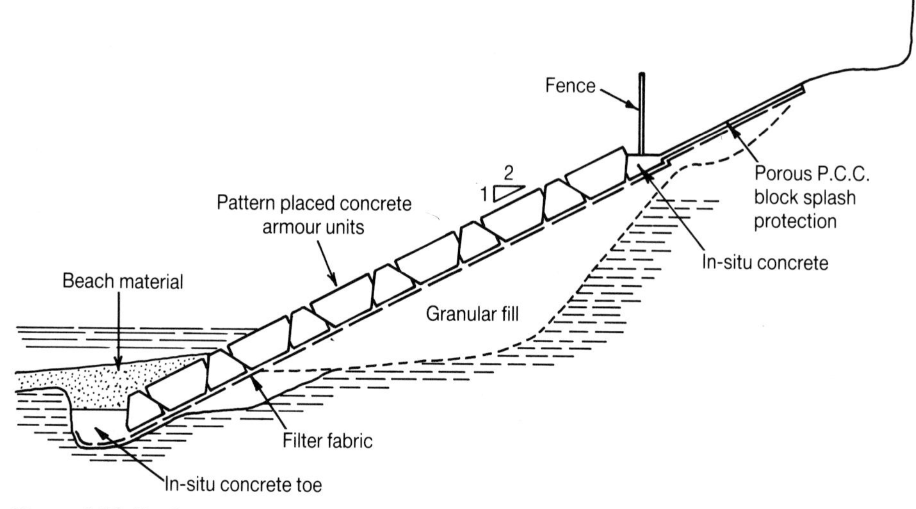

Figure 5.20 Sloping seawall using double-wedge blocks

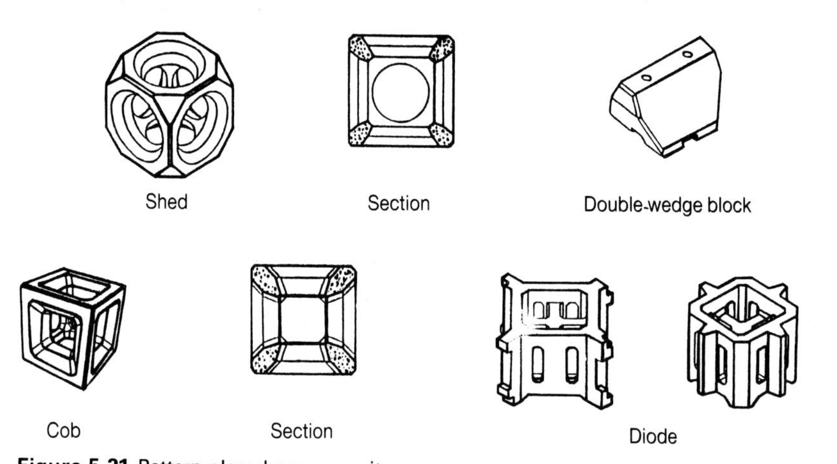

Figure 5.21 Pattern placed armour units

Most of the smaller hand-placed blocks tend to be slab-like and are considered under non-porous slopes (see Section 5.4.3). Of those which form a porous layer there are a large number of proprietary systems that are linked as 'mattresses' by the use of plastic tendons (see below). Independent, small (i.e. man-handleable) porous blocks can be used in protected areas, subject to wave heights of, say, less than one metre. Within this limitation their most suitable application is in areas seldom touched by waves but required as stabilization for extreme events. In more severe wave climates, much larger units such as sheds, diodes, cobs or double-wedge blocks can be used (Figures 5.20 and 5.21). Placing cobs and sheds (a refinement to cobs to ease construction) underwater requires assistance from divers. Diodes and double wedges cannot be placed underwater, requiring too much precision in placing and preparation of underlayers. With the exception of continuous reinforced concrete or mass concrete walls, these units offer the greatest potential stability against wave attack. Diodes, the most intricate armour blocks, require complex shuttering and careful concrete mix design and control and give relatively low resistance to abrasion (by virtue of the slenderness of the members), but offer excellent hydraulic performance (i.e. better than rock armour) with low reflection and run-up. Double-wedge blocks can be cheaper to construct (simple shuttering, less problematical mix design) and have good resistance to abrasion, but do not offer such good hydraulic performance (lying approximately halfway between rock characteristics and a smooth wall).

Cobs and shed units have hydraulic characteristics similar to rock armour. The shuttering is fairly complex (to the extent that it is unlikely to be economical on a small project). They suffer significantly from abrasion in hostile environments (i.e. exposed gravel beaches), but they do not require the precision in grading of the underlayers that is demanded by diodes and double wedges.

Seabees, developed and used in Australia, can be designed for a wide range of wave climates but specialist advice is necessary. For more protected sites (1–2 m wave heights) the units can be made from vitrified clay which gives a hard-wearing, aesthetically pleasing slope that allows ready pedestrian and vehicular access over it.

Pattern placed units and the 'tied' systems described below rely for their stability to a considerable extent on their existence as a homogenous layer. However, if the integrity of the layer is threatened then relatively rapid damage can ensure, with, in the case of the smaller blocks, the armour layer 'peeling' off. To minimize this risk, great care should be taken in detailing to create robust edges to the layer.

Flexible armoured revetment systems (Figure 5.22)

There are a number of different proprietary revetment systems available. The systems consist of small, voided blocks tied together with plastic tendons, to form mattresses of a size that can be lifted into position with a crane. They can be laid directly on a

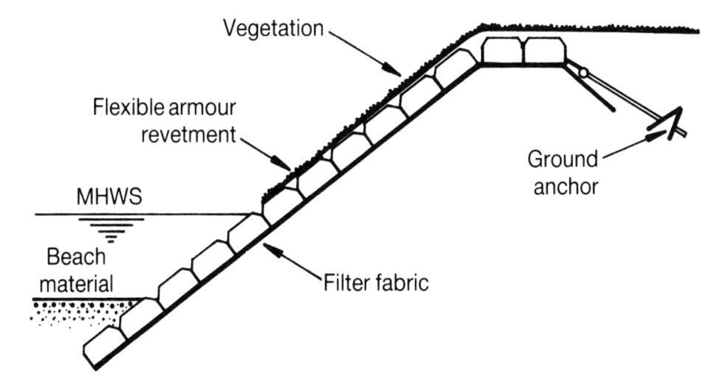

Figure 5.22 Sloping seawall using flexible armour revetment

geotextile on a carefully graded granular fill slope, or the geotextile can be integral with the mattress itself.

Being proprietary systems, full design details and recommendations for use, particularly their hydraulic performance should be obtained from the manufacturers or agents, some of whom have had physical model studies carried out. Design recommendations that are not based on model tests and site data should be treated with caution.

They are subject to suitable access for plant and easy to lay, even underwater. The mattresses can readily be removed and re-used, making them suited to temporary or short-term works. Isolated broken blocks can be replaced with *in-situ* concrete or, in some cases, with new blocks if the tendons can be removed and replaced.

Stone-filled gabion mattresses

This section considers gabion mattresses (or reno mattresses) rather than the more cubical gabions used in steeper walls. Gabion mattresses consist of wire baskets filled with stone, with a wire mesh lid subsequently fixed. They are frequently used laid on a geotextile on granular fill, and allow the use of a 'rubble-type' solution when large rock is not easily available. The system can either be assembled onshore and lifted by crane into position or, if tidal levels allow, be constructed *in-situ* by hand.

Problems with the use of gabions are their susceptibility to vandalism and poor durability. When gabions are subjected to regular impact by waterborne sand they will have a very restricted life and on pebble beaches this life can be reduced to a matter of weeks.

In more severe waves the stone within the basket may move and slump within the mattress. The baskets should therefore be internally partitioned and completely filled. In areas where abrasion is not a problem galvanized plastic-coated gabion mattresses can provide a good solution and, with vegetation becoming established in the stone, have very little visual impact.

Open-stone asphalt (Figure 5.23)

This was developed in Holland, as an alternative to asphaltic concrete, to be more porous and therefore hydraulically better. It consists of a no-fines mix of stone (25 mm approximately) bound with asphalt. Its abrasion resistance in the UK climate is governed by that of the aggregate. Normally it is underlain by lean sand asphalt so that the combined layer is impermeable to wave action but permeable to groundwater flows. The main design criterion is the need to resist hydraulic uplift pressures. The system should be inspected regularly, as once damaged locally it must be repaired rapidly if major subsequent damage is to be avoided. It cannot be laid underwater unless in the form of a pre-formed mattress. However, its open texture allows it to be laid intertidally without the problems of heat retention associated with asphaltic concrete.

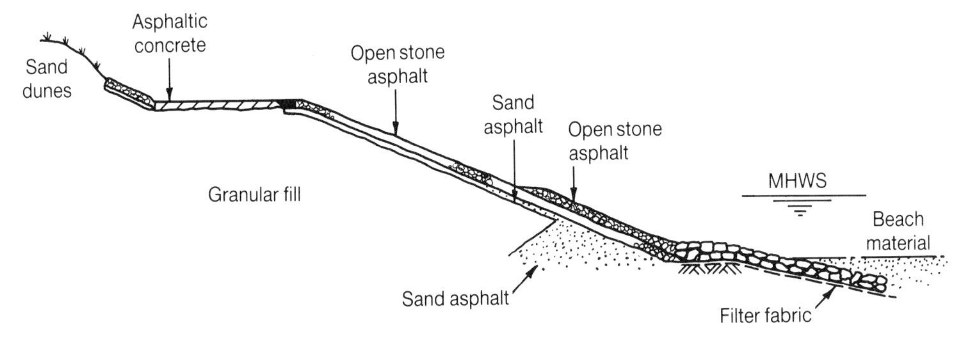

Figure 5.23 Sloping seawalls using open-stone asphalt

Underlayers (including geotexiles)

Beneath the porous slope protection there should be an underlayer. The function of the underlayer (discussed in more detail in Section 6.3.4) can be some or all of the following:

- Filtration and separation between the core and the slope protection;
- Secondary armour and erosion control, during construction and as an integral part of the final protection system;
- To act as a drainage layer;
- To provide a regular surface on which to place the slope protection.

The underlayer usually consists of granular materials, geotexiles or natural fibres either alone or in combination (see Figures 5.17 and 5.18). Granular materials used are rock, gravel or, occasionally, lean sand asphalt. The advantages of the use of gravel or rock are that they form a permeable layer that can greatly enhance hydraulic stability. Their roughness gives a good surface contact between layers above and below which contributes to the overall integrity of the structure. The grains are durable and the layer is relatively easy to repair. Possible disadvantages are difficulties in achieving a consistent layer in terms of composition and thickness.

Lean sand asphalt is as permeable as the constituent sand. It has the advantage over gravel that during construction the presence of the bitumen binder makes it more resistant to wave action. The smoother surface is not so good for the overall integrity of the slope as is gravel, unless the slope protection is asphaltic and the overall integrity is achieved through bonding. Providing the temperature is controlled it can be laid underwater.

Natural fabrics such as woven willow mats have been used extensively in the past and overseas, but recently, geotextiles have been far more widely employed. Geotextiles have the advantages of small construction height (i.e. occupying little space), tensile strength, consistency and cheapness. Their possible disadvantages include:

- Uncertainty in long-term behaviour (e.g. degradation, clogging);

Table 5.4 Functional characteristics of sloping non-porous walls

Type of slope protection	*Range of wave climate*	*Hydraulic performance*	*Visual aspects*	*Ease of access to shore*	*Maintenance*	*Permeability to groundwater*	*Flexibility*	*Durability (assuming good materials)*
Stepped concrete slopes	All	Poor to medium	Have become characteristic of many seaside towns: more obtrusive in rural areas	Good	Low, subject to joints	Impermeable	Inflexible, require good toe and foundations	High
Smooth concrete slopes	All	Poor	Have become characteristic of many seaside towns: more obtrusive in rural areas	Relatively easy to include steps	Low, subject to joints	Impermeable	Inflexible, require good toe and foundations	High
Interlocking concrete slabs and blocks	Mild to moderate	Poor	Generally not over-obtrusive on clay banks. In more exposed sites, careful detailing	Relatively easy	Low, requires regular inspection and rapid response in the event of damage	Impermeable	Medium, will accommodate differential settlement to a degree	High

mattresses						but can be provided with drains		
Grassed slopes	Occasional mild wave action	Poor	Attractive	Good	May require mowing or grazing	Permeable	Flexible	Not to be used in areas regularly subject to wave action
Asphaltic concrete	Mild to moderate	Poor	Colour makes it visually intrusive	Good	Low, requires regular inspection and rapid response in the event of damage	Impermeable	Limited-medium	Medium
Asphalt grouted stone	Normally, mild to moderate. Occasionally has been used in severe wave climate	Poor	Less intrusive than asphaltic concrete but less attractive than native rubble	Fair	Low	Impermeable	Limited	Medium to good

Note: Approximate ranges of wave climate are:
mild, 0–1.5/2 m wave height
moderate, 1.5/2–4 m wave height
severe, greater than 4 m wave height.

- Particularly when clogged, they can form a discontinuity in the permeability of the structure which can lead to a deterioration in hydraulic stability and understreaming of the core along the underside of the fabric;
- They can give a reduction in slope stability due to low friction between the fabric and soil;
- Connections between lapped joints and to other elements have to be made with great care;
- They are easily damaged and rather difficult to repair;
- Geotextiles tend not to follow uneven settlement as well as granular underlayers.

Design guidance on the choice of geotextile fabrics to maximize their advantages while avoiding the problems listed is contained in Section 6.3.4. The nature of the materials and the characteristics that dictate the manner in which they should be used is described in Section 7.3.7. The increasing range of geotextile fabrics available is such that manufacturers' advice should be sought and information on detailing for ease of construction, avoidance of damage, etc. can also be obtained in this way.

5.4.3 Sloping non-porous walls

Non-porous walls will tend not to dissipate wave energy to the same extent as porous walls. Roughness may reduce run-up and flatter slopes will decrease reflections, but overall, the hydraulic performance in respect of run-up, overtopping and reflection will not be as good as, say, rubble. One of the major concerns in design of non-porous walls is their lack of permeability and the potentially damaging internal water pressure that may develop. Particularly with the more flexible systems (such as blockwork and asphalt), uplift due to a build-up in pressure can be very important in overall stability. Since the walls are impermeable the design should be considered with respect to:

- Providing an adequate cut-off if there is danger of liquefaction due to groundwater flows;
- Provision of suitable drainage if it is necessary to avoid obstruction to groundwater flows.

Some characteristics of sloping non-porous walls are given in Table 5.4.

Stepped concrete slopes (Figure 5.24 and Plate 4)

Stepped concrete slopes are widely used in the UK for seawall construction in urban areas. The extent of precasting as opposed to *in-situ* work can be tailored to suit working, tidal and access conditions, and these aspects should be considered carefully at an early stage in the design to ensure that the wall can be built economically (Section 6.4).

The extent to which run-up will be reduced by steps is a function of the size of the steps in relation to wave height. During storm conditions, steps of, say, 200 mm in

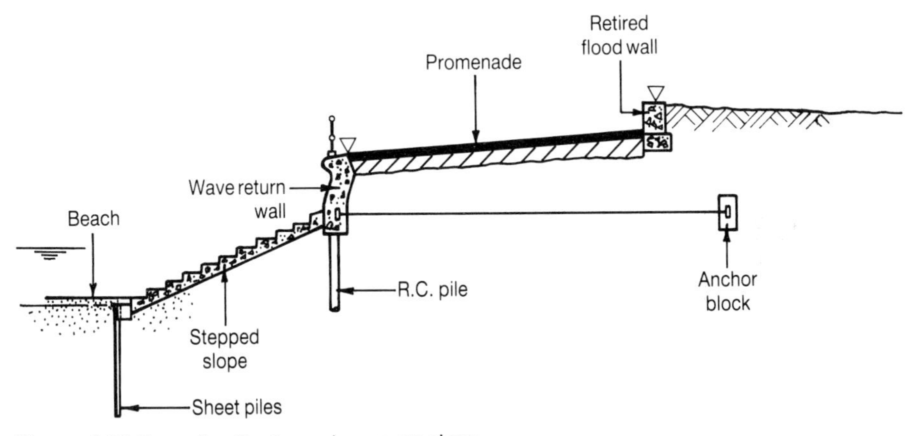

Figure 5.24 Seawall with stepped concrete slope

height are unlikely to give substantial improvement relative to a smooth wall. Much larger steps (say, riser = 1 m) will reduce run-up, although perhaps at the cost of much wave spray and some reflection. Steps of smaller proportions clearly offer good pedestrian access and, correctly detailed, can require little maintenance.

Smooth concrete slopes (Figure 5.25 and Plate 5)

Smooth concrete slopes can be constructed in reinforced or mass, pre-cast or *in-situ* concrete. The decision should be made on the basis of construction and maintenance considerations (Section 6.4) and cost. The creation of pedestrian access is relatively easy, although the slopes themselves can become slippery and dangerous.

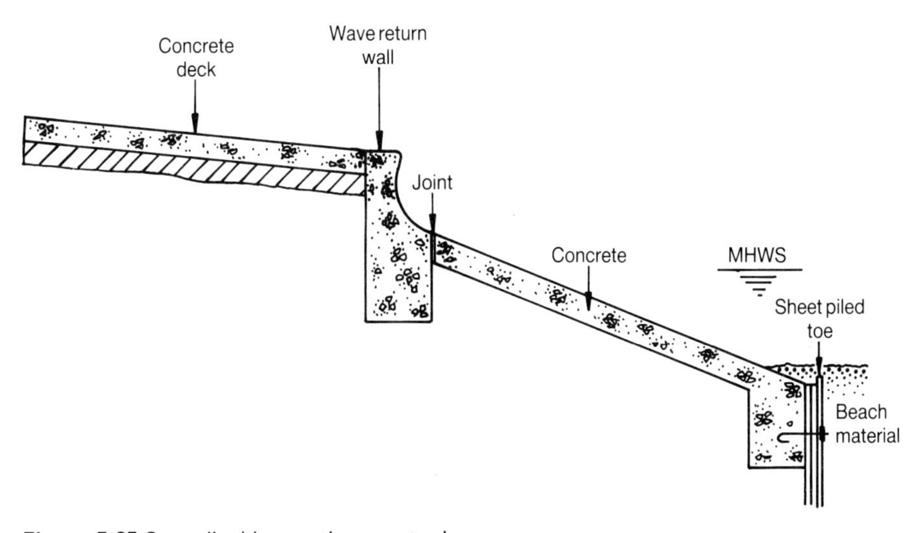

Figure 5.25 Seawall with smooth concrete slope

Concrete slabs and blocks (Figure 5.26 and Plate 6)

Concrete slabs have been used extensively for armouring clay flood banks in estuaries, and larger blocks have been employed in coastal areas of limited exposure. They can be laid by hand and form an effectively impermeable slope, which becomes completely impermeable when the joints are infilled with asphalt. The strength of the system is dependent upon the maintenance of continuity in the sloping face. An interlock between the blocks or slabs is frequently used to achieve some support between adjacent units. While relatively easily maintained, local damage must be repaired quickly to avoid progressive failure.

Grout mattresses (Figure 5.27 and Plate 7)

These are proprietary systems in which a fabric formwork is used to provide an *in-situ* concrete revetment. The fibre used for weaving the formwork is most commonly nylon, polyester or polypropylene. Specially designed cement grout is pumped into the formwork to give a solid armour layer of concrete normally some 100–300 mm thick. The fabric is likely to deteriorate in abrasive environments, and while this gives a temporarily untidy appearance, it is of no structural consequence. Versions can be supplied with fabric filters through the mattress to avoid pressure build-up. In this latter case, in an abrasive environment (on a sand or gravel beach), the filters may be abraded away, so the mattress should be provided with a suitable underlayer to avoid loss of fill. Grout mattresses require specialist experience, so are best laid by specialist contractors.

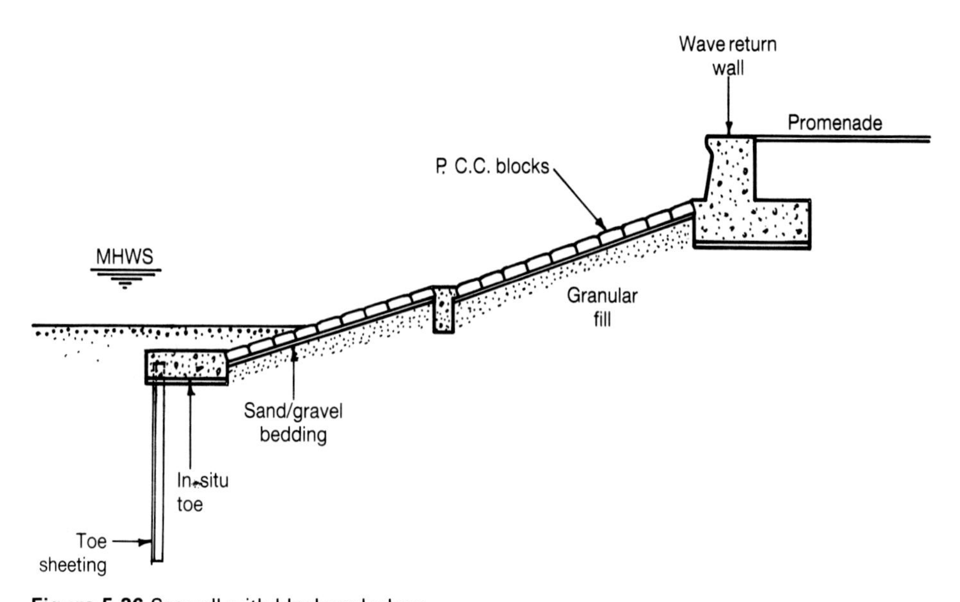

Figure 5.26 Seawall with blockwork slope

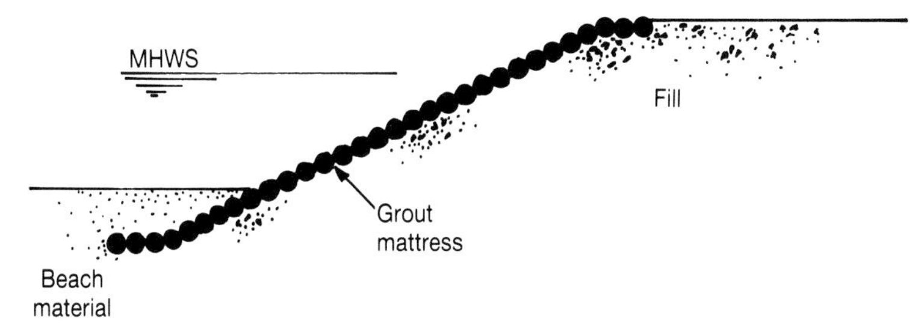

Figure 5.27 Seawall using grout mattress revetment

Hand-pitched stone (Figure 5.28)

This technique was used widely in the past, using basalt, ragstone and limestone. The stones are laid by hand on a granular underlayer with their long axes perpendicular to the slope. Depending on their slope, they can provide ready pedestrian or even vehicle access to the foreshore. Concrete blocks are now available as a proprietary system which can be laid mechanically and are usually cheaper than natural stone.

Asphaltic concrete (Figure 5.29)

Asphalt has not been widely used in the UK, other than in grouting blockwork systems, but is common in the Low Countries, where there is a scarcity of natural stone. Asphaltic concrete is similar to the material used in road construction. It is impermeable, and the main design requirement is the need to resist hydraulic uplift. As with open-stone asphalt, it requires frequent inspection as it will deteriorate rapidly once damaged.

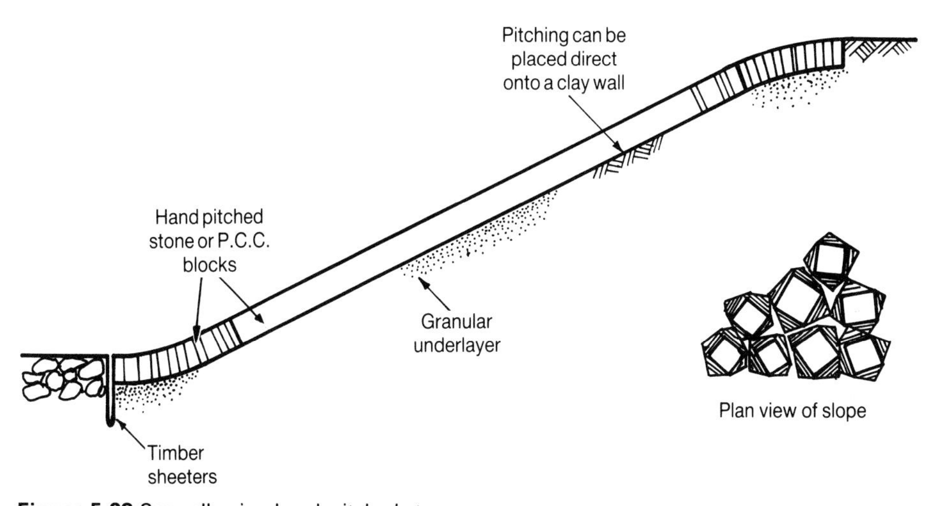

Figure 5.28 Seawall using hand-pitched stone

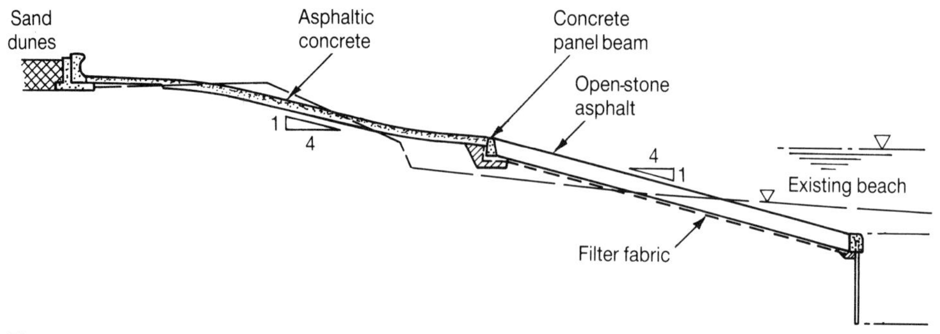

Figure 5.29 Seawall using asphaltic concrete and open-stone asphalt

It should be laid at a slope of 1:3 or flatter to allow the use of conventional asphalt-laying plant and thus to achieve good compaction. Asphaltic concrete is mostly used above the tidal zone in order to limit the layer thickness needed to resist uplift and to avoid steam formation (caused by warm material lying in the seawater) which can weaken the asphalt.

Asphalt-grouted stone

Where suitable rock of only a limited size is available, asphalt grouting can be used to provide an impermeable armour layer of greater resistance to wave action than the component rock alone. This has been used extensively on estuarine flood defences where stone pitching has been grouted (see Figure 5.28). While grouting ties the component pieces of rock together and so forms a linked mattress, it leads to a deterioration in hydraulic performance. Asphalt-grouted stone has been used on breakwaters subject to severe wave climates but only where overtopping can be accepted.

Grassed slopes

Grassed slopes can only be used in protected areas of very limited exposure to wave action and when their level is high enough that they are only occasionally reached by the sea, e.g. at the landward edge of saltings. For this reason, their consideration as an option for a seawall is limited. When suitable, however, they form an environmentally good, cheap solution. Salt-tolerant grasses should be chosen. Their resistance to occasional wave action can be improved either by regular mowing or grazing (to build up the root matrix) or by use of a suitable geotextile within the topsoil.

5.4.4 Vertical non-porous walls

Vertical non-porous walls are very reflective. They have the advantage of occupying little space compared with that required by a sloping structure but require steps or ramps to effect access to the foreshore (Table 5.5). When supplemented by groynes, or when fronted by a beach to the extent that they are only occasionally reached by wave action, the effects of the reflections on beach transport and possible subsequent erosion are mitigated. Built of suitable materials, they can be very durable and can be designed to resist the most severe of wave climates. However, when subject to modest to severe waves the up-rush of water into the air when waves hit the wall can be very great, carrying shingle, sand and other flotsam with it, and overtopping can be serious especially with onshore winds (Section 6.1).

Vertical non-porous walls often prove cost-effective when they also act as retaining walls, for example when at the seaward edge of a promenade or coastal road. In these cases the walls should be designed primarily as retaining walls, taking into account the other functional requirements such as stability, ease of construction, acceptable overtopping, durability, etc. Vertical non-porous walls can therefore be conveniently considered under four headings corresponding to four main types of retaining wall, i.e. gravity, cantilever, anchored and reinforced soil.

Gravity walls (Figure 5.30 and Plate 8)

Gravity walls, by their nature, require to be massive and the most suitable materials are mass concrete, masonry, concrete blockwork and brickwork. Their use was widespread until the last 20–30 years, when increasing labour costs and changing construction techniques often made them more expensive than other types of wall. They require little maintenance subject to sound foundations. In locations such as rocky areas and seaside towns they can blend in well with the local surroundings if faced with local stone.

Reinforced concrete (L-shaped) walls come under the broad heading of gravity walls in that, overall, they function as gravity walls. The 'cantilever' element refers to the front face, which is a vertical cantilever from the base. They can provide considerable potential for precasting, given the requisite access and craneage. Precasting in turn offers improved durability (conditional on adequate reinforcement cover and quality in the finished wall) and alleviates some of the problems associated with tidal working.

Cantilever walls

Unless the wall height is very small, it is unlikely that a cantilever sheet-piled wall would be cost-effective. Sheet-piled walls are normally tied to produce a more effective solution which is more tolerant to variations in soil conditions and ground level (see *Anchored walls* below). Timber or steel sheet-piled cantilever walls have, however, been used as breastworks at the crest of a beach.

Anchored walls (Figure 5.31)

Steel piling is used very widely in seawall construction mainly because of:

- Cheapness;

Table 5.5 Functional characteristics of vertical non-porous walls

Type of seawall	*Range of wave climate*	*Hydraulic performance*	*Visual aspects*	*Ease of access to shore*	*Maintenance*	*Permeability to groundwater*	*Flexibility*	*Durability (assuming good materials)*
Mass concrete gravity wall	All	Poor	In many areas stone-faced walls can be unobtrusive and have become characteristic of some seaside towns	Steps/ramps required	Low	Impermeable	Inflexible	High
Masonry gravity walls	All	Poor	In many areas stone-faced walls can be unobtrusive and have become characteristic of some seaside towns	Steps/ramps required	Low	Impermeable	Very limited	High
Brickwork	Mild to moderate	Poor	Brickwork walls can be unobtrusive in urban areas	Steps/ramps required	Low	Impermeable	Very limited	Medium to poor
Timber sheet piles	Mild	Poor	Can be relatively unobtrusive	Steps/ramps required over high walls	Low	Low permeability	Limited flexibility but piling tends to penetrate to firm soil, so little differential	Medium

Steel sheet piles	Mild to severe	Poor	Fairly obtrusive unless a low wall	Steps/ramps required over high walls	Difficult to maintain once damaged	Low permeability	Limited flexibility but piling tends to penetrate to firm soil, so little differential settlement	Medium to poor
Concrete sheet piles	Mild to severe	Poor	Fairly obtrusive unless a low wall	Steps/ramps required over high walls	Can be repaired	Low permeability	Limited flexibility but piling tends to penetrate to firm soil, so little differential settlement	Medium to good
Reinforced concrete cantilever	All	Poor	Good detailing can make attractive/less obtrusive	Steps/ramps required	Low	Impermeable	Inflexible: can suffer from differential settlement	Good
Reinforced soil	Novel technique but likely to be satisfactory up to moderate climate	Poor	Good detailing can make attractive/ unobtrusive	Steps/ramps required	Low	Low permeability	Inflexible: could suffer badly from differential settlement	Potentially good

Note: Approximate ranges of wave climate are:
mild, 0–1.5/2 m wave height
moderate, 1.5/2–4 m wave height
severe, greater than 4 m wave height.

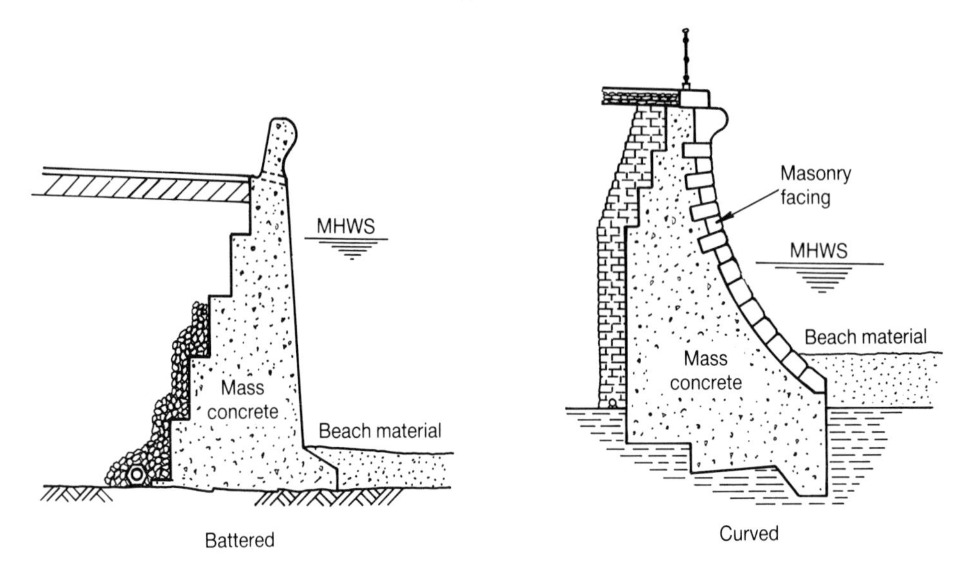

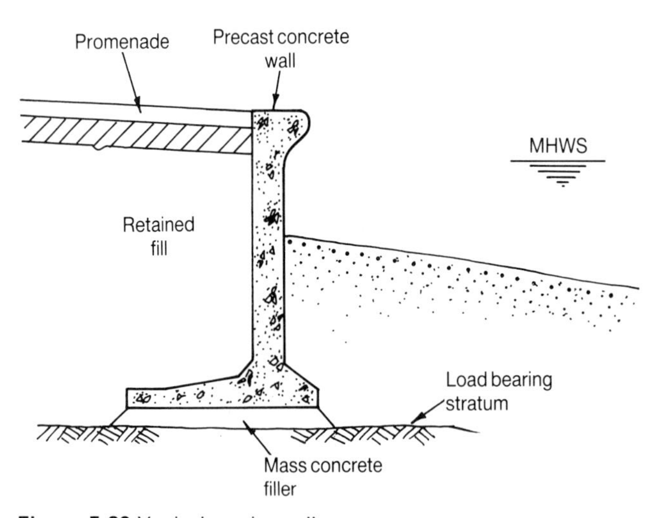

Figure 5.30 Vertical gravity walls

- Flexibility in being able to accommodate variation in ground levels and conditions along its length;
- Relative ease of construction: access for pile-driving plant is necessary but, since piles can be driven through water, and there is no need to excavate for foundations or shuttering, there are no restrictions due to tidal working.

Exposed steel sheet piling lacks durability when used in a coastal environment. Its disadvantages include:

- Corrosion, particularly between high- and low-water levels;
- Abrasion from beach material moved by waves;
- An unsightly appearance;
- Difficulties of maintenance and repair.

The rates of loss to be expected from corrosion and abrasion are discussed in Section 7.3. Used with steel sheet piling, concrete, being less sensitive to abrasion, makes a suitable medium for the construction of tied walls. The cross sections shown in Figure 5.31 indicate some ways in which the two materials may be combined to utilize the advantages of each.

Reinforced soil (Figure 5.32 see page 162)

Reinforced soil is a relatively new system of construction, and has only had very limited use on seawalls. At present, as design techniques are advancing, the engineer should seek assistance from manufacturers of the reinforcing system and/or specialist consultants. The system, in situations which can be kept dry during construction, offers potential for substantial cost savings. The fill must, however, be placed carefully and be well controlled, which militates against tidal working. The construction does not require heavy plant. Providing measures are taken to ensure durability of the reinforcing strips and to avoid any loss of fill, i.e. by installing geotextiles down the back face of the facing blocks and by constructing an effective toe, the wall should be effective.

5.4.5 Vertical porous walls

Vertical porous walls offer the potential for reducing somewhat the high reflections that occur with non-porous walls. Unlike non-porous walls, they also have the advantage of being permeable, so the potential problems of blockage of groundwater flow are minimized. Two types of walls have been used in the UK, i.e. gabions and cribwork. These basically comprise stone or rock held at a vertical or near-vertical slope by a framework or mesh. Other types of vertical porous wall have been used overseas, notably in Japan, and consist of concrete blockwork with built-in voids. They were developed, and are more widely used, for breakwater construction (Table 5.6).

Stone-filled gabions (Figure 5.33)

Gabions, conditional on suitable stone fill being available (which is normally the case), offer a cheap solution. However, they are not durable (see Section 5.4.2). In areas of limited public access and where they are only occasionally reached by the sea they have performed successfully. In such cases they offer a flexible solution (which

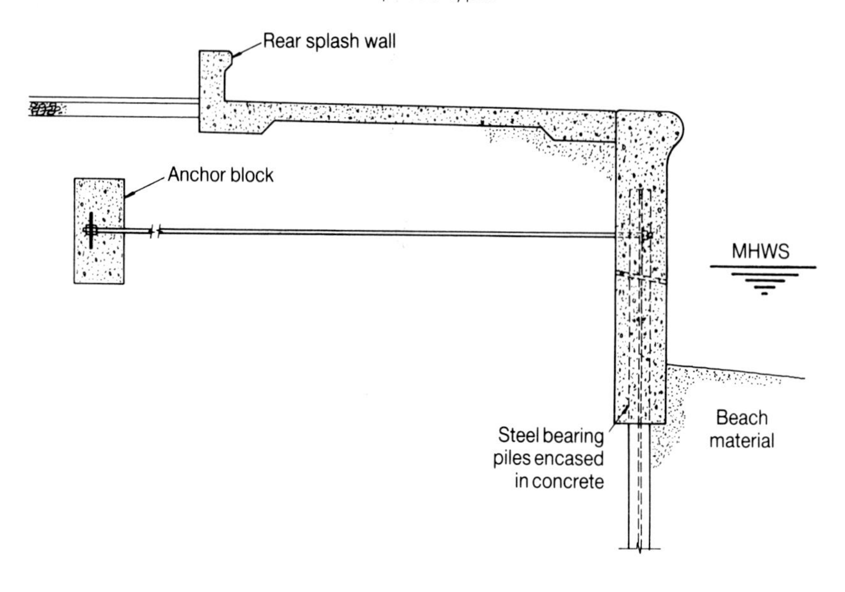

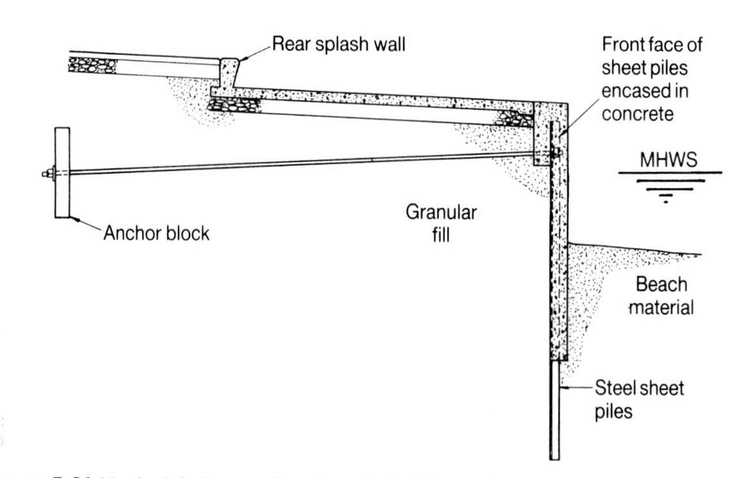

Figure 5.31 Vertical tied seawalls using steel piling and concrete

can accommodate differential settlement to a degree) and can be aesthetically pleasing, particularly in rural areas. When acting as a retaining wall, care should be taken in the design to include suitable filters down the back face to prevent leaching out of fill and to allow provision for toe scour.

Table 5.6 Functional characteristics of vertical porous walls

Type of seawall	*Range of wave climate*	*Hydraulic performance*	*Visual aspects*	*Ease of access to shore*	*Maintenance*	*Permeability to groundwater*	*Flexibility*	*Durability (assuming good materials)*
Gabion gravity wall	Mild	Fairly absorptive	Can be attractive in local stone	Steps/ramps required – difficult to make durable	High maintenance	High	Fairly flexible	Very poor
Cribwork/ breastwork	Mild to moderate	Good if single-sized rock and sufficient width of section	Can be attractive in local stone	Steps/ramps required	Moderate	High	Fairly flexible	Medium, depending on whether crib is steel or timber, hardwood or softwood

Note: Approximate ranges of wave climate are:
mild, 0–1.5/2 m wave height
moderate, 1.5/2–4 m wave height
severe, greater than 4 m wave height.

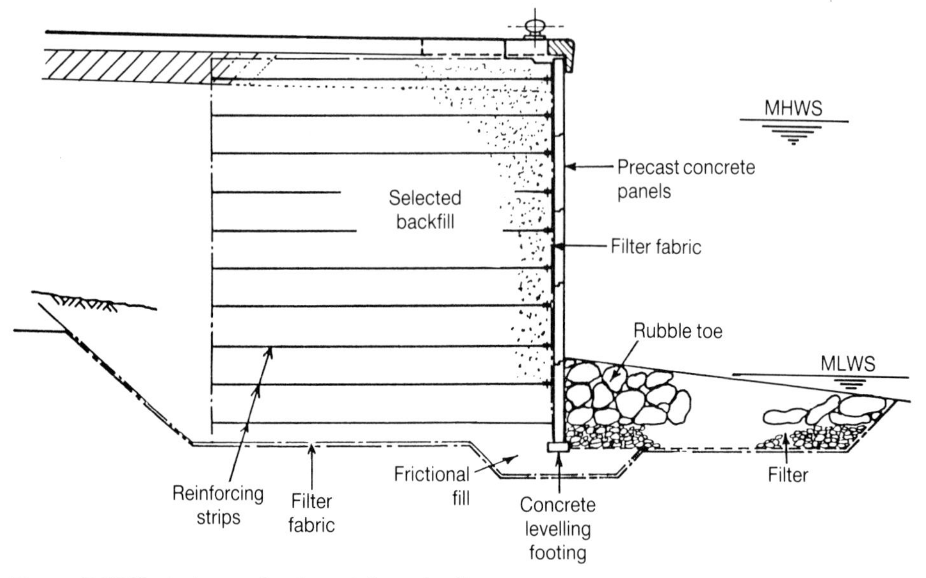

Figure 5.32 Vertical seawall using reinforced soil

Cribwork and breastwork (Figure 5.34)

Cribwork and breastwork have been used a number of times within the UK, often to protect the base of cliffs from erosion. A cribwork is normally constructed of vertical or sloping timber or steel with cross members. This retains rubble infill, as indicated in Figure 5.34. For the most part, cribwork systems are used as conventional types of seawall, i.e. as abutments to land which might otherwise erode. On occasions they have been used seawards of the toe of a cliff. In this case they act to reduce, rather than eliminate, the wave energy reaching the cliff.

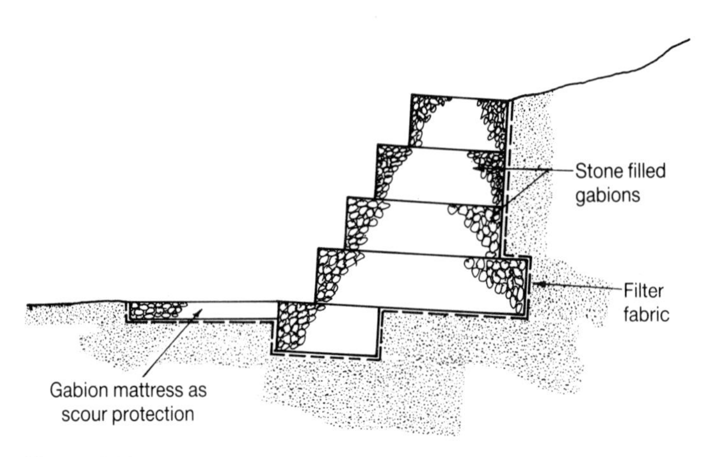

Figure 5.33 Vertical porous seawall using gabions

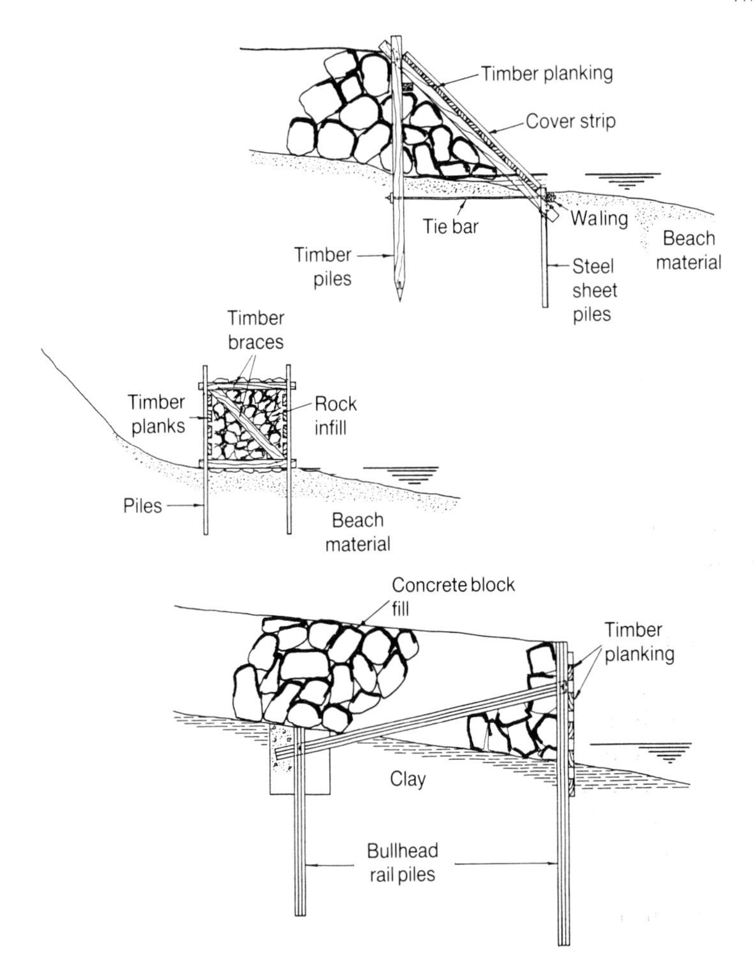

Figure 5.34 Porous seawalls using stone-filled cribwork

5.5 The toe of the wall

The toe of the seawall terminates the base of the wall on its seaward face. It is located in that critical zone where the rigid or semi-rigid seawall structure meets the mobile material of the foreshore. CIRIA Report TN 125 indicated that toe erosion is the most common cause of seawall failure, which emphasizes the importance of toe design.

The term 'apron' is often used to describe a sloping or horizontal construction whose primary purpose is to provide protection against scour and which is located either seaward of the toe or between the body of the wall and the toe. In this book the toe includes any such aprons.

The primary purpose of the toe is to prevent undermining of the wall. In addition, it may:

- Protect the beach or sub-strata in front of the wall against scour;
- Improve the hydraulic performance of the wall;
- Provide structural support to the wall against sliding or toppling forward;
- Provide a part of the structural foundation of the wall;
- Prevent or restrict seepage.

While these apply to consideration of a new seawall, they apply equally well to the case when works are being carried out to the toe of an existing wall. In satisfying these purposes the toe is likely to be of major significance in the overall stability of the wall.

The most likely cause of toe failure is a fall in beach levels which, with a new seawall in place, cannot be accurately predicted. Even with a model, the sensitivity of the beach to variations in wave conditions, tides and other changes along the foreshore means that no absolute minimum beach level can be reliably predicted unless the fall is restricted by a hard stratum. Having regard to the potential for overall failure if the toe is undermined, the engineer should be conservative in his estimate of minimum beach levels, and he should also carefully consider the consequences of a fall in beach level below that predicted.

5.5.1 Nature of the toe

In order for it to be successful the toe needs to be able to extend down to a level sufficiently below the lowest likely beach level to ensure that it can perform all its functions listed above. Alternatively, it can be designed in the knowledge that the beach may well fall below the toe, but that it is sufficiently flexible to drop down to the new lower level without damage. Introducing an apron into the toe construction has the advantage of taking the scour problems further away from the foundation of the wall.

The method of founding the toe may be selected from the following:

Founded in resistant strata

Where strata, which are relatively resistant to erosion, are exposed or occur within a reasonable depth of beach level, the toe is founded on the stratum with little risk of undermining.

Founded in formation with limited resistance

In many instances, clay or other strata with limited resistance to erosion occurs at a shallow depth below the beach and erodes only slowly when it is uncovered. Founding within such strata usually reduces the risk of undermining arising from unexpected beach changes.

Founded in beach or other erodible material

Where there is no resistant formation at reasonable depth in which to found the toe it is necessary to predict the lowest beach level during the design life and found below this level. The risk depends largely on the reliability of prediction and the degree of conservatism adopted.

Falling apron in erodible material

As an alternative, provision can be made to accommodate a fall in beach level below the underside of the toe by means of an apron of rock or other construction which is sufficiently flexible to adjust to the lower beach without suffering damage.

Provision for toe extension

As another alternative, provision can also be made for the construction of a seaward extension to the toe at some future date when the beach falls below a certain level. Such a policy carries a high degree of risk, requires careful monitoring and calls for the ability to mobilize resources at short notice for emergency works. It may nevertheless be the most acceptable solution in economic terms where future changes are uncertain.

5.5.2 Design considerations

The hydraulic performance of the toe should be considered in general terms in conjunction with the whole seawall (see Sections 5.3.2 and 6.1). Particular consideration should be given to the effect of changes in beach level on the toe design and the possible progressive exposure of surfaces which were originally buried and which may give rise to wave reflection. Where an apron is being added to an existing seawall then a specific investigation into the combined hydraulic performance may be necessary. Environmental aspects arising from possible future changes must also be considered in relation to access, amenity and appearance. This can be the overriding consideration on an amenity beach.

The design of the toe should also be considered in relation to the overall structural design of the wall (Sections 5.3.4 and 6.2). In many cases the toe can be designed to assist in resisting sliding, rotation or toppling movements or as a foundation. Structural analysis is normally carried out on the basis of the worst design foreshore conditions that can be expected (Section 5.5.3).

Consideration of construction problems, always essential in seawall design, becomes particularly important at the toe because of tidal working (see Section 6.8). Account must be taken of the nature of the subsoil and the overlying beach both in terms of:

- The ease of construction of a particular solution;
- The effect of the construction on the subsoil.

Both pile driving and excavation for the toe can affect the structure of the subsoil, leading to additional local scour if it becomes exposed.

Design considerations relating to water pressure are described elsewhere (Sections 6.2 and 6.3–6.5). If the toe design is such that it will affect the flow of tidal and groundwater under the seawall, the impact of such changes will need to be analysed.

On shingle and cobble beaches, and under exposed conditions, abrasion is likely to be most severe at beach level, i.e. at the toe. The effect of temporary or progressive exposure of the toe to abrasion due to changes in beach level should be taken into account. Steel sheet-piled toes in particular are vulnerable to perforation from abrasion. If this occurs below the level of any backing concrete, the fill or underlying beach may be washed out by wave, tidal and groundwater flows. This has in several cases led to seawall collapse.

5.5.3 Toe construction – non-porous

Steel sheet piling (Figure 5.24)

Given suitable ground conditions for pile driving, steel sheet piling can provide a deep cut-off without the problems of foreshore excavation or the damage to the subsoil. In consequence it is used extensively in situations where cyclical or progressive beach changes are expected. It is particularly vulnerable to combined abrasion and corrosion. The vertical face of the piling can become unsightly and cause wave reflection should it become exposed above beach level. It is therefore usually designed so that it is not exposed above beach level under normal conditions.

Steel sheet piling can be used at the toe of a large variety of forms of construction of the body of the wall. These uses may be divided into two categories:

- Where the piling is structurally separate and usually of cantilever construction, as in the case of a rock armoured slope or pattern placed armour units;
- Where the piling is structurally connected to form an integral part of the body of the wall, such as in a reinforced concrete wall.

In the former case steel sheet piling is usually provided with a waling or other stiffening members but is self-supporting. In the latter it is most commonly used in conjunction with some form of concrete construction which provides the necessary stiffness and support. Structural considerations usually require adequate attachment to transfer loading from the pile head to the seawall. Where steel sheet piling is used with a concrete cap and backing, to form a composite toe, the concrete backing can provide a safeguard against loss of fill due to perforation of the piling and the concrete should extend below the lowest design beach level. Steel sheet piling also offers an effective means of constructing a new toe to underpin an existing seawall where excavation would cause undermining and consequent risk to the wall.

Concrete (see Figure 6.29)

Concrete is particularly suitable for seawall toe construction where the toe is to be founded in a relatively resistant material or on a reasonably stable beach. The use of reinforcement in the toe and the extent of precasting is largely a matter for structural considerations and design for construction (see Sections 6.8 and 6.9).

The profile of concrete as used in toe construction can vary from a narrow vertical cut-off to a horizontal slab. The profile is determined both by structural requirements and the practicalities of construction. The latter is often related to the slopes at which the excavated subsoil will stand. In the cases of a toe in resistant strata it is usually important to completely fill the excavated trench with concrete.

Asphalt and bitumen (see Figure 5.23)

Asphalt and composite bitumen and stone materials are used as flexible scour aprons to protect structures or as aprons in front of existing seawalls in order to improve the hydraulic performance. Where it is necessary to make provision against undermining, the slope of the material is flattened to provide a 'falling apron' which will, to a degree, settle into a cavity created underneath it by undermining. However, care should be taken in using such a toe on a coastal beach. The rapid fall in beach levels that can occur within a few hours of a storm can be too rapid for the asphalt to accommodate without rupture.

Timber

A low timber breastwork can contain and protect the seaward edge of other materials forming a sloping seawall or apron. This is normally either a continuous line of timber sheet piles with a top waling or capping or timber king piles with horizontal planking.

Other materials

Grouted stone, pre-cast concrete revetment blocks and other materials laid to slope to form the body of the seawall may be extended below beach level to form a toe. Some edge restraint (e.g. a toebeam) is required to preserve the overall integrity of the revetment.

5.5.4 Toe construction – porous

Armour

Armour comprising either rock or pre-cast concrete units can provide a flexible toe in the form of a 'falling apron'. It can adjoin all forms of wall construction and has the advantage that it can be durable and flexible. However, it can make access to the beach difficult.

Rip-rap

Graded rock rip-rap can also provide a flexible toe either in the form of a berm or a flattened slope particularly when there is a possibility of extensive redistribution of the material under extreme conditions. It has similar advantages to armour, although the smaller pieces of stone inherent in the wider grading of rip-rap may well cause abrasion problems, when they are moved in storms if the main seawall consists of, for example, steel sheet piling.

Gabions

Gabions and Reno mattresses provide a porous semi-rigid form of toe construction, although they lack durability.

Cribwork

Design considerations relating to the use of either sloping or vertical cribwork in a toe are usually similar to their use in the body of the wall (see Section 5.4.5).

5.6 The crest of the wall

The crest provides the interface between the seawall and the land behind. As such, on flood defences the crest has been taken to include the back face of a flood embankment or dyke. In addition to forming an element of new walls, crests can be added to existing walls to improve their hydraulic performance. An analysis of failure modes by CIRIA, Report TN 125, has indicated that partial crest failure is the second most common type of seawall damage. The most common cause of breaching of flood banks is erosion of the back face as a result of overtopping.

The primary function of the crest is to prevent overtopping, that is to satisfy one or more of the following:

- Prevent flooding of the land behind;
- Prevent scour of the back face or crest itself;
- Contain the beach and prevent it from being washed onto the land behind; and
- Prevent the build-up of water on the crest which may result in excessive water loads on the land immediately behind the crest (such as a promenade).

Additionally, the crest may well be required to:

- Resist scour if the wall does overtop;
- Provide a collecting area for spray;
- Provide access (for public, amenity, construction and maintenance);
- Retain or collect fallen rock or soil movement behind the wall;
- Provide a termination to the body of the wall (e.g. crest beam for concrete slabs).

Other functional requirements of the overall wall (see Section 3.4.2) which relate particularly to the crest are:

- Hydraulic, structural and visual compatibility with the rest of the wall;
- Overall visual acceptability;
- Ease of access along and across the wall;
- Safety to those using and near the wall;
- Drainage.

In most circumstances, the choice of crest should follow that of the body of the wall. Exceptions arise where the main purpose of the wall is in the crest, e.g. provision of a road along a causeway or the base of a cliff. With its primary function likely to be the prevention of overtopping, we discuss first the hydraulic performance in Section 5.6.1 and subsequently the other design considerations in Section 5.6.2. Various types of crest are described in Section 5.6.3.

5.6.1 Hydraulic performance

The toe and body will govern the nature of wave run-up that reaches the crest, and so an evaluation of hydraulic performance should be based on considerations of the overall wall. Nonetheless, the crest itself does offer considerable potential for improving the hydraulic performance of the wall with respect to overtopping. It is unlikely to make much difference to wave reflections.

The crest can prevent or alleviate overtopping in three ways:

- By virtue of height alone;
- By increasing the amount of dissipation (e.g. by providing a promenade, doubling as a high-level berm with a stub wall to landward);
- By deflecting the uprushing wave back to the sea.

Some quantitative information on these options available to the engineer is discussed in Section 6.1.

5.6.2 Design considerations

Crest level

The cost of reducing overtopping should be weighed against the damage that is caused by it. This is discussed in Chapter 8, but of particular relevance to crest design is whether the designer should spend money on making the crest (including the back face) resistant to erosion if it is overtopped or whether that money is better spent on reducing the risk of overtopping happening at all.

The discounted costs of flood damage and wall repairs can be assessed as described in Chapter 8 and used to assist in making a choice between these two options. The economic optimum can also be estimated using techniques discussed in that chapter. However, in evaluating the various options the engineer should take into account the reliability of the various parameters making up the estimate of the extreme event (wave heights, beach levels, water levels, secular changes to water level, etc.) over the life of the structure. This may well lead him to conclude that a more pragmatic approach is to adopt a solution resistant to overtopping erosion which is less sensitive to errors in the estimate of the extreme event.

Allowable overtopping discharge should also be considered in relation to the penetration of seawater under non-porous slabs where there is a risk of uplift. Sloping wall facings on granular material are particularly vulnerable.

Beach levels and overtopping

Changes in beach level may affect overtopping discharge by effectively altering the seawall profile or allowing larger waves to reach the wall. Overtopping combined with high beach levels may also result in beach material being washed over the wall. In developed frontages this may be a serious problem.

Spray and windblown sand

Once created, spray is difficult to control (see Section 6.1.4). The incorporation of wide paved areas into the crest of the wall with seaward drainage may mitigate the effect of dense spray. In a few instances the nuisance caused by sand blown over a seawall may be significant, requiring the incorporation of a windbreak into the crest. Overwashed or windblown beach material can be a nuisance to surface water drainage both for the seawall itself and for adjoining highways and properties.

Structural, construction and maintenance considerations

While the design of the crest should be considered in relation to the structural design of the wall, this is not normally a major consideration. The structural design of the crest itself, however, may involve the following:

- Wave loadings on parapets, floodwalls and other cantilevered structures;
- Bearing loads and settlement problems over backfilled areas;
- Stability of back slopes;
- Support to coastal slopes or cliffs;
- Impact loading from cliff falls;
- Access and traffic loading.

Consideration of construction and maintenance problems is an essential part of crest design, particularly in respect of maintaining plant access for construction as the work proceeds. (Section 6.8).

Environmental considerations

Because the crest is at the interface between the seawall and the land the design may involve planning and/or environmental considerations which either override or modify purely technical considerations of hydraulic performance and structural design. These may include provision for:

- Safety of those on or near the wall;
- Pedestrian or vehicular access along the wall or across to the beach;
- Boat launching or other special facilities;
- Floodgates or scuppers in connection with the above;
- Special finishes for appearance;
- Limitation of crest level to avoid interference with views from properties behind.

Consideration should be given to the appearance, particularly the detailing of joints in areas where the public may be expected to walk. Areas with poor drainage falls or discharges from weepholes should be avoided, as slippery surfaces may develop and become a risk to the public.

Drainage

Surface water drainage will need to be considered both in terms of rainwater and the potentially larger flows involved in spray and overtopping.

5.6.3 Types of crest

Taking account of the general discussion of the functions of the crest (including the back face of an embankment), the crest of a seawall should consist of one or more of the following:

- Walls (to increase the effectiveness of the seawall in preventing overtopping);
- Slope protection;
- Decking and surfacing.

Wave return walls (Figure 5.25)

The purpose of these is to divert the uprushing wave seawards and so reduce overtopping. They are most effective when used at the top of a smooth slope, so that the run-up of water is guided smoothly around the face of the wall and thrown back. Wave return walls atop a rubble slope, which produces more turbulent run-up, are less likely to be so successful, although it must be remembered that rubble walls in themselves will produce much less run-up in the first place (see Section 6.1).

Wave return walls need to be carefully dimensioned, smooth and structurally strong, so are normally built of concrete. A crest wall is a strong visual feature and care is needed to achieve a shape and surface finish that is both initially acceptable and will weather in a pleasing way. Concrete is very adaptable in that a wide variety of special surface textures or colours can be provided where required to enhance the visual impact. Access to the shore past large wave return walls is difficult if the hydraulic performance is to be preserved. Sometimes there is little choice but to leave gaps and install floodgates at points of access. The concrete of the wall will require to be strong and durable to resist reinforcement corrosion, and adequate joints will be required if settlement is likely.

Parapet walls

Where there is limited space, the crest of a sloping seawall can be raised with a vertical wall, although this is unlikely to be as effective in resisting run-up as would be an extension of the slope up to the same level. On more exposed walls, they are used to retain the top of armoured slopes. In urban areas they are normally constructed in concrete which, with careful detailing, can produce an aesthetically suitable result. As for wave return walls, the concrete should be adequately designed in respect of durability and joints. In rural areas, on clay banks, cantilever steel sheet piles have been used to provide a modest (say, 0.6 m) raising in the wall which also overcomes some of the problems due to fissuring (see Section 5.4.1). This piling can, however, lead to problems because of:

- Pressure build-up at the pile toe during driving, which locally reduces the strength of the soil;
- Concentration of seepage around the pile toe which leads to washing out of fill.

Splash walls, flood walls and flood banks

Wave return and parapet walls are intended to resist waves at the top of the slope. Alternatively, or in addition (see Figure 5.24), a wall can be placed further landwards. This has advantages that:

- The wall is removed from the full force of wave attack so it need not be so strong;
- Waves are allowed to spend their energy before reaching the wall, thus making it more effective than if it were further seawards;
- It allows easy access and uninterrupted sight from the decking (between the wall and the slope) to the beach and sea.

However, it does mean that the seawall overall occupies more space than with a parapet at the top of the main body of the wall. Another consequence is that the decking between the splash wall and the seaward slope is not fully protected against waves and flooding.

Depending on location, space and available funds, sheet piling (timber, steel or concrete), concrete, brickwork or an earth bank could be used to form the splash wall or flood wall.

Slope protection and deckings

The degree and nature of slope protection at the crest varies a great deal with the severity of the wave climate, the nature of the body of the wall and the additional uses to which the crest is put (e.g. a roadway). A vertical wall in a severe wave climate will generate large amounts of spray which will be carried onto the land in onshore winds. The land immediately adjacent will be subject to quite heavy dynamic loads from water falling. On the other hand, a flood bank should be designed so that it will not breach if design wave/water level conditions are exceeded, when it will be subject to water flowing down the back face. Types of slope protection and deckings are broadly similar to those that might be used on the front face (see Sections 5.4.2 and 5.4.3), but of a lighter weight because they are less exposed. The following systems are particularly appropriate to the crest and back face of a seawall.

1. *Concrete slabs* (Figure 5.35). These can be used for pedestrian access on a flat crest or berm and are resistant to modest overtopping. They should be designed for occasional vehicular loading, during maintenance.
2. *Concrete decks* (Figure 5.36). These are less flexible than a slab system and can crack seriously if the supporting soil settles. They can readily be designed to resist moderate or even severe overtopping, conditional on being well founded, or they can be designed as conventional pavement slabs to take pedestrian or vehicular access.
3. *Asphaltic concrete* (Figure 5.23). As used in road construction, this can be effective as a surface protection, whether it be sloping (a maximum slope of 1:3 to allow use of conventional road plant) or horizontal, when it can provide good pedestrian or vehicular access. Somewhat more flexible than concrete, asphaltic concrete can again be designed to resist severe overtopping. Visually, asphaltic concrete is probably less appealing on prominent slopes than well-detailed concrete surfaces.
4. *Hoggin*. Where fissuring is a problem in clay flood banks, a layer of hoggin, a well-graded clayey sandy gravel, can be placed over the crest of the bank to provide a layer (say, 0.6 m thick) which will not fissure. It will, however, require some form of surface protection if overtopping is to be resisted.
5. *Grass*. Where only occasional and limited overtopping is envisaged then grass can provide good protection to the crest and back face (see Section 5.4.3). The grass

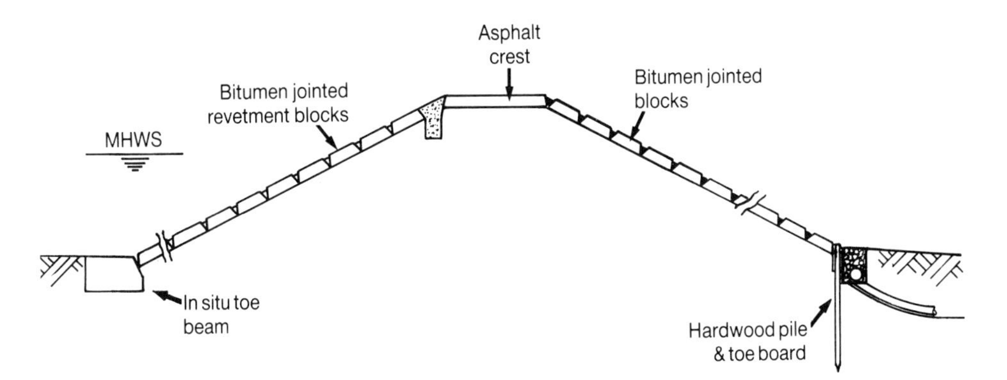

Figure 5.35 Concrete slabs on back face

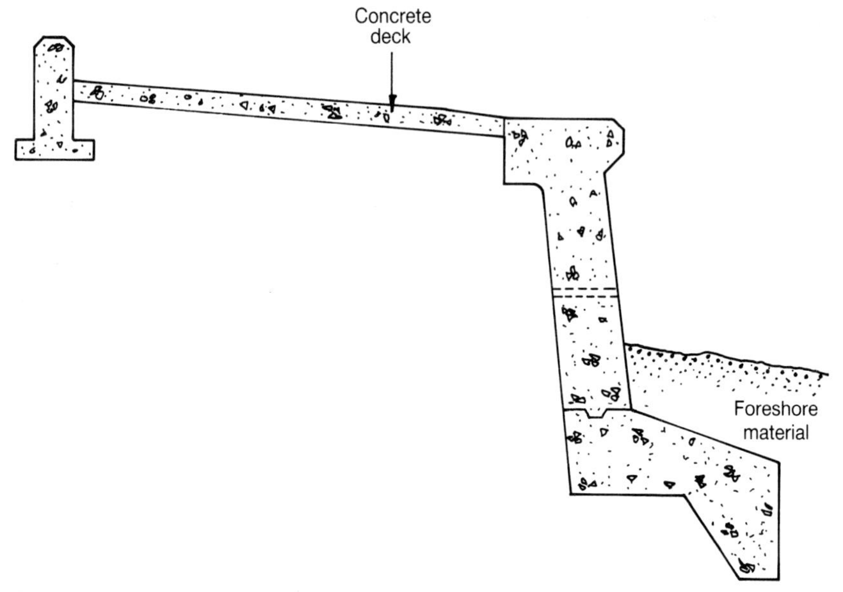

Figure 5.36 Concrete deck

mat may be strengthened by provision of a suitable geotextile at the surface or hardened for light traffic by incorporating open blockwork[3].

Other systems of slope protection can be employed as discussed in Sections 5.4.2 and 5.4.3 for the front face.

5.7 Rehabilitation

A substantial proportion of current and potential coastal defence works in the UK comprises rehabilitation (upgrading or renovation) of existing seawalls. In a number of cases the existing wall may not be suitable or of adequate strength to be upgraded, but it may still be of use in the construction of the new wall. This section covers considerations which are unique to works and which have not therefore been included in earlier sections. The broad nature of upgrading and renovation works is discussed in Sections 5.7.1 and 5.7.2, after which the philosophy of design is considered in Section 5.7.3. Particular problems and possible options are discussed in Sections 5.7.4-5.7.7.

5.7.1 Upgrading

Upgrading involves the improvement of the structure or performance of a seawall. The need for such improvement may result from inadequacies in the original design or from changes in:

- Conditions of the seawall environment;
- The required function;
- Design standards.

as considered in the fault trees of Section 5.1.

The objectives of the upgrading are commonly one or more of the following:

- To prevent undermining;
- To improve overall stability of the wall itself or the adjoining land;
- To reduce potential overtopping discharge;
- To reduce spray;
- To mitigate future deterioration of seawall components or to reduce the need for maintenance;
- To accommodate a change in function of the seawall;
- To improve hydraulic performance in relation to the foreshore;
- To improve its environmental impact.

In the event that the marine environment at the seawall has changed since the wall's construction the causes of those changes should be assessed on the basis of the investigations referred to in Section 4.11.4.

5.7.2 Renovation

Renovation involves the reinstatement or replacement of components to restore a seawall to its original standard and function. It does not, by definition, have upgrading as its objective, although it may well be convenient and/or cost-effective to incorporate some improvements into renovation works. It can also provide an opportunity to review the original design parameters, if known, and consider the need for upgrading.

Renovation is normally necessary when a structure reaches the end of its working (or structure) life. This may be determined either by the life of key items such as toe piling or by the scale of replacement of components. The dividing line between maintenance and renovation is difficult to assess. The need for renovation may arise from:

- The expiry of the structure life;
- Premature failure due to neglect;
- Premature failure due to a change in conditions.

5.7.3 General considerations

In a high proportion of cases it is advantageous to incorporate existing structures into the revised works. Reasons may include:

- Avoiding expense of demolition;
- Retaining a degree of protection afforded by remains of the existing structure during construction;
- Contributions to the total mass of the new structure from the existing components;
- The need to retain the visual character of existing facing.

Data required for works to existing seawalls are discussed in Section 4.11. These are necessary to:

- Assess the problems to be dealt with where the existing structure has failed in some way;
- Define what is actually there so that the existing and proposed structures can be analysed (as discussed in Section 5.1.5).

The gathering of sufficient data to achieve these two aims is often not feasible without major destructive investigation. It may not be until excavation for construction begins that the full nature of the wall and the problem to be solved become apparent. This is not undesirable in itself but calls for a considerable degree of flexibility in financial control, contractual matters and a very good liaison between all parties involved in the works (e.g. contractor, engineer, client, funding agency). In these circumstances the engineer should pay particular attention to the form of contract which should allow for substantial variations as the work proceeds, both in terms of quantity and of type of works.

When designing works to an existing wall it should be remembered that discontinuities in the structure of the wall tend to lead to weaknesses. Such discontinuities may occur in:

- Flexibility – where a flexible system adjoins one that is less flexible (perhaps an asphalt patch in a concrete wall or rigid concrete grouting on a flexible rip-rap slope);
- Foundations – where the new works settle more or less than the existing (perhaps a well-founded piled new toe on the front of a sloping concrete wall).

Joints between new and old works are difficult to make good and if there is differential movement between new and old works this is likely to lead to future problems.

5.7.4 Improvement of seawall stability

The prevention of undermining or the provision of additional resistance to horizontal or vertical movement at the foot of a wall usually involves additional works at the toe. Other work to improve stability may require stabilization of the land or coastal slope behind, possibly including drainage, or additional restraints such as anchorages to the seawall itself.

Design considerations for the addition of a toe to an existing seawall are similar to those in Section 5.5. Where a new toe is added for structural reasons then particular attention to the method of attachment (between the new toe and existing wall) will be necessary. It is also essential that the new toe be designed so that the existing wall is not put at risk during construction. This may involve siting the new toe well seaward of the old wall and providing a connecting apron. At the same time, the effect of an additional toe on subsoil drainage should not be overlooked.

5.7.5 Improvement of hydraulic performance

Improvements in hydraulic performance may be either:

- To reduce reflections from the existing wall (which may be causing scour);
- To reduce overtopping.

When assessing the effectiveness of the new works the hydraulic performance of the overall structure should be assessed. As discussed in Section 5.3.2, wave energy hitting a seawall will reflect, overtop or dissipate. A decrease in one element must be accompanied by an increase in one or both of the others.

Limited improvements can be made by a change in profile to concrete, masonry and steel piling walls using concrete encasements and other additions. These include:

- Bullnoses and wave returns;
- Parapet walls and other forms of heightening;
- Stepwork;
- Projecting blocks or shaped walls cast onto existing aprons and sloping surfaces.

In such cases consideration should be given as to where the energy may be diverted and to problems which might result.

More major improvements can be effected by the addition of entirely new structures in front of the existing wall specifically designed to dissipate wave energy. These include:

- Wide, sloping or composite, non-porous aprons in concrete or asphalt;
- Sloping porous aprons of rock, pre-cast concrete armour or pattern placed units;
- Porous cribwork.

The design of such additions involves the same considerations as would that for an entirely new wall and the hydraulic performance should be assessed for the combined effect of the existing and new works acting together. Further, a porous apron or cribwork added to the seaward side of an existing impermeable structure provides a potential for back pressure, the effects of which are difficult to evaluate with confidence.

The reduction of overtopping discharge may require additional works to the crest. Design considerations for this case are given in Section 5.6. The structural implications of such additions (e.g. surcharge) must be taken into account.

5.7.6 Restoration and upgrading of components

In some cases components can be replaced and at the same time upgraded. Examples are:

- Renewal of rock and concrete armour slopes using larger units or partial grouting;
- Replacement of timber and steel breastworks using larger members (wearing timbers can also be fitted to protect against abrasion).

Certain components such as armoured slopes, gabions and pattern placed armour can be given additional stability by grouting with concrete or asphalt. This requires careful consideration of consequential changes in hydraulic performance, potential problems of wave uplift pressures and discontinuities in flexibility.

The most adaptable forms of (existing) construction are concrete, masonry or steel sheet piling where an entirely new face can be cast onto the existing wall in mass or reinforced concrete. Such encasements are probably the most common form of seawall renovation. Sprayed concrete encasements can be used in the same way. In addition, these encasements provide an opportunity to upgrade existing walls and may include:

- Sacrificial surfaces for abrasion;
- Changes in profile to improve hydraulic performance such as the addition of a bullnose;
- Reinforcement of weak components;
- Environmentally acceptable surface finishes;
- Amenity features.

Consideration should be given to the effect of differential shrinkage between concrete encasements and the parent material and to the method of attachment. This is usually achieved by a close pattern of steel dowels grouted in or welded on as appropriate. It is essential that the old and new act monolithically under wave loading. The use of encasements to protect seawalls undergoing chemical deterioration requires special consideration of the factors involved. These include:

- The rate of deterioration and eventual condition of the existing wall;
- Possible chemical attack on the encasement;
- Interaction between the old and new concrete such as between high-alumina and ordinary Portland cement concrete.

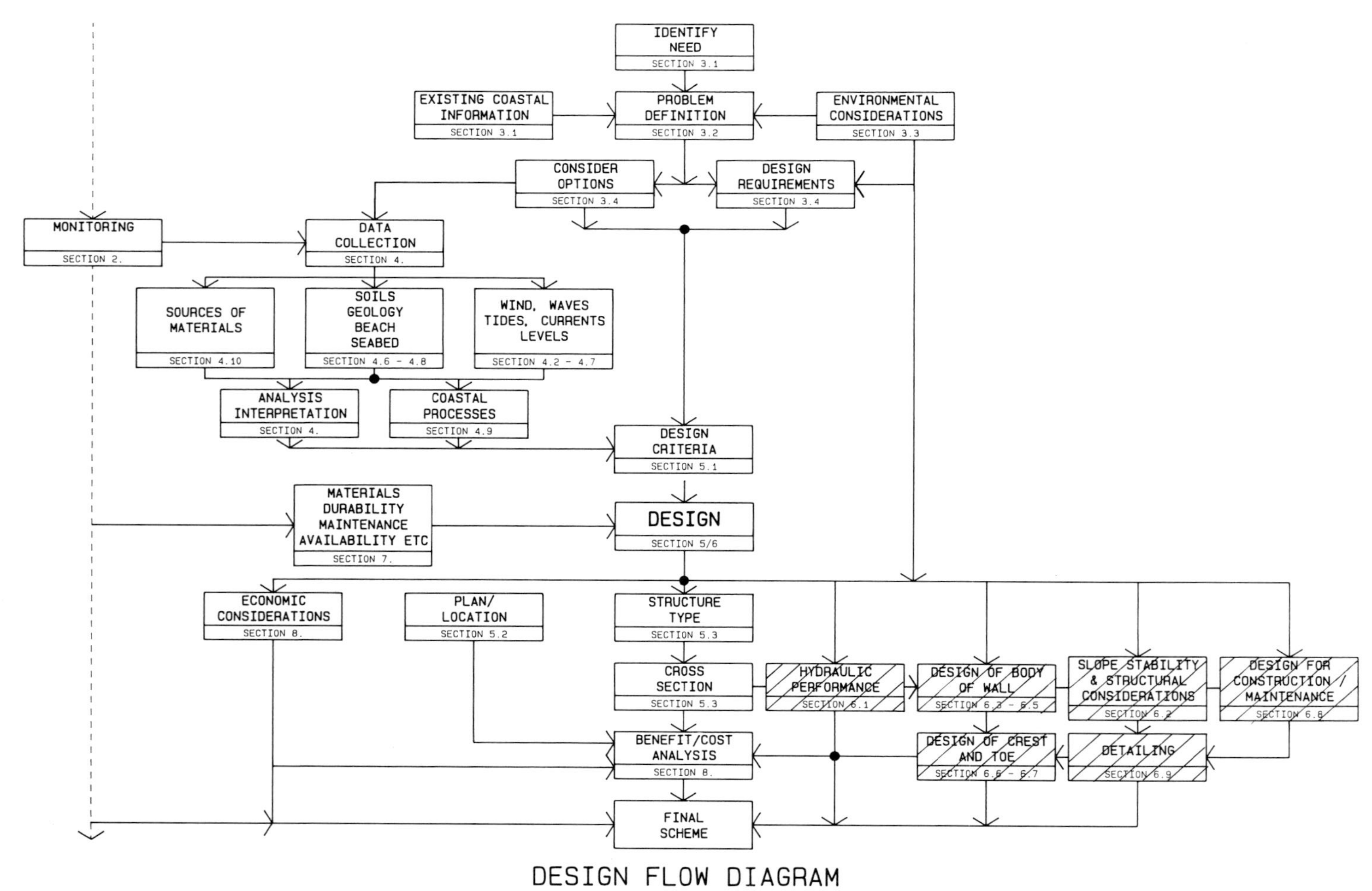

DESIGN FLOW DIAGRAM

6 Design

The overall philosophy behind design, and the various options available for the elements of a seawall, have been discussed in Chapter 5. Section 6.1 gives detailed design considerations, starting with hydraulic performance. Section 6.2 considers the overall stability of the embankment and coastal cliffs as well as structural loads. Sections 6.3 to 6.5 deal with design of the wall itself, taking particular account of geotechnical aspects, waves and water pressure. Section 6.6 and 6.7 cover design of the crest and toe.

Construction and maintenance are often difficult at the coast. Aspects of design which can facilitate matters are considered in Section 6.8. Finally, in the marine environment it is crucial to optimize the design with respect to durability and general adequacy of performance as well as to environmental aspects such as access and visual impact. This is considered in Section 6.9.

The essence of the design process is to consider possible modes of failure. In studying soil mechanics, aspects of overall coastal slope, embankment and wall design will need to have adequate factors of safety against failures, and guidance is given in BS 6031[44]. Where the structural performance of individual elements is being considered, limit state design should be used. In this respect the designer should take into account:

- The likelihood of failure, bearing in mind the frequency of occurrence of the load case;
- The consequences of failure;
- The reliability of the assumed load case;
- The reliability of the assumed structure strength.

The question of wave heights for use in design is discussed in SPM[6], which recommends the following:

- For 'rigid' structures or elements of structures, e.g. cantilever steel sheet-piled walls where a single wave may cause failure: $H_{1/100}$;
- For 'semi-rigid' structures or elements of structures such as a tied sheet pile wall: $H_{1/10}$ to $H_{1/100}$;
- for 'flexible' structures such as rip-rap, $H_{1/3}$ to $H_{1/10}$.

Further discussion on parameters for use in design is given in this chapter where appropriate.

6.1 Hydraulic performance

When waves meet a seawall their energy is spent by two main processes: 'dissipation' and 'reflection'. Dissipation is the conversion of the wave energy into turbulence by the surface roughness of the seawall, by flow in and out of its pores and by wave breaking. The energy which is neither dissipated nor transmitted past the structure by overtopping must return to the sea by way of a reflected wave.

Hydraulic performance is concerned with the ways in which a seawall accommodates the processes mentioned above. The effects which are of greatest engineering importance are:

- Wave run-up;
- Wave overtopping;
- Wave reflection.

The parameters listed above are illustrated in Figure 6.1 The prediction of these parameters using analytical and empirical techniques is the subject of this chapter.

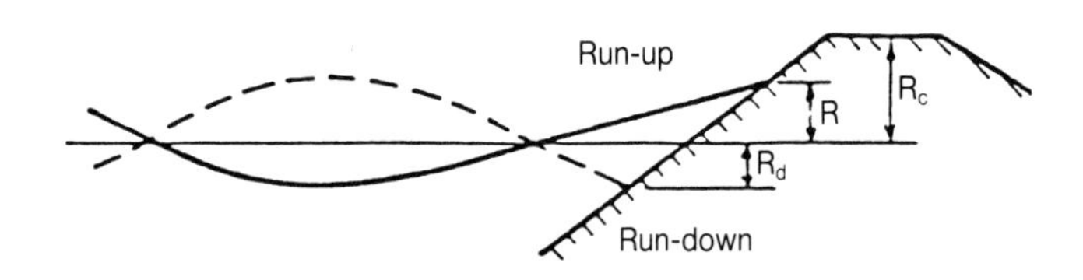

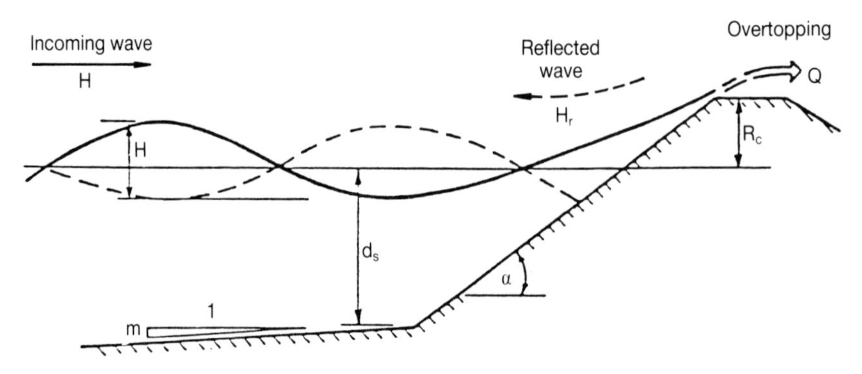

Figure 6.1 Seawall hydraulics—definition sketch

Recommendations regarding hydraulic modelling are also made (see also Appendix B). The forces which are imparted to the structure by waves are described in Section 6.2.

6.1.1 Surf similarity parameter

Run-up, overtopping and reflection are influenced by:

- Structural form and features of the wall – its height, slope, shape, roughness and porosity;
- Foreshore slope and level;
- Water level;
- Water depth;
- Wave conditions (height, period);
- Wave direction.

In describing the behaviour of a wave on a beach or seawall slope, many coastal engineers have made use of a non-dimensional parameter known as the surf similarity parameter (or Iribarren number), *Ir*. This has been widely used to categorize the form and severity of wave breaking on a slope, and may be employed in the calculations of run-up and wave reflections. The Iribarren number is defined, in regular wave terms, by the following:

$$Ir = \frac{\tan\ \alpha}{(H/L_o)^{\frac{1}{2}}} \tag{6.1}$$

where α = structure slope angle;
H = incident wave height at the structure;
L_o = deep water wave length, given by $gT^2/2\pi$;
T = wave period.

For smooth or porous rough slopes Gunbak[1] has summarized wave breaking in terms of the value of *Ir* as follows:

Breaker type	*Limiting criteria*	
	Smooth slope	Rough, porous slope
Plunging	$Ir < 2.5$	$Ir < 2.0$
Plunging/collapsing	$2.5 < Ir < 3.2$	$2.0 < Ir < 2.6$
Collapsing/surging	$3.2 < Ir < 3.4$	$2.6 < Ir < 3.1$
Surging	$3.4 < Ir$	$3.1 < Ir$

When considering irregular waves one can use a modified Iribarren number Ir_p, defined by:

$Ir_p = \tan \alpha/(s_p)^{\frac{1}{2}}$
where $s_p = 2\pi\ H_s/gT_p^{\ 2}$ (6.2)

6.1.2 Type of wall

Research into the hydraulic performance of seawalls has focused on particular types of wall and some wall types have been more extensively researched than others. It is important, when using the design charts and formulae which are presented in the following sections, to identify the most appropriate category of wall. Table 6.1 shows the categories that have been considered.

6.1.3 Run-up

The 'run-up' and 'run-down' levels are defined as the maximum and minimum levels reached by waves at a seawall relative to still water (Figure 6.1). If the run-up level exceeds the crest freeboard R_c, then overtopping will occur.

Under the action of random waves, run-up levels will vary from wave to wave. It is therefore more meaningful to determine a characteristic measure of run-up, which is typical of the sea state. Three measures of run-up may be considered in accordance with the following definitions:

R: the mean run-up (also run-up of regular waves);

R_s: the significant run-up (analogous to significant wave height H_s), i.e. the average of the highest one third run-up levels reached;

R_2: the run-up level exceeded by only 2% of the waves. R_2 has been used in the Netherlands as a basis for establishing crest level, and has been assumed to produce 'very small' overtopping.

Vertical non-porous walls

The prediction formulae for run-up vertical walls are all based on regular waves, and generally assume deep water at the seawall toe. An expression for the run-up of a non-breaking wave on a vertical wall based on the work of Sainflou[2] is:

$$R = H + \frac{\pi H^2}{L} \coth \frac{2\pi d_s}{L} \tag{6.3}$$

The *Shore Protection Manual*[7] gives prediction graphs based on model tests for relative run-up R/H'_o where the wave height H'_o is the deep water height. For a vertical wall, data points are presented for a range of wave steepnesses and relative water depths. Similar graphs are given for curved walls (not reproduced here). Graphs are given for a range of relative depth ratios d_s/H'_o when the approach beach was 1:10 (Figures 6.2–6.4).

Prediction graphs are also given for $d_s/H'_o = 2.0$ and $d_s/H'_o \geq 3.0$ for the case of horizontal seabed (Figures 6.5 and 6.6). For all these graphs the SPM recommends

Table 6.1 Wall types

Category	*Wall type*	*Example*
a	Vertical, battered or recurved walls steeper than 1:1	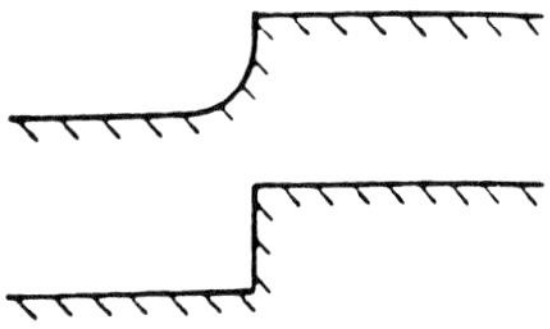
b	Simple, smooth, non-porous slopes	
c	Simple, rough, non-porous slopes	
d	Simple, rough, porous slopes	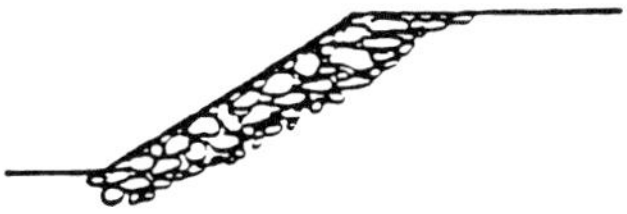
e	Composite, multiple or bermed slopes	

that a correction be applied for model scale effects, generally leading to an increase in the predicted value of around 10–20% (Figure 6.7).

Data on run-up levels on vertical, battered or curved walls under random wave attack are not generally available except for slopes close to 1:1, where it is possible to use the method suggested by Ahrens[4]. Simple prediction methods for wave run-up on near vertical walls are reviewed in SR1[3]. No data on wave run-down levels on vertical walls under random waves are available, although the method given by Ahrens for slopes of 1:1 or shallower may give a first estimate of the lower extent of wave action at the wall.

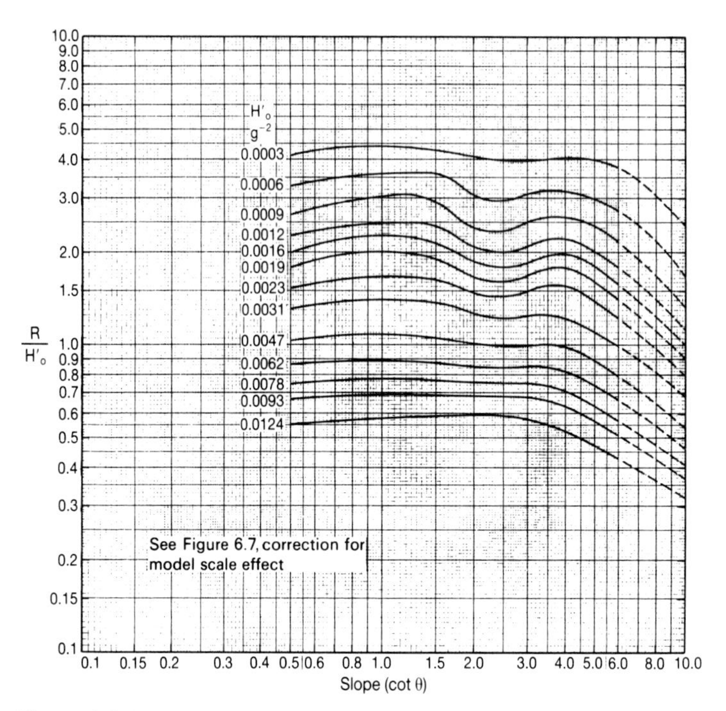

Figure 6.2 Wave run-up on smooth, impermeable slopes when $d_s/H_0=0$ (structures fronted by a 1:10 slope)

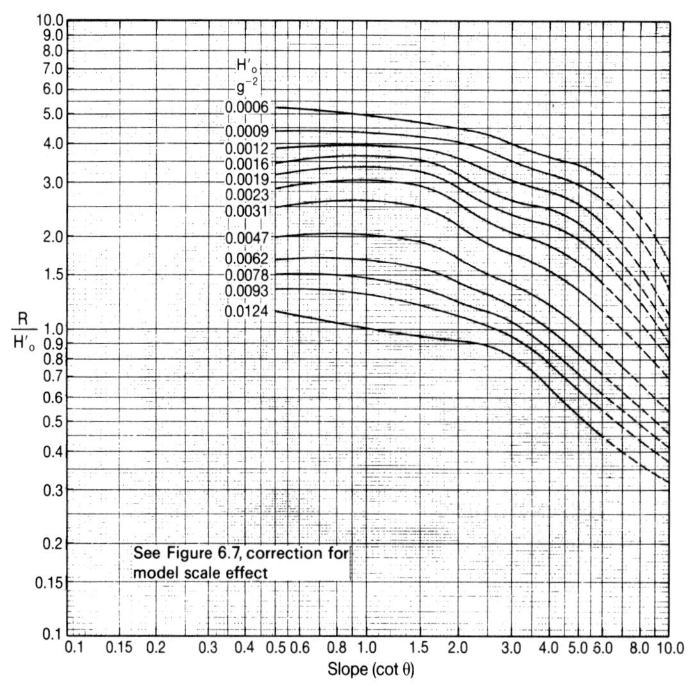

Figure 6.3 Wave run-up on smooth, impermeable slopes when $d_s/H_o=0.45$ (structures fronted by a 1:10 slope)

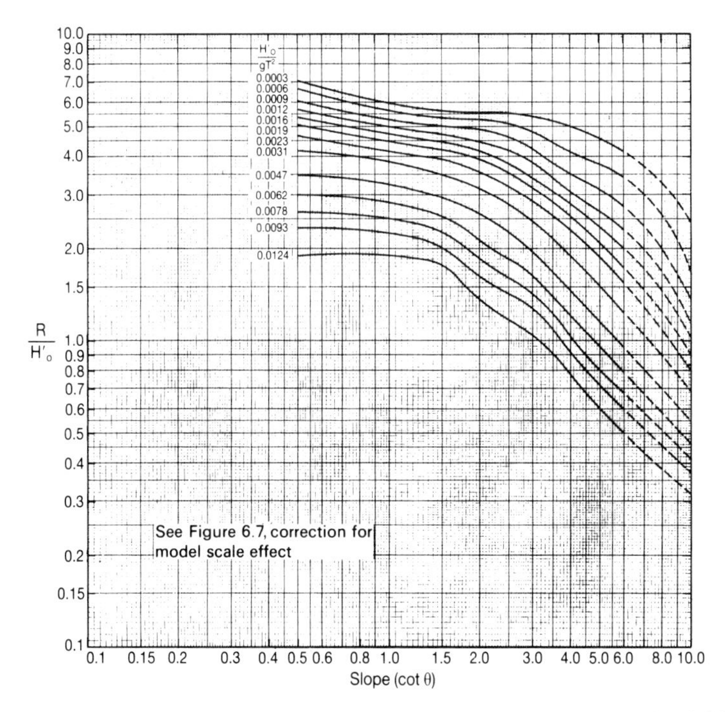

Figure 6.4 Wave run-up on smooth, impermeable slopes when $d_s/H_o=0.80$ (structures fronted by a 1:10 slope)

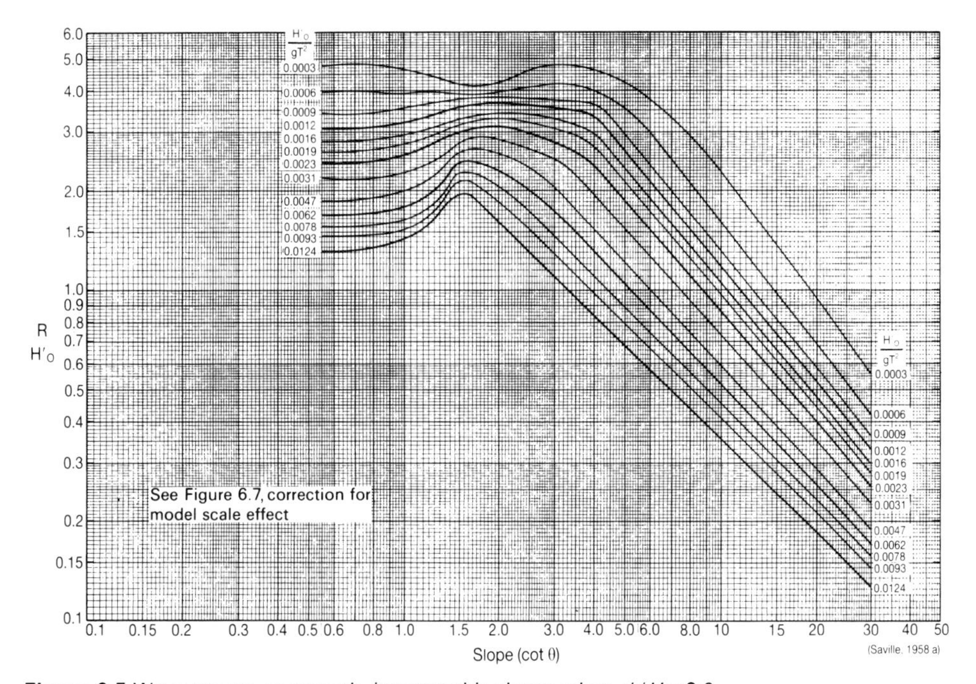

Figure 6.5 Wave run-up on smooth, impermeable slopes when $d_s/H_o=2.0$

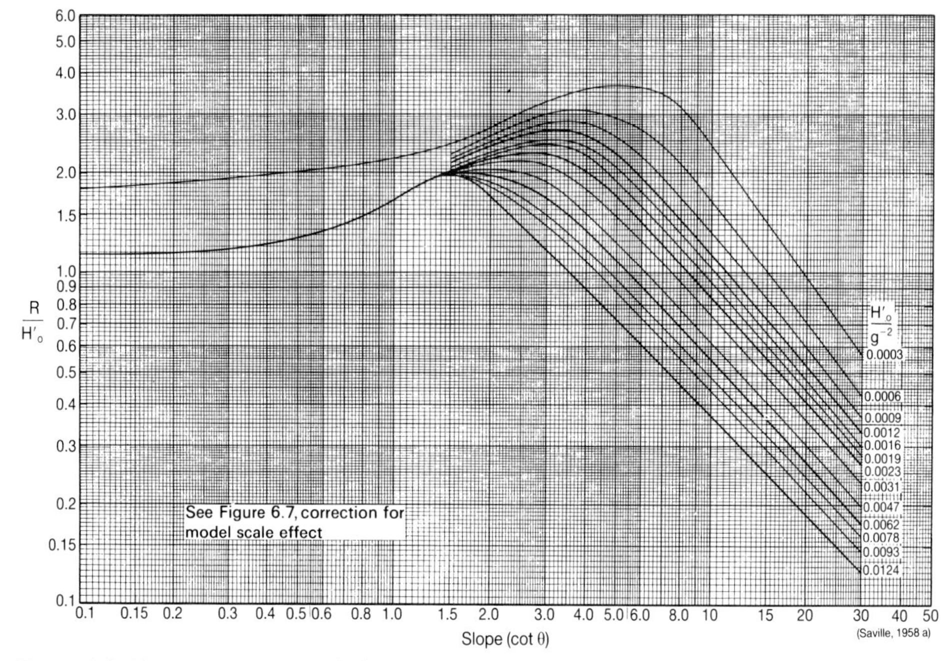

Figure 6.6 Wave run-up on smooth, impermeable slopes when $d_s/H_o \geqslant 3.0$

Simple smooth non-porous slopes

The prediction of wave run-up levels on smooth slopes has received relatively more attention than vertical walls. Methods are available for the calculation of run-up levels under either regular or random waves (discussed below) but no single method is universally applicable.

Predictions of relative run-up R/H'_o for regular waves of equivalent deep water wave height H'_o may be made using Figures 6.2–6.7 as discussed above. These graphs cover a range of structure slopes.

The Iribarren number (Section 6.1.1) has been used by Losada[5], in a prediction method for run-up on simple smooth slopes, in which the relative run-up R/H is determined by:

$$\begin{aligned} R/H &= Ir && \text{for } 0 < Ir < 2.5 \\ R/H &= 2.5 - \frac{(Ir - 2.5)}{3.0} && \text{for } 2.5 < Ir < 4.0 \\ R/H &= 2.0 && \text{for } 4.0 < Ir \end{aligned} \tag{6.4}$$

This approach is too coarse to provide a detailed assessment but allows an initial estimation of the run-up level on smooth slopes for regular waves.

The results of irregular wave test by Ahrens and those reported in SR2[6] have been used to give prediction methods for R_s and R_2. The former method allows the calculation of mean, significant and 2% run-up levels on structure slopes between 1:1 and 1:4. The method is valid for relative depths d_s/H_s greater than 3, and is therefore

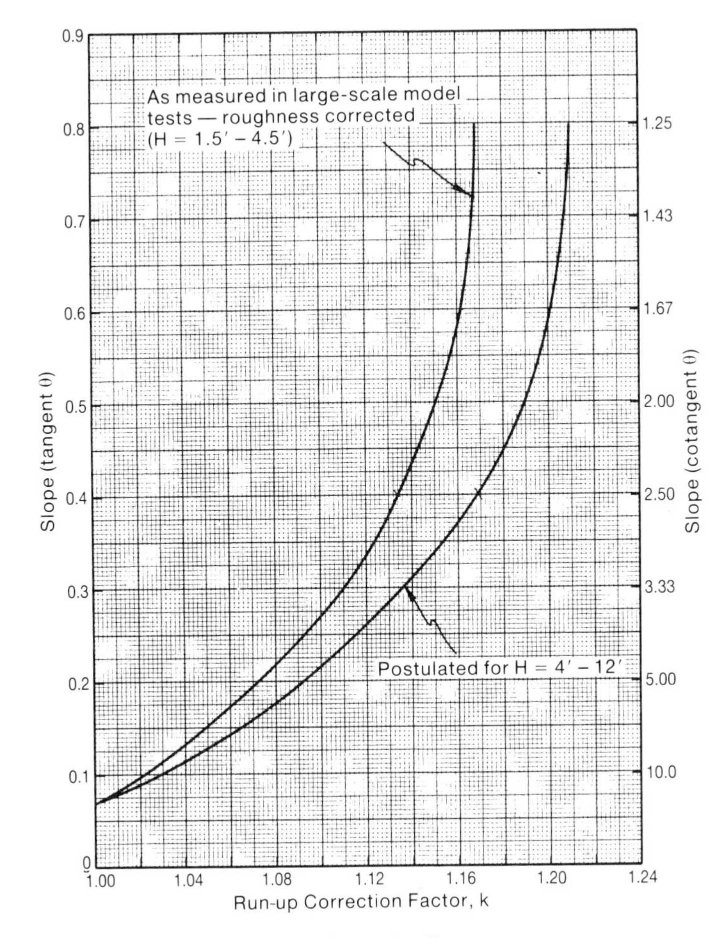

Figure 6.7 Run-up correction for scale effects

not appropriate for seawalls in more shallow water, although it can be used with caution to compare the potential overtopping of different walls. The results of random wave tests on smooth slopes between 1:1.33 and 1:2.0 are also reported in SR2. Prediction equations are suggested for R_2 and R_s for a restricted range of wave conditions.

For smooth slopes SR2 gives the following empirical equations for R_2 and R_s based on test results (for which the slope was in the range 1:1.33 to 1:2.0 and Ir ranged from 2.7 to 5.5):

$$R_2/H_s = 3.39 - 0.21\ Ir_p \qquad (6.5)$$

$$R_s/H_s = 2.11 - 0.09\ Ir_p \qquad (6.6)$$

Ahrens suggests a general prediction equation for R, R_2 and R_s which may be written in the form:

$$\frac{R_x}{H_s} = C_1 + C_2\frac{(s_p)}{Z} + C_3\frac{(s_p)^2}{Z} \quad (6.7)$$

in which values for coefficients C_1, C_2 and C_3 are given in Table 6.2.

Equation (6.7) generally predicts run-up levels somewhat greater than those given by equations (6.5) and (6.6). The reasons for this difference are not clear, but serve to demonstrate that the designer should not rely on one technique but should base his judgement on all available information.

In some instances it may be useful to estimate run-down. The run-down level, analogous to R_2, may be defined as the level on the slope below which only 2% of waves reach, and is given by Ahrens as:

$$\frac{R_{d98}}{H_s} = 2.32 \exp(-2.46/Ir_p) \quad (6.8)$$

He gives a wide scatter of the data, and emphasizes that this method should only be used to estimate approximate run-down.

Simple rough non-porous slopes

The prediction of run-up on rough non-porous slopes is a modification of that for smooth slopes. The effects of roughness on run-up can be described by run-up reduction (or roughness) factor, r. This is defined as the ratio of the run-up on the

Table 6.2 Coefficients for run-up on smooth slopes (for use in conjunction with equations (6.3)–(6.7))

R_x	cotα	C_1	C_2	C_3
R	1.0	0.71	110	− 8070
	1.5	0.75	197	−11400
	2.0	0.93	242	−19300
	2.5	1.00	278	−31300
	3.0	1.19	209	−29600
	4.0	1.47	72.5	−17000
R_s	1.0	1.34	66.1	0
	1.5	1.38	318	−19700
	2.0	1.64	357	−30900
	2.5	1.94	279	−32100
	3.0	2.11	187	−26700
	4.0	2.52	−79.4	0
R_2	1.0	2.32	71.5	0
	1.5	2.52	195	0
	2.0	3.21	71.9	0
	2.5	3.39	129	−16100
	3.0	3.70	0	−17000
	4.0	3.60	−222	0

rough slope to that on the equivalent smooth slope. Values of r have been derived from model test results and suggested values are given in Table 6.3. It is reasonable to suppose that values of r derived from regular wave tests will be applicable to random wave prediction methods such as discussed above, but this assumption has not been confirmed.

Simple rough porous slopes

Two approaches may be taken for the evaluation of run-up on rough porous slopes. One method entails the application of the roughness factor r (Table 6.3) to the results from Section 6.1.4. Another approach is to make use of the results of laboratory measurements on porous slopes.

Prediction curves for regular waves on various rubble slopes are given by SPM (Figures 6.8 and 6.9). These two graphs give values which are assumed to be directly applicable to the prototype without need for scale correction.

Limited measurements have also been made of random wave run-up levels on porous armoured slopes in the range 1:1.33 to 1:2.0 and for a range of wave conditions, given by Ir', from 2.7 to 5.6. Prediction formulae are suggested for rubble slopes armoured with concrete armour units, of which the following give reasonable estimates:

$$\frac{R_s}{H_s} = 1.32\,(1 - \exp\,(-0.31\, Ir_p)) \qquad (6.9)$$

$$\frac{R_2}{H_s} = 1.83\,(1 - \exp\,(-0.31\, Ir_p)) \qquad (6.10)$$

Composite slopes

The methods discussed so far have all been developed for simple slopes. In some cases local geometric restrictions require a bermed or composite slope. Such a cross section may also arise where a roadway is incorporated for access or where the structure is extended or upgraded. A berm at or close to design still water level will often reduce

Table 6.3 Values of run-up reduction (roughness) factor, *r*

Slope surface characteristics	*Roughness value, r*
Smooth, impermeable	1.00
Concrete blocks, fitted	0.90
Stone blocks, pitches or mortared	0.90
Grass	0.85–0.90
Rough concrete	0.85
One layer of quarrystone on impermeable foundation	0.80
Stone set in cement mortar	0.75–0.80
Rounded quarrystone	0.60–0.65
Two or more layers of quarrystone on rubble layers	0.60–0.65
Concrete armour units (at 50% void ratio)	0.45–0.50

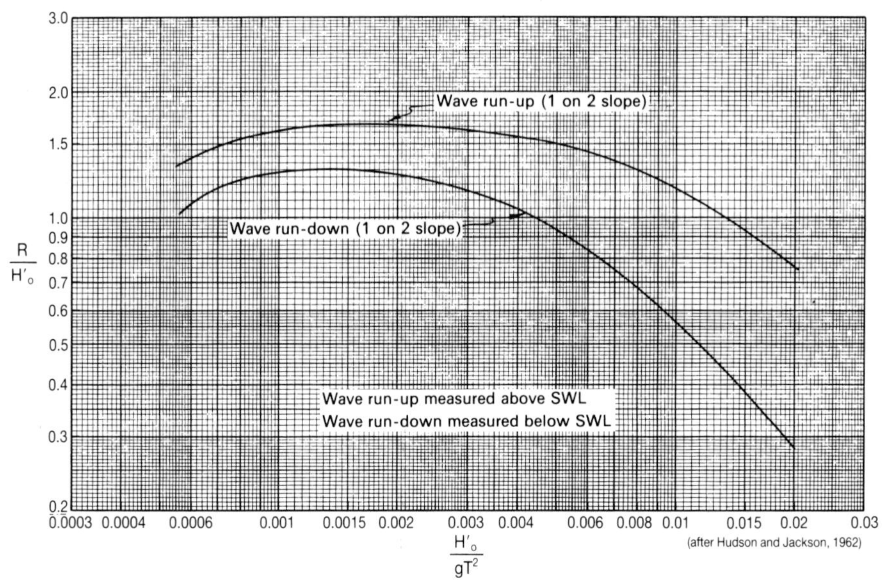

Figure 6.8 Wave run-up and run-down on graded rip-rap, 1:2 slope, impermeable base, H_o/gT^2 (data for $d_s/H_o > 3.0$)

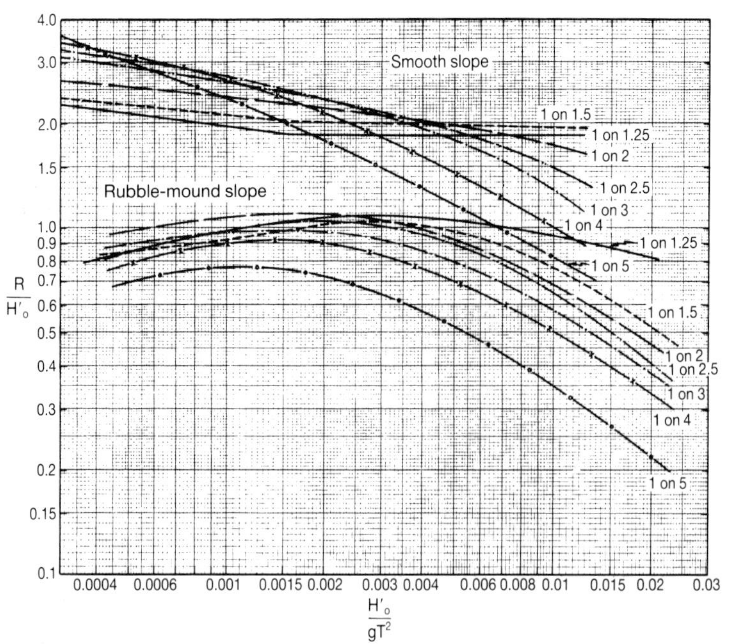

Figure 6.9 Comparison of wave run-up on smooth slopes with run-up on permeable rubble slopes (data for $d_s/H_o > 3.0$)

both run-up and reflections. No data are available to predict the reduction of run-up under random waves on a bermed slope.

Methods to estimate run-up on composite or bermed slopes under regular waves are discussed in the *Shore Protection Manual* and by Thompson[59]. Both are based on the estimate of an equivalent simple slope. Neither method has been tested or validated for random waves. The effect of a berm on overtopping discharges under random waves is discussed in Section 6.1.4.

6.1.4 Wave overtopping

Wave overtopping is most conveniently expressed as the discharge per unit length of wall, given by Q in $m^3/s/m$. This is usually described as the mean discharge, Q, for a particular crest elevation, still water level, and wave condition. The number of waves causing overtopping may also be required in some applications.

Most likely, the engineer will wish to design the seawall so it limits overtopping to a specific quantity or rate, given the design wave and water level. Guidance on acceptable amounts of overtopping is given by Owen[10], which takes account of:

- The stability of the crown and back face of the seawall;
- The discharge capacity of drainage channels behind the seawall;
- The total volume available for storage of flood waters behind the seawall until the tide level falls sufficiently for tidal outfalls to come into operation;
- The possibility of damage or injury to buildings, vehicles or members of the public located behind the seawall.

In discussing the overtopping of seawalls a distinction is drawn between 'green water' (or 'solid') overtopping and spray (or 'white water'). The differences are not well identified, although both terms refer to water passing over the seawall as a result of wave action. In general, the volume of water due to 'green water' overtopping is many times greater than that due to spray, although with some walls severe spray may frequently occur. Spray is not correctly simulated in hydraulic model tests, due to surface tension effects, and it has not therefore been possible to study it to any significant extent in the laboratory. Very little guidance is available to the designer to determine the volume of wind-driven spray that might pass over a seawall. The engineer should therefore rely on experience to produce a wall that is not too susceptible to spray.

Prediction methods for overtopping of different seawalls vary considerably. Methods based solely on regular wave testing are available for some vertical or curved walls and some smooth non-porous, rough or armoured slopes. Prediction methods based on random wave tests are available for non-porous sloping and bermed seawalls, and may be extended to rough non-porous and armoured slopes. There are no analytical prediction methods presently available to predict the overtopping discharges for seawalls incorporating parapet or crown walls but this is currently being researched (1989). The principal methods available are discussed below in which the sources of information are *Shore Protection Manual*[7], Goda[9] and Owen[10–12].

Vertical walls (non-porous and porous)

Overtopping of non-porous vertical walls has been considered by Goda and in the *Shore Protection Manual.* Both sources are based on regular wave tests, but postulate methods by which these results might be extended to random waves. Both methods involve considerable assumptions, and neither has been validated for random waves. Douglass[14] has compared the use of these two methods for various cases (Figure 6.10). The engineer should use these methods for preliminary design but will need model tests to gain more reliable values for detailed work.

No prediction method is available to describe overtopping of porous vertical walls such as cribwork or gabions. In the absence of better information it should be assumed that they behave as the equivalent non-porous structure.

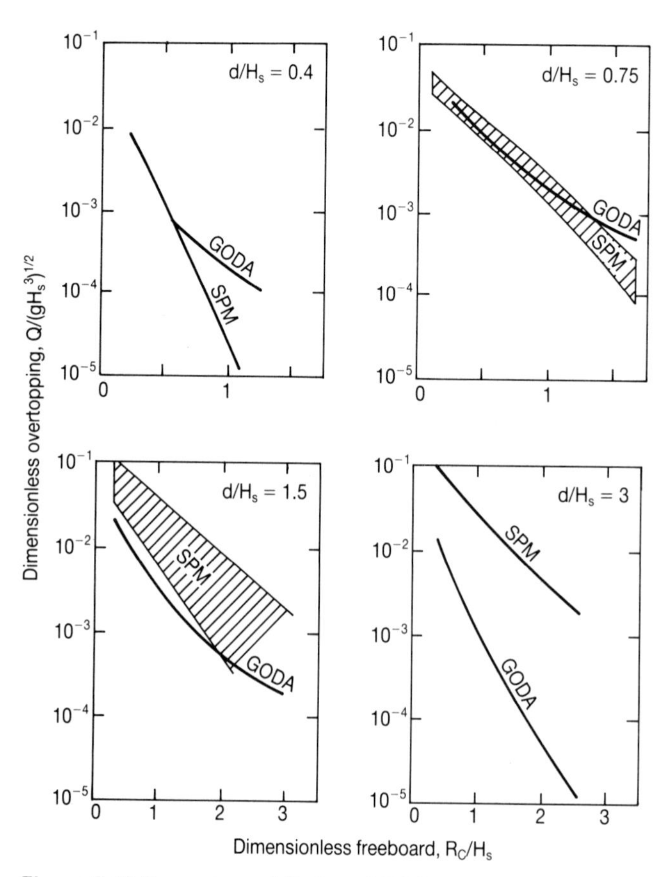

Figure 6.10 Comparison of Goda and SPM methods for estimating overtopping of a vertical wall

Simple smooth non-porous slopes

For this type of face a method for the prediction of overtopping to seawalls under random waves is the application of test results from *HR*, which include walls of slope 1:1 to 1:4, with waves of steepness, H_s/L_o, from 0.035 to 0.055. The test results were used to define values of empirical coefficients, *A* and *B*, in a general equation for overtopping discharge, which may be written:

$$Q^* = A \exp(-BR^*/r) \tag{6.11}$$

where the non-dimensional discharge, Q^*, and non-dimensional freeboard, R^*, are defined by:

$$Q^* = \frac{Q}{(gH_s^3)^{\frac{1}{2}}} \left(\frac{(s)^{\frac{1}{2}}}{2\pi}\right) \tag{6.12}$$

where $s = 2\pi\, H_s/gT^2$:

$$R^* = \frac{Rc}{H_s} \frac{(s)^{\frac{1}{2}}}{2\pi} \tag{6.13}$$

and r is the roughness factor (note $r = 1.0$ for smooth slopes). Values of the coefficients *A* and *B* are given in Table 6.4 for simple seawalls. Owen[10] also gives design curves allowing interpolations for wall configurations not covered by the test conditions.

Model tests have shown that overtopping is most severe at angles of wave attack of approximately 15°. Figure 6.11 gives correction factors for the coefficients *A* and *B* to allow for oblique wave attack.

Simple, rough, porous and non-porous slopes

Rough slopes generally absorb significantly more wave energy than the equivalent smooth slopes, and both run-up and overtopping will therefore be reduced. Methods

Table 6.4 Values of the coefficients *A* and *B* for simple seawalls

Seawall slope	*A*	*B*
1:1	7.9×10^{-3}	20.12
1:1½	1.02×10^{-2}	20.12
1:2	1.25×10^{-2}	22.06
1:2½	1.45×10^{-2}	26.1
1:3	1.63×10^{-2}	31.9
1:3½	1.78×10^{-2}	38.9
1:4	1.92×10^{-2}	46.96
1:4½	2.15×10^{-2}	55.7
1:5	2.5×10^{-2}	65.2

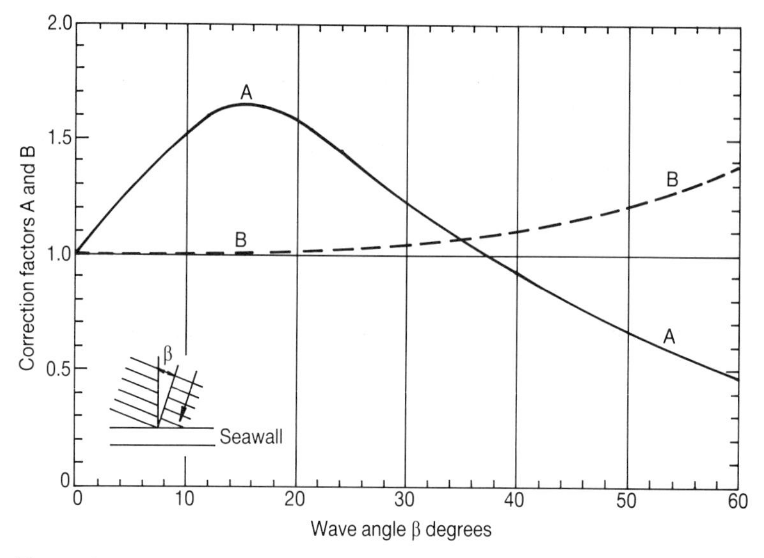

Figure 6.11 Correction factors for angled wave attack

of predicting overtopping of rough slopes are based on the prediction methods for smooth slopes, as shown in equations (6.12) and (6.13), in which the roughness value r is obtained from Table 6.3.

Composite or bermed slopes

The overtopping of composite or bermed slopes may again be estimated with equations (6.12) and (6.13) but using coefficients A and B obtained from Table 6.5.

Validity of methods

The value of overtopping calculated by the above methods is subject to some uncertainties, due to the assumptions and limitations connected with each method. None of the methods presented has been validated by field measurements, or by large-scale laboratory tests. Owen[10] suggests that a 95% confidence interval from $Q/3$ to $3Q$ should be used for predictions. Douglass[13,14] suggests that the correct value should be considered to be within an order of magnitude of the calculated value. This implies that, for a maximum permissible value of overtopping, Q, the seawall should be designed for, at best, $Q/3$, and more conservatively for $Q/10$. If this is considered to produce an uneconomic design, hydraulic model tests with random waves will be required to refine the estimates.

Wind effects

Almost all data on wave overtopping have been obtained in laboratory studies without taking wind effects into account. However, in nature, larger waves will

Table 6.5 Values of the coefficients *A* and *B* for bermed seawalls

Seawall slope	*Berm elevation (m SWL)*	*Berm width (m)*	*A*	*B*
1:1	−4.0	10	6.40×10^{-3}	19.50
1:2			9.11×10^{-3}	21.50
1:4			1.45×10^{-2}	41.10
1:1	−2.0	5	3.40×10^{-3}	16.52
1:2			9.80×10^{-3}	23.98
1:4			1.59×10^{-2}	46.63
1:1	−2.0	10	4.79×10^{-3}	18.92
1:2			6.78×10^{-3}	24.20
1:4			8.57×10^{-3}	45.80
1:1	−2.0	20	8.80×10^{-4}	14.76
1:2			2.00×10^{-3}	24.81
1:4			8.50×10^{-3}	50.40
1:1	−2.0	40	3.80×10^{-4}	22.65
1:2			5.00×10^{-4}	25.93
1:4			4.70×10^{-3}	51.23
1:1	−2.0	80	2.40×10^{-4}	25.90
1:2			3.80×10^{-4}	25.76
1:4			8.80×10^{-4}	58.24
1:1	−1.0	5	1.55×10^{-2}	32.68
1:2			1.90×10^{-2}	37.27
1:4			5.00×10^{-2}	70.32
1:1	−1.0	10	9.25×10^{-3}	38.90
1:2			3.39×10^{-2}	53.30
1:4			3.03×10^{-2}	79.60
1:1	−1.0	20	7.50×10^{-3}	45.61
1:2			3.40×10^{-3}	49.97
1:4			3.90×10^{-3}	61.57
1:1	−1.0	40	1.20×10^{-3}	49.30
1:2			2.35×10^{-3}	56.18
1:4			1.45×10^{-4}	63.43
1:1	−1.0	80	4.10×10^{-5}	51.41
1:2			6.60×10^{-5}	66.54
1:4			5.40×10^{-5}	71.59
1:1	0.0	10	9.67×10^{-3}	41.90
1:2			2.90×10^{-2}	56.70
1:4			3.03×10^{-2}	79.60

frequently be associated with onshore wind. These winds may influence the overtopping discharge in several ways, including:

- Raising the still water level (wind set-up);
- Increasing wave run-up on the seawall;
- Blowing spray over the seawall.

The relative importance of each of these factors will depend largely on the type of seawall being considered. For example, a vertical seawall can result in a considerable volume of water being thrown into the air when the waves break against it; with a moderate onshore wind a significant proportion of this will be blown over the seawall. For simple slopes and bermed seawalls the quantity of water thrown into the air by waves breaking on the wall can be relatively small.

The *Shore Protection Manual* quotes a formula for wind effect. Although it is said to be unverified, the formula is 'believed to give a reasonable estimate of the effects of onshore winds of significant magnitude'. The formula based on regular waves can be applied for seawalls with slopes up to vertical. Calculated overtopping rates are multiplied by a wind correction factor K_w, where

$$K_w = 1.0 + W_f \left(\frac{(h - d_s)}{R} + 0.1 \right) \sin \alpha \tag{6.14}$$

where h is the height of the seawall (crest to toe) and W_f is a wind factor, whose value depends on the onshore component of wind speed. For no wind W_f has a value of 0: for a wind speed of 13.4 m/s W_f is 0.5, and for a speed of 26.8 m/s W_f is 2.0. Values of W_f for intermediate speeds can be derived by interpolation.

For most new seawalls, designed for little overtopping, the value of K_w used will probably approach the upper end of the range of possible values.

6.1.5 Wave reflections

The interaction of incident and reflected waves often leads to a confused sea in front of the structure, with occasional steep and unstable waves of considerable hazard to small boats. Reflected waves can also propagate into areas of a harbour previously sheltered from wave action. These will lead to increased peak orbital velocities, increasing the likelihood of movement of beach material. Under oblique waves, reflection will increase littoral currents and hence local sediment transport. All coastal structures reflect some proportion of the incident wave energy. This is often described by a reflection coefficient, C_r, defined in terms of the incident and reflected wave heights, H_i and H_r, respectively, or the total incident and reflected wave energies, E_i and E_r:

$$C_r = H_r/H_i = \sqrt{(E_r/E_i)} \tag{6.15}$$

When considering random waves, values of C_r may be defined using the significant incident and reflected wave heights as representative of the incident and reflected energies.

Vertical non-porous walls

Vertical, battered, curved or recurved and other non-porous steeply sloping walls in deep water will reflect almost 100% of the incident wave energy, i.e. $C_r = 1.0$. Only if the water depth is sufficiently shallow to promote wave breaking on the approach slope, or at the wall, will significant energy be dissipated, rather than reflected. If waves can reach a wall substantially unmodified by depth effects, a coefficient of reflection of unity should be assumed. Wall roughness or corrugations are unlikely to reduce this significantly unless large in relation to the wave (say, greater than $L/10$).

Simple smooth non-porous slopes

Seawalls with non-porous sloping faces will reflect significantly less than vertical walls, depending upon wave steepness and the seawall slope. Much of the most useful information for the prediction of wave reflection from non-porous sloping structures is presented by Seelig[15].

Seelig advocates the use of the expression:

$$C_r = \frac{a.Ir^2}{Ir^2 + b} \qquad (6.16)$$

with values of $a = 1.0$ and $b = 5.5$ for smooth slopes of 1:6.0 or steeper.

The recommendation is based upon the results of regular wave testing only. Recently the results of tests with random waves have been analysed[16,17]. The results have been presented again in terms of the Iribarren number, but defined for random waves, and equation (6.16). For impermeable smooth slopes the value of Ir used in equation (6.16) may be given by Ir_m:

$$Ir_m = \tan\alpha / s_m^{\frac{1}{2}}$$

$$s_m = 2\pi H_s / g T^2_m$$

Random wave tests reported by Allsop[17] then support the use of coefficients in equation (6.16):

$$a = 1.02, \ b = 5.57$$

For structures in shallow water Seelig recommends the use of reduction factors in the calculation of C_r. In use these factors have given values of C_r which appear to be unrealistically low. No reduction factor is therefore recommended for shallow water.

Table 6.6 Values of coefficients for equation (6.16)

Armour	*Iribarren No. used in equation (6.16)*	*Range of validity*	*Coefficients used in equation (6.16)*	
			a	*b*
Dolos	Ir	$1.5 < Ir < 5.5$	0.56	10.0
Cob	Ir	$1.5 < Ir < 4.5$	0.50	6.5
Tetrapod	Ir_p	$2.5 < Ir_p < 6.0$	0.48	9.6
Stabit	Ir_p	$2.5 < Ir_p < 6.0$	0.48	9.6
Shed	Ir_p	$3.0 < Ir_p < 6.0$	0.49	7.9
Diode	Ir_p	$3.0 < Ir_p < 6.0$	0.49	7.9
Rock	Ir_m	$2.0 < Ir_m < 10.0$	0.64	8.8
Rock (large)	Ir_m	$2.0 < Ir_m < 10.0$	0.64	9.6
Rock (one layer)	Ir_m	$2.0 < Ir_m < 8.0$	0.64	7.2

Simple rough non-porous slopes

It is generally believed that a rough impermeable slope will reflect slightly less wave energy than the equivalent smooth type. In practice any reduction measured in model tests has proved to be small. It is not therefore recommended that the value of C_r used should be less than that for a smooth slope, unless specific model test data are available.

Simple rough porous slopes

Analysis of recent random wave test results has been used in equation (6.16) by Allsop[16,17] to generate new values of coefficients a and b. These cover a number of armour units and configurations. It should be noted that some of the test data were generated in slightly different ways, and that the value of the Iribarren number used in analysis of some configurations was given by Ir_p:

$$Ir_p = \tan\alpha / s_p^{\frac{1}{2}} \qquad (6.17)$$

$$s_p = 2\pi H_s / g T_p^2 \qquad (6.18)$$

Composite or bermed slopes

Bermed and composite slopes with berms close to the still water level may offer considerable reductions in the magnitude of wave reflections from a seawall. However, very few data are available to allow these reductions to be calculated without specific test data. Results for a series of rock armoured slopes with berms at the water level have been presented by Allsop and Channell[17]. The results from these tests show C_r plotted against B/L_{ms} for the value of B/h_s; where B = berm width, h_s = water depth at structure toe, L_{ms} = wave length of mean wave period, T_m, in water depth, h_s.

The reflection coefficient, C_r, does not provide a measure of the bed velocities resulting from reflections, for which model tests would be required.

6.2 Slope stability and structural loads

In this section guidance is given regarding the overall considerations of stability of the coastal slope and of the core or embankment (Sections 6.2.1 and 6.2.2). The design of the wall will require as good a knowledge as possible of live loads, including those from wave action. These are discussed in Sections 6.2.3 and 6.2.4.

6.2.1 Stability of coastal cliffs

Where the coastline consists of cliffs or a coastal slope, the design of a seawall should be viewed in the context of the overall stability of the coastal slope. The stability of the cliff is clearly important since the integrity of the wall may be affected by any future landslips. This section gives a brief introduction to the subject of cliff stabilization and gives the engineer appropriate references which provide much greater detail.

The investigation and analysis of coastal landslides, and the design of suitable remedial works, requires an adequate geotechnical understanding of the various factors involved. In all but the most straightforward cases it is advisable to consult specialist geotechnical engineers with experience of stabilizing coastal landslips.

General

Coastal cliffs that require protection from erosion generally consist of soil (cohesive or granular) and/or soft rock (e.g. chalk, mudstone), and in both cases erosion of material from the toe results in an oversteepening of the slope. The coastline retreats due to periodic landslips in this material, with the debris being carried away by the action of the sea. Even if a seawall is built to halt the erosion at the toe, the slope will continue to regress (unless stabilized) over time as a result of further mass movements, but only if they are not themselves stabilized.

Thus there are two important aspects in the overall stabilization of an eroding cliff: first, the construction of a suitable seawall to prevent futher toe erosion, and second the implementation of appropriate cliff-stabilization measures to ensure satisfactory long-term slope stability. The phasing of these two interrelated elements will depend on the particular site conditions.

In certain limited cases it may be possible to omit any stabilization works and allow the slope to regrade naturally by itself. Where this course of action is adopted the designer should be sure that future landslides will neither endanger the stability of the seawall nor pose any threat to the public at either the top or bottom of the slope.

When a seawall is being designed to replace an existing structure the coastal slope may already have benefited from remedial measures as part of a previous scheme. It is still important to assess the security of the slope, particularly if the new scheme involves a change of drainage conditions or loading at the toe of the slope. The existence of an apparently stable slope now does not guarantee its stability in the future, as it can take a very long time for pore-water pressures to rise to their equilibrium values, especially in heavily overconsolidated clays.

Modes of failure

A number of classification schemes has been proposed which identify different types of landslide and their particular modes of failure. The classification given by Hutchinson[39] is reproduced as Figure 6.12. Although it is one of several classification schemes, it has been chosen to illustrate possible modes of failure because it deals specifically with coastal landslides. Other classifications are given by Broms,[35] Varnes[45] and BS 6349,[47] with a more comprehensive one contained in the Department of the Environment Review of Research in Landsliding in Great Britain.[56]

Figure 6.12 shows the main types of instability to be found in coastal cliffs. Slides can be broadly classified as rotational, compound or translational. Instability can also occur due to seepage erosion, principally in fine-grained granular material. There are also various types of falls, flows and toppling failures.

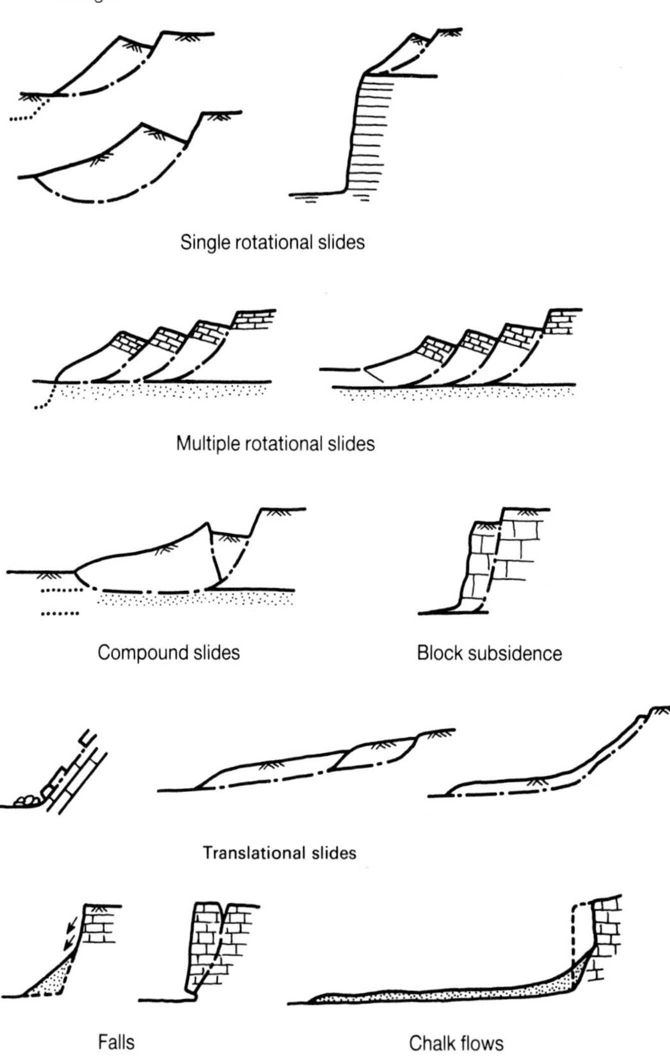

Figure 6.12 Main types of coastal landslides (after Hutchinson)

One of the aims of the geotechnical investigation (Section 4.8) is to identify, where relevant, the existing modes of failure. The main objective of the design regarding cliff stabilization is to devise a scheme which possesses an adequate factor of safety against all existing and potential modes of failure.

Stability analysis

Methods of analysis for slope stability are given in BS 6031[46] as well as in standard textbooks (for example, Bromhead[34]). In analysing the stability of coastal cliffs, which often have complex geometry and uncertain stratigraphy and soil properties, the use

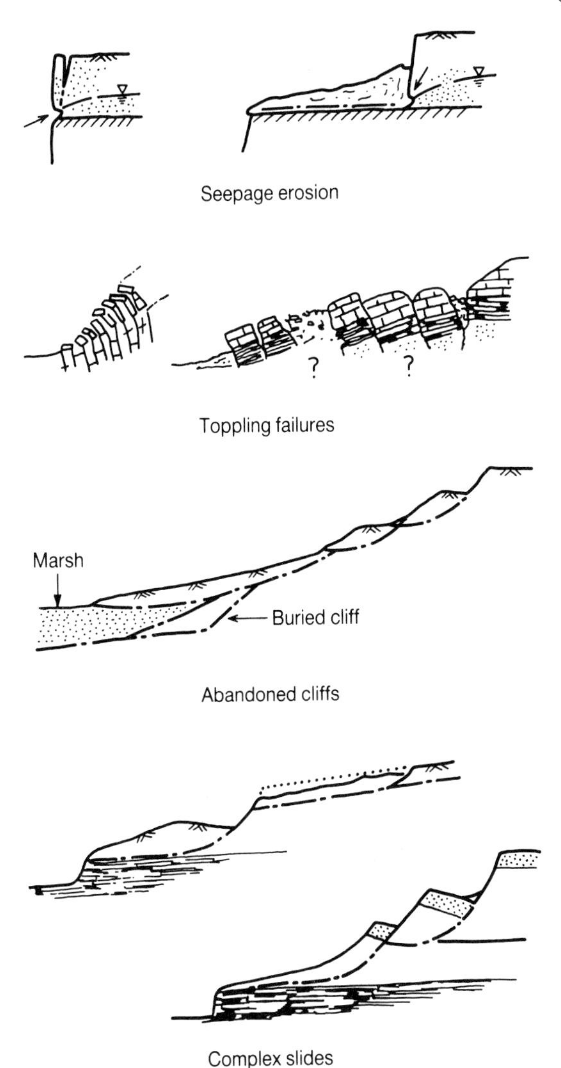

Figure 6.12 (continued)

of sophisticated methods of analysis will not always be justified. Shallow surface slides may be adequately analysed using an infinite slope analysis or Janbu's simplified method of slices[41], compound slides, which can often be represented by several straight lines, may also be treated as a number of sliding wedges. The use of Bishop's simplified method[32] to analyse potential circular slip surfaces may often not be appropriate, as circular slides will only occur in fairly homogeneous materials.

Generally, stability analyses should be carried out in terms of effective stresses. Considerable care needs to be taken in the choice of shear strength parameters, particularly in the case of over consolidated clays of high plasticity. Where large shear displacements have taken place on previous slip surfaces it is appropriate to adopt residual shear strength parameters. When considering potential failure surfaces through intact material, peak angles of friction may be used, although non-zero values of effective cohesion intercept (c') should be employed with caution.

Equally important in the analysis is the appropriate choice of pore-water pressures. Knowledge of the existing pore-pressure regime within the cliff is essential if any back-analysis of past failures is to be undertaken. It is therefore important to install piezometers as part of the ground investigation (see Section 4.8.4). The stability of the final scheme will depend on correctly predicting the maximum long-term pore pressures in the slope. Depending on the disposition of the phreatic surface, care must be taken when flattening a slope to ensure that its stability is not reduced.

Methods of stabilization

The main methods of slope stabilization which are employed on coastal cliffs are:

- Modification of the slope profile;
- Drainage;
- Restraining structures;
- Prevention of seepage erosion;
- Vegetation (surface erosion control);
- Combinations of the above.

Modifications to the slope usually consist of the provision of additional weighting at the toe or a general flattening of the slope angle. Sometimes the top of the slope is unloaded by the removal of material, although this is less common. The effect of any slope modification on the factor of safety can be assessed using the neutral-line concept as discussed by Hutchinson[40]. The provision of substantial toe weighting which results in the seawall being sited substantially to seaward should be undertaken with caution for the reasons discussed in Section 5.1.

Drainage can be used to improve the stability of the slope by reducing the pore-water pressures in the ground. Surface water should be led away, and in some cases it may be possible to prevent sub-surface water entering the slope from above by means of a cut-off drain. Sub-surface water within the slope can be drained by a wide variety of techniques which have been reviewed by Hutchinson[37]. In each case it is necessary to identify the objectives of the drainage scheme, which in turn requires a good understanding of the hydrogeology of the cliff.

With any drainage scheme it is important to monitor its long-term performance. Particular care needs to be taken to guard against clogging of the drains, due either to siltation or to chemical action. The life of the drainage system can be shorter than the design life of the seawall, so that mid-term renewal of the drainage system may be required.

The use of restraining structures is often less appropriate than slope modification to drainage, as it can introduce an element of brittleness into the slope. Generally, restraining structures are only used when space is restricted. Figure 6.13 shows the stabilization of the chalk cliffs at Kingsgate by rock anchoring.

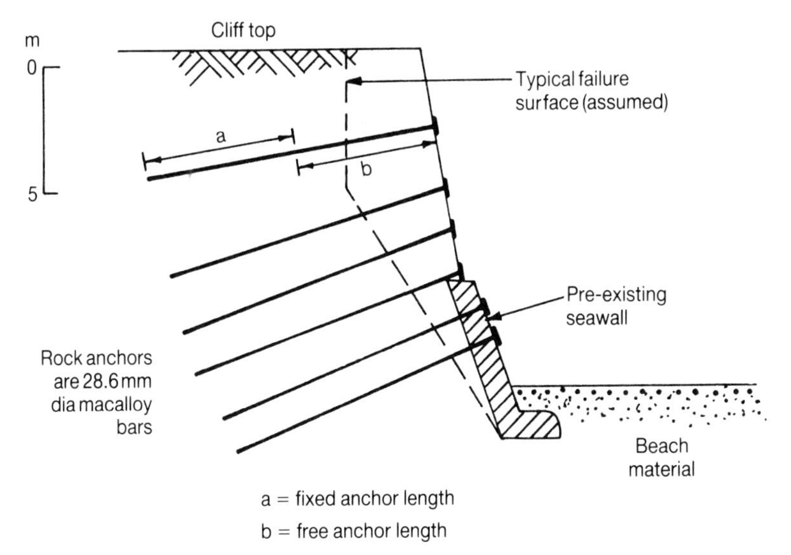

Figure 6.13 Use of rock anchors

Seepage erosion can be halted by the provision of a suitable filter layer on the surface of the eroding stratum. Alternatively, the groundwater which is emerging at the slope face and causing the problem can be intercepted and led away by suitable drainage measures. A review of recent cases of seepage erosion is given by Hutchinson[38].

Vegetation can help to reduce surface erosion through the strengthening and binding action of the roots. This is in addition to the drainage function it performs in reducing pore-water pressures in the ground. Geotextiles may also be used to provide temporary or permanent reinforcement to the root structure. In the former case a natural fibre is used which biodegrades as the plant growth is established. Information on grass reinforcement is given in Coppin and Richards[36].

6.2.2 Design of embankments

This section deals with the stability and design of flood banks. Much of the material is also relevant to the overall stability of the core of coast protection works which have a sloping seaward face.

The design procedure consists of identifying potential modes of failure, assessing the factors of safety against these failure modes occurring, modifying the embankment geometry and/or composition where necessary, and thus producing a stable overall profile for the bank in both the short and long terms. Short-term failures could, for example, be due to construction being too rapid or to rapid drawdown. As well as checking stability, consideration must also be given to the long-term settlement performance of the bank.

The overall slope stability of the embankment is dealt with here in purely geotechnical terms. The surface stability of any slope protection will also depend on other factors, principally the dynamic effects of wave action. These considerations are dealt with in Section 6.3 in terms of porous slopes and Section 6.4 for non-porous slopes. In many cases the slope protection will govern the choice of slope angle.

Modes of failure

Generally, the modes of failure that can occur in sea defences are similar to those found in other classes of earthworks, and as such they are adequately covered in BS 6031[46]. However, it is often possible to utilize low-grade locally available fill materials in the construction of sea defences that would never be allowed in, say, a highway embankment. This can often lead to substantial costs savings, but may in turn require careful geotechnical analysis to ensure satisfactory performance.

Figure 6.14 illustrates three common types of rotational failure that can occur in embankments. Deep-seated circular slips are generally characteristic of short-term failures, and can be viewed as a failure of the founding stratum. Non-circular slips may occur when there is a layer of weaker material beneath the embankment along which preferential sliding occurs. As this type of failure also involves the foundation, it is likely to be more critical in the short term, although it can occur in the longer term if pore pressures are controlled by an underlying granular stratum connecting to the sea. Shallow circular slips within the fill material usually represent longer-term failures, and can occur in both the seaward- and landward-facing slopes.

Where marsh clays – often available at seawall sites – are used to form a flood defence embankment the material placed above high water level will dry out and become fissured. When this type of embankment is subjected to extreme water levels, breaching in the fissured zone is a potential mode of failure. Marsland[61] investigated this problem and proposed a method of analysis to evaluate a failure situation.

Consideration should also be given to the possibility of a seepage-induced failure due to piping or internal erosion. This can occur when an embankment is constructed on ground containing permeable layers of granular material without an adequate groundwater cut-off being provided.

Analysis

Conventional methods of analysis can be used in embankment design and these are covered in BS 6031 and soil mechanics textbooks. Bishop's simplified method of analysis[32] can be used for any potential failure surface that approximates to a circular arc. Preliminary analysis can also be carried out very rapidly using the stability charts of Bishop and Morgenstern[33]. When failure surfaces are considered which are markedly non-circular, an analysis which allows any general shape of slip surface must be used (for example, Morgenstern and Price[42] and Sarma[43]). Alternatively, a multiple-wedge analysis can be used if the potential slip surface can be approximated by a series of straight lines.

Short-term stability should be analysed in terms of total stresses using undrained shear strength parameters for cohesive soils. Long-term stability should be analysed

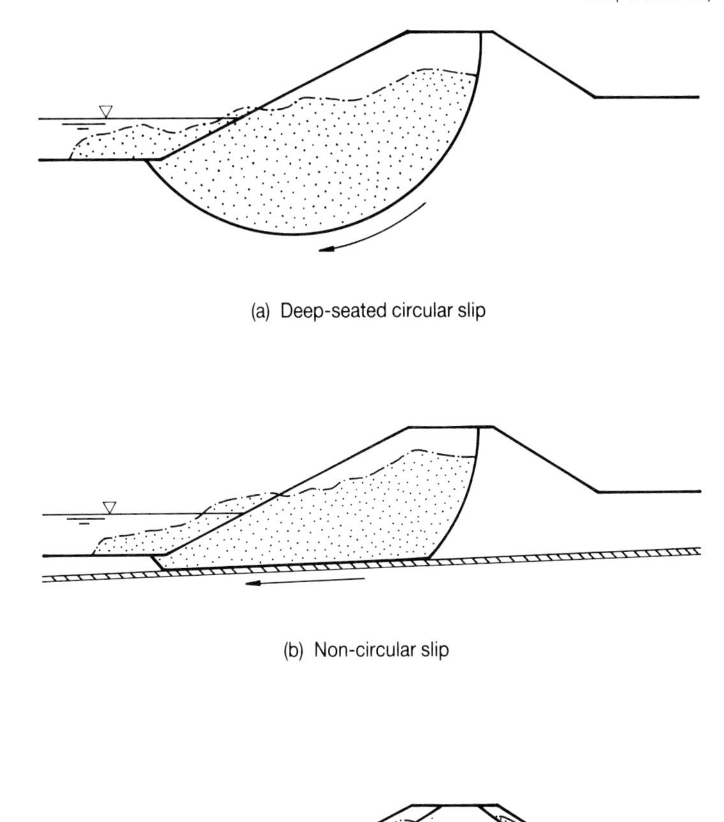

(a) Deep-seated circular slip

(b) Non-circular slip

(c) Shallow circular slips

Figure 6.14 Examples of modes of failures in embankments

in terms of effective stresses using the maximum predicted pore-water pressures. The choice of shear strength parameters for use in analysis should only be made after the raw data have been carefully interpreted. When the material of the embankment is cohesive, allowance should be made in the analysis for the presence of tension cracks.

When an embankment is to be constructed on soft ground, an estimate of the likely long-term consolidation settlement of the fill and the ground should be made, so that a settlement allowance can be built into the design crest level. The calculated settlement should include an estimate of the secondary compression of the ground, which can account for a significant percentage of the total settlement. Where the material of the embankment is prone to fissuring an alternative may be used above the high water level or an allowance added to the crest level adopted.

6.2.3 Wave loads

The most rigorous treatment of wave loads on vertical walls has been prepared by Goda as presented in AMD 5488 to BS 6349. Goda's work, however, relates to breakwaters and seawalls tend to be in shallower water. Nonetheless this work is probably the best means of gaining an indication of the level of force. At the time of writing the only way to gain an accurate prediction of wave loads is with physical model studies.

Observations of existing seawalls around the UK have suggested that wave loading will generally fall within the range 50 to 150 kN/m^2. Where the wall is very high, lower pressures may be applicable. Although the limits above are large it is often the case that the requirement for robustness and durability means that the design is not over sensitive to wave loads. Where there are substantial potential cost savings to be gained by obtaining better estimates of wave loads, or where the wall is in a very exposed area, the engineer should use model studies. In their absence he should adopt a conservative approach.

The structural design of the wall should take account of the uncertainties surrounding the current state of the art in assessing wave forces. It is necessary to consider how wave forces are transmitted by the wall to the supporting soil. Where the seawall is partly supported either by retained soil or undisturbed ground, wave forces are transmitted by the wall and dissipated by the elastic deformation of the material behind. In such cases the estimation of wave forces is not usually critical. A material which would be suitable for acting as filling behind a retaining wall is likely to be adequate to sustain these pressures.

Specific circumstances where the consideration of the wave force may be critical can be summarized as follows:

- During construction;
- Unsupported crest or parapet wall;
- Uplift on wave return nosing;
- Structure supported partially or wholly independent of the retained material;
- Seawall units or components are too small to distribute wave loadings.

The most critical condition in many cases is after the construction of the wall but before the supporting backfill has been placed. This is the ruling structural condition, and it has to be a matter of judgement as to whether it is considered necessary to design for storm wave loading with the wall unsupported.

The permanently unsupported crest or parapet wall is a clear case where the full wave loading should be taken into design. Uplift on the wave return nosing has resulted in local failures of blockwork type walls where the nosing blocks have been inadequately secured to the body of the wall. It has proved sufficient in the past to apply a pressure of the same magnitude as the chosen wave pressure normal to the inclination of the nosing and consider the structural design accordingly. This aspect of design should be considered, particularly when it is intended to attach a new nosing to an existing wall or when the nosing is not monolithic with the remainder of the wall.

6.2.4 Other live loads

Live loads experienced by a seawall other than those discussed in Section 6.2.3 will be surcharge due to traffic, pedestrians or special load cases.

Consideration of seismic loading in the design of seawalls is rarely a problem around the UK coastline. However, where sensitive installations (e.g. nuclear power stations) are being protected special attention will be necessary. In such cases textbooks on seismic design should be consulted.

6.3 Design of sloping porous walls

This section deals with the design of porous slope protection, as introduced in Section 5.4.

The essential functional requirement of a slope protection system is to prevent erosion of the slope. The active forces to be resisted are primarily wave attack and the erosive action of groundwater and surface water. It follows that the slope protection system must satisfy geotechnical as well as hydraulic criteria. Other functions which should be considered in the design of the slope protection system are: hydraulic performance, durability and flexibility. Hydraulic performance and durability are dealt with in Section 6.1 and Chapter 7. Flexibility is considered in Section 6.9.2.

6.3.1 Modes of failure

Considering wave action first, Figure 6.15(a) shows two phases of wave breaking on an embankment. In (i) the upward movement behind the breaking wave draws particles away from the slope while the up-rush and down-rush shear the surface and cause erosion. In (ii) the plunging wave causes local increases in pore-water pressure, capable of liquefying the soil and washing it away in the subsequent flow of water down the slope.

The slope protection system is required to insulate the embankment from this destructive action of the impinging waves. Moreover, the system must itself be stable in the given wave condition, the size and type of components which make up the armour or cover layer being primarily dependent on the severity of wave attack.

The effects of steady flow are demonstrated in Figure 6.15(b), which shows an embankment subject to potentially damaging situations. A large difference between the groundwater level and the sea level can exist because the rate of drainage from the land cannot keep pace with the fall of the tide. In Figure 6.15(b)(i) the resulting flow is seen to exit close to the bottom of the embankment. The weight of the individual soil particles is insufficient to resist the seepage and they are lifted from the surface and carried down the slope – a process known as piping. The downward flow also causes shear, resulting in further erosion. In Figure 6.15(b)(ii) the shear is caused by the runoff of surface water which might be due to wave overtopping, possibly elsewhere along the seawall. The method of preventing piping and erosion must allow for the fact that the vulnerable section of the embankment will change position, depending upon the groundwater level and the tidal level. The effect of a layered slope protection system

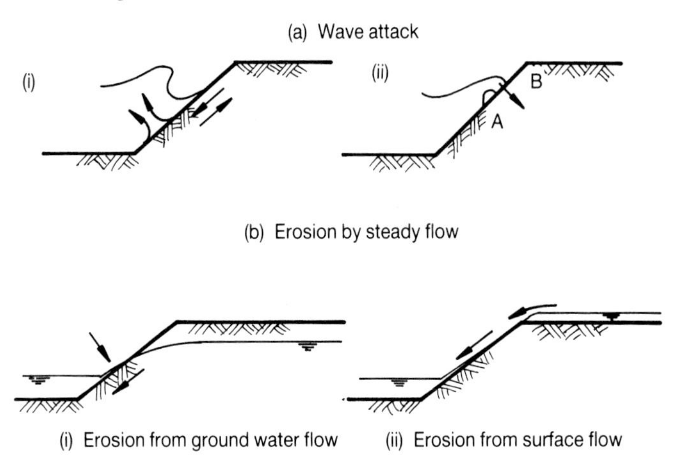

Figure 6.15 Modes of erosion

on the drainage of the structure (seawall and embankment) depends crucially on the relative permeabilities of the various layers and this is demonstrated by the examples shown in Figure 6.16 (reproduced from reference 38).

Permeability in terms of groundwater drainage is different from permeability in the terms of wave action. Groundwater flow is effectively steady and the flow velocities are low. Consequently the shape and orientation of the pores are less important for drainage than in the dynamic case (although these properties do have a bearing on the particle-retention properties of the medium).

In the context of wave action, 'permeability' refers to the rapid drainage response of the medium to the cyclic applications of hydrodynamic load. In the cover layer especially, the hydrodynamic loads consist of high-velocity jets which are reduced to turbulence by collisions with the armour surface and within the voids. Hence the shape, size and orientation of the voids are highly relevant to the permeability.

6.3.2 Conceptual design

Slope protection consists of (Figure 6.17):

- An armour, or cover layer;
- Underlayers;
- The embankment.

There is considerable overlap in the different systems that might be used, and at the conceptual design stage alternative systems should be considered. Initial thinking should be targeted on the type of external protection or armour. An early evaluation of the viable options should be based on an assessment of the likely wave severity. Table 5.3 indicates the approximate ranges of application of various systems. The stability of the embankment is considered in Section 6.2.

Top layer	Under-layer	Subsoil	
H	H	H	
H	H	L	
H	L	L	
L	L	L	
L	L	H	
L	H	H	
L	H	L	
H	L	H	

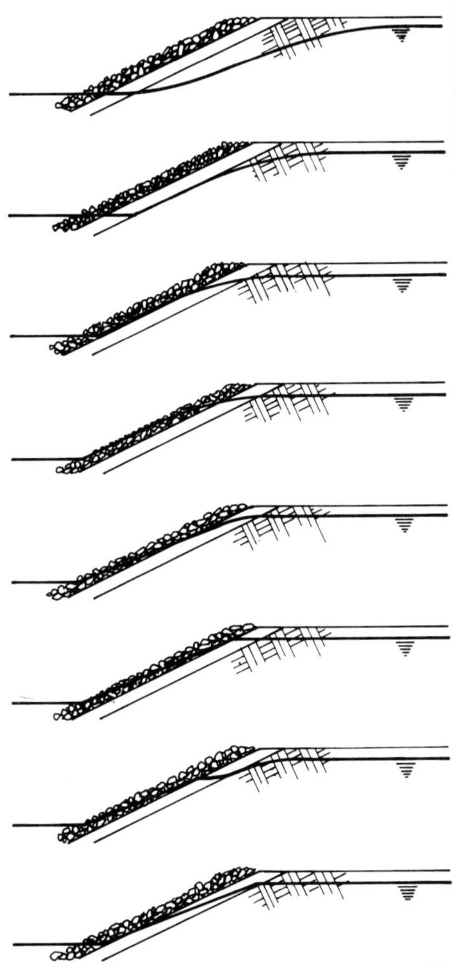

H = High permeability L = Low permeability

Figure 6.16 Groundwater flow-effect of relative permeabilities

Having confined the design options for the armour to those which satisfy the requirements for wave attack, the slope protection system should be considered in terms of the groundwater (and surface water) flow. The relative permeabilities of the layers should be examined with the view to avoiding the problems highlighted by Figure 6.16 and described below.

A high-pressure gradient across a layer causes a high load on it but reduces the load on the other layers, as shown by the final example in Figure 6.16. In this situation the

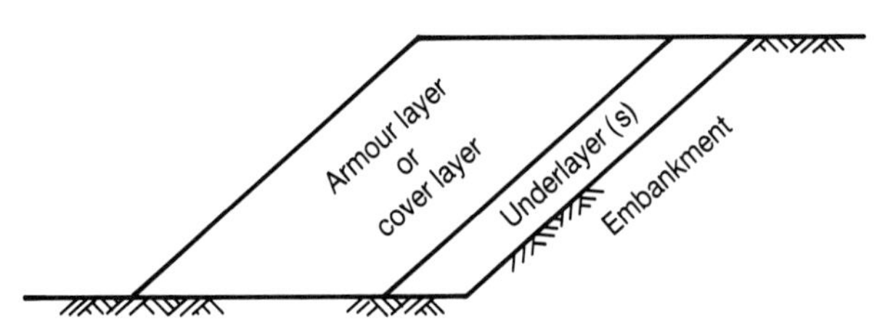

Figure 6.17 Slope protection system elements (schematic)

layer in question is of low relative permeability and is vulnerable to uplift due to the normal force, and this in turn could lead to failure of the system.

Incorrect selection of the relative permeabilities can also lead to seepage problems in the embankment or other layers, resulting in the piping of soil particles at the surface between layers – a condition known as streaming.

To summarize: the main criteria governing the design are:

- External stability of the slope under wave attack;
- Control of internal erosion at the interface between layers;
- Drainage.

Aspects of hydraulic performance (relating to overtopping and reflections) are likely to be major functional requirements which will be important in the selection of the slope protection system (summarized in Table 5.3). Flexibility is important in that settlement will normally occur, and this should be allowed for in design to ensure that it does not invalidate the initial design assumptions (e.g. with regard to the allowable gap between the units comprising the cover layer). Settlement can be caused either by the consolidation of the subsoil or by movement or localized minor losses from the underlayers.

6.3.3 Armour layer design (see also Section 5.4.2)

The objective of detailed design is to select the form of the structure, including the specifications of the armour type, size, grading and thickness and the corresponding properties of the underlayers (Section 6.3.4). The capacity of an armour system to resist a given wave attack can, in broad terms, be measured by the ratio of the wave height at the toe of the wall to some characteristic dimension of the armour layer. Introducing the parameter Δ ($= \rho_a/\rho - 1$) to allow for the submerged weight of the armour, and describing its size by the characteristic length D, then the ratio takes the form $H_s/\Delta D$. This ratio is sometimes referred to as the stability number N_s.

The hydrodynamic loads imparted to the seawall depend upon the types of waves arriving there. The wave type can be theoretically characterized by the surf similarity parameter Ir (Section 6.1), in which the seawall slope angle α is used. It should be noted that this implies that the structure is solely responsible for determining the wavebreaking characteristics, whereas the shape and slope of the foreshore will also condition the waves, and, in shallow water this may be the dominant influence.

Figure 6.18 shows how N_s varies with Ir. The additional factors such as permeability, armour type, thickness of armour, etc. are discussed in the context of the various methods described below.

All the quoted methods for deriving stable armour sizes should be regarded, at best, as a guide to engineering judgement. Moreover, the reliability of the answers is governed by the quality of the wave data for the structure. In exposed situations and cases where the incident waves are difficult to assess because of a complex foreshore bathymetry then physical hydraulic modelling may well be necessary to confirm hydraulic performance and revetment stability. Modelling should also be considered when the hydraulic properties of the slope protection system cannot reliably be assessed using existing data, as outlined below.

Rock armour and rip-rap

Probably the most commonly used method for determining the size of rock armour is the Hudson formula. The formula does not take account of wave period, required stone weight being given as a function of wave height, armour slopes and density and a stability coefficient K_D:

$$W = \frac{\rho_a . H^3}{K_D (SR - 1)^3 \cot \alpha} \tag{6.19}$$

where:

W = weight (or mass) in kg of an individual armour unit in the primary cover layer (see below);
ρ_a = mass density of the armour material (kg/m^3);
Sr = specific gravity of the armour unit relative to water at the structure $= \rho_a/\rho$;
H = design wave height (m) at the structure toe. The *Shore Protection Manual*[7] recommends $H = H_{1/10}$;
α = angle of structure slope measured from the horizontal;
K_D = stability coefficient (values are given in the *Shore Protection Manual*).

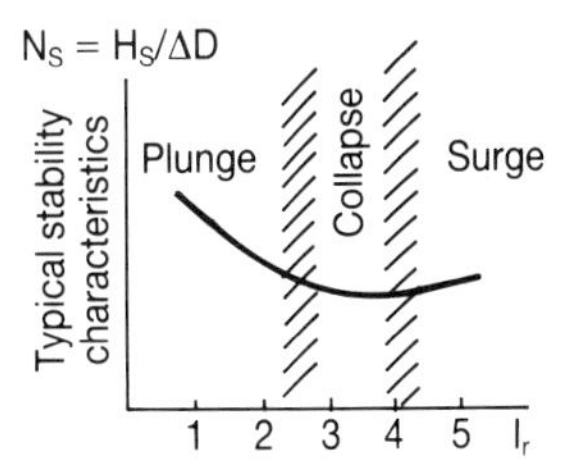

Figure 6.18 Variation of stability with Ir

The *Shore Protection Manual* discusses various factors affecting the validity of equation (6.19). Furthermore, it should be noted that the equation assumes that the structure crest is sufficiently high to prevent major overtopping.

Following the SPM recommendations, when the cover layer consists of two layers of quarry stones, then the stones comprising the primary cover layer can range from $0.75W$ to $1.25W$ with 50% of the individual stones weighing more than W.

For graded angular rip-rap, W is replaced by W_{50} and the rock grading used may then range from $4.W_{50}$ (max.) to $0.125W_{50}$ (min.) and in this case K_D takes the value appropriate to rip-rap (denoted K_{RR}).

The values arrived at by this method refer to a so-called 'no damage' criterion which actually allows 0–5% damage. (The damage is defined as the percentage volume of armour units displaced from the zone of active armour unit removal, this zone being defined as extending from the middle of the breakwater crest down the seaward face to a depth equivalent to one 'zero-damage' wave height below the still water level.) The *Shore Protection Manual* also provides information enabling higher percentages of damage to be considered in the selection of armour size. This is done by factoring the wave heights according to the allowable percentage damage, using values advised in the *Shore Protection Manual*. The *Manual* expresses caution in using this approach for breaking wave conditions, structure heads or structures other than breakwaters or jetties, noting that 'the damage zone is more concentrated around the still water level on the face of a revetment than on a breakwater'. Damage levels in excess of 30% represent complete failure of the armour to a revetment.

The experiments of Hudson were conducted using regular waves. Experimental work described in Thompson and Shuttler[19] (now being revised) used random waves. Different wave-breaking conditions were identified on the various slopes examined, it being observed that the form of breaking and the movement of the stones were very dependent on the slope. The displaced stones were found to move quickly down the 1:2 slope with no healing whereas on the flatter slopes (1:4 and 1:6) the stones oscillated up and down the slope but with a net drift down the slope.

Work by the Delft Hydraulics Laboratory[20] in the last ten years has shown a more marked influence of wave period on armour stability than did that of CIRIA. This work is continuing. The factors examined included the following:

- Wave height;
- Wave period;
- Number of waves (storm duration);
- Armour grading;
- Spectrum shape;
- Groupiness of waves;
- Permeability of core.

The results culminated in different solutions which depend upon wave breaking conditions as characterized by the Iribarren number Ir, the critical value of which was given by:

$$Ir_c = (6.2P^{\alpha 31} \sqrt{\tan\alpha}) \frac{1}{P+0.5} \qquad (6.20)$$

The stability equations for rock armour are:
for plunging waves (I_r less than I_{rc}):

$$H_s/D_{n50} = 6.2P^{-0.18} \left(\frac{(S)}{\sqrt{N}}\right)^{0.2} Irp^{-0.5} \qquad (6.21)$$

for surging waves (Ir greater than Ir_c):

$$H_s/D_{n50} = P^{-\alpha 13} \frac{(S)}{\sqrt{N}} \cot Ir_p \qquad (6.22)$$

Where P = permeability coefficient (see below); N = number of waves to cause damage; D_{n50} = nominal diameter of the armour rocks. Note that the results of this work[4] concluded that the grading of the rocks had no influence on stability although his experiments were conducted on rocks of gradings $D_{85}/D_{15} = 2.25$ and $D_{85}/D_{15} = 1.25$. Hudson, on the other hand, does recognize rock grading and this is reflected in the different values for K_D and K_{RR};

S = damage level = A/D_{n50}^2

where A = eroded cross-sectional area of the profile,
S = 1 to 3 corresponds to the Hudson definition of no damage.
S = 8 to 17 represents failure according to the slope angle in accordance with Table 6.7.

Figure 6.19 gives examples of P values for different cover/underlayer/core particle size ratios.

The results are sensitive to the value of P selected, which at present is a question of subjective judgement. Also, the answers depend crucially upon the value Ir by virtue of which equation to use, i.e. (6.21) or (6.22). The two equations give quite different answers, and, as noted previously, these solutions assume that the wave breaking is conditioned by the structural slope whereas in shallow water the natural slope of the foreshore may be the major influence on the wave characteristics. Work by others suggests that damage may be underpredicted and/or values P less than 0.1 may need

Table 6.7

Slope angle	Damage level S	
	Onset of damage	Failure
1.5	2	8
2	2	8
3	2	12
4	3	17
6	3	17

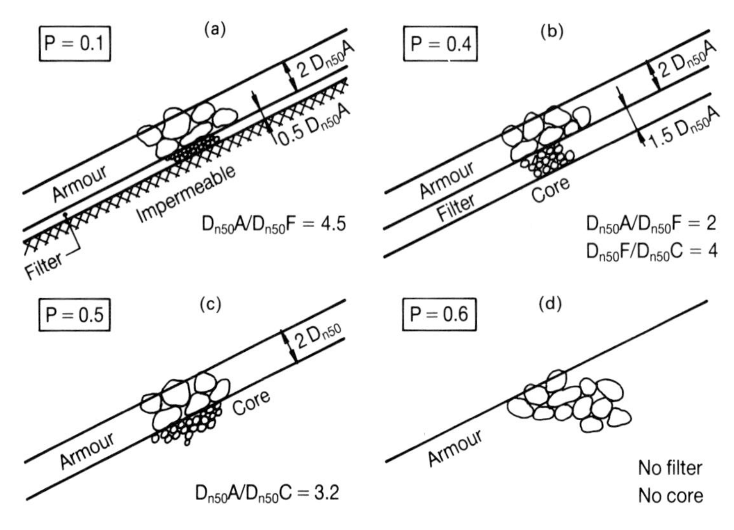

$D_{n50}A$ = nominal diameter of armour stone
$D_{n50}F$ = nominal diameter of filter material
$D_{n50}C$ = nominal diameter of core

The structure on Fig. a, b and c have been tested
The value of P for Fig. d has been assumed

Figure 6.19 Permeability coefficient P

to be reconsidered. In short, a range of conditions should be examined, varying P and varying H_s, T_z combinations.

To summarize: rock armour, rip-rap, can be sized for stability using the methods described above, but caution must be exercised in particular with regard to:

Hudson:
- limitations of experimental conditions;
- non-recognition of wave period;
- doubtful application to random waves;
- non-recognition of storm duration.

Delft work:
- limitations of experimental conditions;
- subjective selection of P value;
- sensitivity of Ir;
- implicit rock grading.

Random placed concrete armour units (see Figure 5.19)

The design methods which follow consider 'gravitational' and interlocking stability, but do not cater for armour breakages. This can be a serious problem particularly with slender or larger armour units ($W > 15$ tonnes, say) and the designer is recommended to seek specialist advice in such circumstances.

Hudson[29] conducted tests on model tetrapods and arrived at a stability coefficient

K_D for use in equation (6.19). The optimum number of layers was found to be $n = 2$. In subsequent work various other types of breakwater armour unit were investigated. K_D values are given in the *Shore Protection Manual*. Experience has suggested that K_D for dolos lower than those quoted in the *Shore Protection Manual* should be used.

The research work of Delft Hydraulics[21] has now been extended to the stability of cubes, tetrapods and accropodes. Accropodes were tested as a single-layer armour unit and are discussed in the next sub-section. In the tests, the slope of the structure was a constant for each type of armour unit: 1:1.5 for cubes and tetrapods. Hence, because the slope was not varied, the Iribarren number could not be identified as an independent variable. In the equations, therefore, Ir is replaced by wave steepness (S_z). No distinction was made in the equations between plunging and surging waves.

As all the armour units in an artificial layer are the same size, the relative damage is defined by n_o, being the actual number of displaced units related to the nominal width D_n of one unit.

For cubes and tetrapods, once damage started to occur the number of units displaced (n_o) became a function of the storm duration (N).

Cubes:

$$H_s/\Delta D_n = (6.7 n_o^{0.4}/N^{0.3} + 1) S_z^{-0.1} \quad (6.23)$$

Tetrapods:

$$H_s/\Delta D_n = (3.75 n_o^{0.5}/N^{0.25} + 0.85) S_z^{-0.2} \quad (6.24)$$

When using the equations above, the engineer should be aware of the limitations of the experimental work, particularly with regard to the limited slopes that were examined.

Pattern placed concrete armour units (see Figures 5.20 and 5.21)

In model tests, pattern placed single-layer concrete armour units exhibit stability which is significantly better than randomly placed units, or units with lower degrees of interlock. The types of armour used in this application are generally those which allow close placing so that voids are sufficiently small to prevent the egress of the underlayer material; or the porosity is controlled by voids within the units. Armour units which fall into this category are the shed, cob, seabee, diode and accropode (see Section 5.4).

Accropodes. Losada[5] investigated the stability of a single layer of accropodes on a 1:1.33 slope. Unlike cubes and tetrapods, storm duration had very little influence on damage, the no damage ($n_o = o$) and failure damage ($n_o > 0.5$) conditions being much closer. This was attributed to high interlock, and hence its ability to behave as a 'blanket' rather than as discrete units. Wave period was also found to have little effect on the results which were summarized as follows:

Start of damage ($n_o = o$) $H_s/\Delta D_n = 3.7$ (6.25)

Failure ($n_o > 0.5$) $H_s/\Delta D_n = 4.1$ (6.26)

Seabees. The seabee was conceived and developed using Blanket Theory[25,26]. The theory, using considerations and some model tests, allows unit dimensions to be derived, given wave conditions. A factor of safety is used together with the minimum stability condition, and the results should be used to develop designs for model testing.

Sheds and cobs. Sheds and cobs have been used successfully at a number of exposed sites around the UK. Data on their performance have demonstrated that their resistance to wave action is high with minimal armour movement (in model studies) for wave heights up to $H_s/\Delta D_n = 5.7$. Dead loads acting down the slope are more likely to be the governing factor in their use and research is proceeding on this aspect. Units weighing two tonnes have performed successfully at sites with design wave heights up to 6.5 m. Since internal stresses rather than stability against wave attack are likely to govern the design, and design rules are not available for determining these stresses, the engineer should consult specialists in the detailed design process.

Flexible armoured revetment systems

Flexible armoured revetment systems comprise those systems with discrete concrete armour units connected together to form a continuous protection system. The systems may be categorized as follows:

- Dual-cable interlocking blocks;
- Single-cable interlocking blocks;
- Two-dimensional interlocking blocks (interlocking in plan and depth);
- One-dimensional interlocking blocks (interlocking in plan only).

Currently (1989) such systems provide for a primary armour weight of 160 kg/m^2 to 500 kg/m^2 with associated unit block weights of approximately 15 kg to 110 kg. Block thicknesses vary between 0.1 m and 0.25 m with porosities in the range 5% to 30%, though none of the systems provides for lateral porosity within the block shape.

Some of the block systems have been model tested, but mostly with regular waves. Most of the blocks are limited to use within the 'mild' category of wave attack. This is consistent with the recommendations made by the Flexible Armoured Revetment Association, which states that the heavier systems (415–500 kg/m^2) are suitable for a wave exposure of $H_s = 2.0$ m on a slope of gradient 1:3.

The stability of a given system can be assessed on the basis of the simple equation:

$$H_s/\Delta D = \frac{\Psi}{\sqrt{Ir}} \tag{6.27}$$

in which Δ = relative density of block material,
Ir = Iribarren number,
Ψ = strength coefficient,
D = depth of block system.

The most subjective part of the equation is the so-called strength coefficient and its variation from one system to another. Other constraints that will need to be examined when using the equation are the values of Ir and revetment slope for which it was determined. The engineer should seek the advice of the manufacturer, who can utilize the results of previous research or, depending upon the scale of the project, commission tests specific to the project.

Pilarczyk[22] reviewed the test results of various block systems, quoting the minimum stability condition ($H_s/\Delta D$ minimum). A further review was undertaken by Hydraulics Research[14]. The main aspects relating to the stability of flexible armoured revetments subject to wave action are identified as:

- Block weight and shape;
- System permeability;
- Relative permeability of primary armour with respect to underlayers;
- Degree of interlock, friction or grouting.

The 'grouting' of flexible revetment systems refers to the inclusion of a uniform granular material (12 mm down) to infill the cells and interstices between the concrete blocks. This can increase stability by 25% (Allsop *et al.*[6]) but reduces porosity and will tend to increase wave run-up and reflections.

Selection of the correct relative permeability of the slope protection system layers is important, the main factors being the prevention of:

- High-pressure gradient due to groundwater, leading to rupture of the revetment;
- Piping in the underlayers or embankment soil.

Concrete blocks on clay sublayer

Revetments have been formed by placing concrete blocks directly onto a layer of clay, with no intermediate filter. The systems require very precise placing to avoid gaps between the blocks. The recommended maximum stability number for this type of revetment quoted by Pilarczyk was $N_s = 6$.

Gabions

Gabions have received less attention than rock and concrete armour in terms of stability research and design. This can, in part, be attributed to the application of gabions which would normally only be considered in locations of very mild exposure. Also, the problems with gabions tend to be initiated by wire abrasion resulting in loss of stones rather than structural collapse. Gabion stability was examined by Brown[26]. Initial guidance on stone fill and placing can be obtained from manufacturers' literature.

6.3.4 Underlayer design

The underlayer can fulfil some or all of the following functions:

- Filtration – to prevent the core material from being washed out through the armour;
- Erosion control – to prevent the surface of the core from being eroded;
- Separation – to prevent the armour layer from settling into the core and the core from penetrating into the armour;
- Drainage – to act as a drainage layer;
- Secondary armour – the underlayer can play an important part, together with the primary armour, in providing an overall armouring system;
- Energy dissipation – the underlayer can assist in dissipating wave energy;
- Regulation – in providing a regular surface on which to place the armour.

The underlayer should retain the underlying material without giving rise to unacceptable pore-water pressures, i.e. the function of filtration. Secondary benefits of the underlayer are the strengthening of the underlying soil surface and the provision of a mechanical interlock with the cover material. The underlayer may consist of granular materials and geotextiles, either alone or in combination. The objective of the design is to specify the composition, type and hence porosity of the underlayer(s), its thickness and grading composition.

Granular underlayers for rip-rap

Commonly quoted ratios for the sizing are as follows:

$$D_{85}\text{ (underlayer)} > \frac{D_{15}\text{(rip-rap)}}{5} \tag{6.28}$$

$$D_{15}\text{ (underlayer)} < 5D_{85}\text{ (embankment)} \tag{6.29}$$

These identities are in agreement with the *Shore Protection Manual*; D_{15} (rip-rap), i.e. the diameter exceeded by 85% of the rip-rap by weight should be no more than five times D_{85} (underlayer), i.e. the diameter exceeded by 15% of the underlayer by weight.

The thickness of the underlayer will depend on the size of the stones in the cover layer. Construction tolerance, particularly with regard to placing stones underwater, may dictate that a greater thickness is specified in order to achieve the required minimum value.

Depending upon the size of the rip-rap and the particle size of the embankment, it may not be possible to satisfy both inequalities (6.28) and (6.29), with a sensible grading of material. In this case more than one underlayer may be required, or further filtering may be achieved by the use of a geotextile.

Granular underlayers for rock armour and concrete armour units

The *Shore Protection Manual* recommends, in reference to breakwaters, that the first underlayer should have a minimum thickness of two quarrystones of mean weight approximately one-tenth ($W/10$) of the weight of the armour units. However, if the armour consists of units with a very high stability coefficient (e.g. dolos or tribar) then the first underlayer should consist of stones weighing about $W/5$. This larger size is suggested in order to provide adequate interlock between the armour layer and the filter so that the inherent high stability of the armour is not compromised.

The actual grading of the first underlayer or filter will depend upon the specific nature of the application; the slope, the breaking characteristics of the waves and the type of the armour unit used. Its ability to resist movement of the armour subject to wave attack should be confirmed by model testing.

Recommendations for the grading of subsequent filter layers (if necessary) are given in the *Shore Protection Manual*.

Granular underlayers for slopes of low permeability

The permeability of a slope protection system can be significantly reduced by armouring it with closely packed or interlocked concrete units, or by full bitumen grouting. In such cases, the stability of the slope can be endangered by the accumulation of water pressure behind the facing. The pressure can take the form of pore-water pressure in the embankment or in the filter layer, or a combination of the two.

The stability of the system can be improved by providing seepage holes through the armour. If this is not feasible, then the armour itself can be placed on an impermeable clay layer as noted in Section 6.3.3. The likelihood of washout can be assessed on the basis of the particle size distribution of the clay, compositions containing silt or sand lenses being most vulnerable. Where filters are provided these should consist of a layer 150–200 mm of crushed stone ranging 1–50 mm diameter.

Use of geotextiles

The functions of geotextiles in slope protection systems are:

- Filtration;
- Separation;
- Erosion control;
- Drainage;
- Reinforcement.

The function of filtration is to separate the fine-grained granular soil beneath from the coarser-grained stones or armour units above the fabric. In order to fulfil this requirement, the size of the openings in the fabric must be small enough to prevent the underlying soil from passing through. It should, however, achieve this function without impairing the permeability of the system, and this will generally mean that the permeability of the geotextiles is at least as good as that of the underlying soil.

Design criteria for geotextiles

Veldhuizen Van Zanten[23] gives various design considerations to determine the requirements of a geotextile. The considerations of importance to this section of the guidelines are the 'hydraulic' and 'mechanical' properties. Hydraulic properties are considered in terms of 'soil retention' and 'permeability'.

Soil retention is the primary requirement for a geotextile to act as a filter. The retention properties of the geotextile depend on:

- The type of geotextile–woven, non-woven, etc.;
- The type (granular or cohesive), density and grading of the soil;
- The hydraulic gradient.

The size of the openings in the geotextile are expressed in terms of the symbol O_p (being analogous to d_n, the size of the soil retained by the geotextile), in which p usually takes the value 90 or 98.

Methods of evaluating the pore size O_p vary, depending upon the size of sieve test that is used, and these can include dry sieving, wet sieving and sieving with alternating flow. The type of test should reflect the service conditions of the geotextile. Having selected the relevant definition of O_p, its actual size is related to the characteristic dimension of the retained soil, d_n, by a constant of proportionality:

$$O_p - \lambda d_n$$

Veldhuizen Van Zanten[23] and PIANC[24] give examples of λ values with respect to inland waterways, but the design engineer should be aware of the differences that exist between navigation channels and coastal environments, especially with regard to reversing (tidal) flow and the nature of the wave attack. It should be noted that a geotextile designed to retain the material may be relatively impermeable to the rapid flow fluctuation due to wave action, and that this could jeopardize the stability of the cover layer.

It has already been stated that the *permeability* of the geotextile should be at least as good as that of the underlying soil in order to avoid unacceptable load upon the fabric. There are cases where the permeability of the geotextile should be adapted to suit the overlying layer. This can happen if the contact area between the geotextile and the top layer comprises the available area for normal flow, e.g. by the placing of the concrete blocks directly onto the fabric. As a consequence of this, flow develops in the plane of the fabric (transmissivity).

Although the transmissivity may be very low, the routing of flow can lead to excess pressure beneath the concrete blocks during wave attack, leading to instability in the cover layer. It follows that the problem is aggravated by increasing the permeability of the geotextile in an attempt to compensate for the reduction in normal flow area (Figure 6.20).

Permeability (K_g) is the ratio of the rate of flow (q) in a unit area (A_g) (normal to geotextile) to the hydraulic gradient, i.e.

$$K_g = \frac{q}{\Phi_g} \div \frac{\Delta H}{t_g}$$

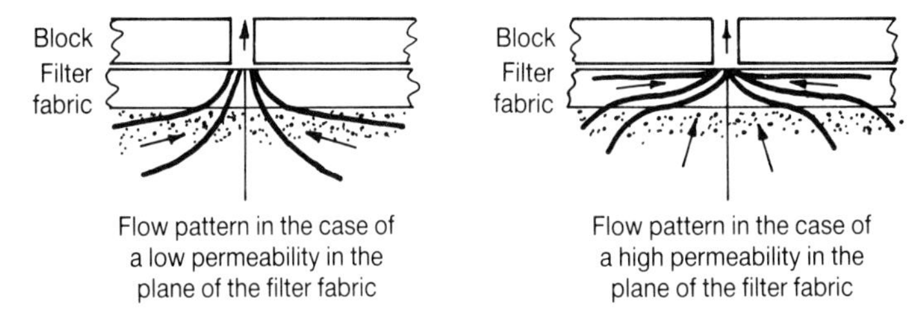

Figure 6.20 Flow patterns beneath concrete blocks

where H is the head loss and t_g the thickness of the fabric.

The thickness t_g depends upon the applied pressure; therefore in practice the ratio K_g/t_g, the permittivity (Φ), remains fairly constant for a given material. Typical values of Φ lie between 0.01 to 10.

As noted above, transmissivity refers to flow in the plane of the fabric. Thick non-woven geotextiles have a higher transmissivity than flat woven fabrics.

In order to select a geotextile permeability (K_g) which is better than that of the soil (K_g) then a substantial factor of safety (η) is introduced[8] to cater for clogging and blocking (see below):

$$K_g \geq K_g/\eta$$

Blocking is the loss of permeability resulting from soil particles getting trapped within the geotextile matrix. Clogging is the loss of permeability resulting from matter (silt, soil chemicals, vegetation) accumulating on the face of the geotextiles.

There are various mechanical failures against which a geotextile must be designed. These include the conditions known as flapping, overlap stability, uplift, subsoil deformation and layer sliding. Information on these may be obtained from Reference 7, but it is worth mentioning here the last item, layer sliding. Friction will generally be better between the geotextile and the subsoil than between the geotextile and the coverlayer, and when the geotextile is anchored then clearly the latter condition predominates. The steepest slope that should be considered for placing rip-rap on a geotextile is 1:2 in order to prevent sliding of the cover stones.

6.4 Design of sloping non-porous walls

As with sloping porous walls (Section 6.3), the essential functional requirement of the slope protection system is to resist wave attack and the erosive action of ground and surface water, and so contribute to the stability of the wall.

6.4.1 Modes of failure

Sloping non-porous walls are likely to be predominantly impermeable unless specific weepholes and drainage layers are introduced. Drainage measures are discussed in detailing (Section 6.9.7). Certainly, however, non-porous walls will be relatively impermeable to wave action and for this reason the main modes of failure against which the wall should be designed are:

- Collapse of the face into the slope due to wave impact;
- Hogging failure of the slope due to wave-induced uplift during wave drawdown, perhaps supplemented by excess groundwater pressure acting upwards on the slope protection;
- Sliding of the slope protection down the slope – which is dealt with by the provision of an adequate toe;
- Deformation (the flexing of the slope under wave attack leading to a fatigue failure).

Non-porous walls, as defined in this book, are non-porous in relation to the hydraulic performance of the wall with respect to waves. They will not therefore normally be expected to experience the short-term fluctuations referred to above, although liquefaction of saturated sand beneath a non-porous slope as a result of alternative shock pressures from breaking waves has been recorded.

6.4.2 Analysis

The relevant modes of failure vary between different protection systems, as does the method of analysis. For this reason, the analysis is discussed under three headings.

Precast and in-situ concrete (smooth and stepped slopes)

Rigid slopes should be capable of resisting wave impact forces. Providing they are founded on and are in complete continuous contact with good-quality fill, the loads will adequately be taken by the fill. However, when they are not founded on the core (e.g. on piles) or when local voids occur between the slope protection due to differential settlement, consolidation or loss of fill, they will be required to withstand wave loads. Bearing in mind the lack of data on wave loads (see Section 6.3.3), at the time of publication of this book, definitive techniques of analysis are not available. However, on the coast around the UK seawalls have performed successfully when designed to resist wave pressures of 50–100 kN/m^2, assuming that the fill supports the lower half of the slope and the slab is thus designed to span the upper half.

Rigid concrete walls will normally have sufficient self-mass to resist uplift forces and resistance to wave impact will normally govern the design. As a general rule, however, it has been found that in order to resist uplift the thickness of the concrete layer should be at least one tenth of $H_{1/3}$ at the toe of the wall.

Interlocking blocks, slabs and pitched stone

Resistance to uplift tends to be the governing design case, although, particularly with newer cable-linked systems, deformation can be important. Work published by

Pilarczyk[22] gives guidance on the required minimum layer thickness required. In this case the layer thickness, D, is related to the wave climate by the formula

$$\frac{H_s}{\Delta D} = \Psi \frac{\cos\alpha}{\sqrt{Ir}} \approx \frac{\Psi}{\sqrt{Ir}}$$

where
Ir = Iribarren number (see Section 6.1.1) [the formula applies for $I_r < 3$ (breaking waves)],
α = slope angle (the formula applies for slopes with $\cot\alpha \geq 2$),
Ψ = strength coefficient.

The following values are suggested by Pilarczyk:

Ψ	*Type of protection*	*Comments*
3 to 4	Pitched stone, loose blocks, blocks connected by geotextile	For long-term loading increase D by 25%
4 to 5	Blocks, interlocking due to friction, grouted blocks connected by geotextile, cable-linked blocks	Blocks laid directly on geotextile and well-compacted sand. Max $H_{1/3} = 1.2$ m
greater than 5	Grouted cable linked blocks, mechanically interlocking blocks	Should be very thoroughly designed to ensure true system strength is achieved (i.e. require model studies)

Asphaltic concrete

This should be designed to resist uplift, deformation and sliding. Detailed guidance is given in reference 60.

As an example, for an asphaltic concrete revetment with a slope of 1:3 placed on a sand core with a modulus of subgrade reaction of 10^8 Nm^{-3} (compacted sand), the following layer thicknesses would be derived:

$H_{1/3}$*	Layer thickness
m	m
2	0.1
3	0.2
4	0.3

*at the toe of the wall

6.4.3 Foundations

Where walls are founded directly on the core it is vital that the core remains in place. This is largely a function of adequate provision of drainage, as already discussed and in Section 6.9, and of good toe design.

Bearing piles can be used to support elements of sloping concrete walls. Wave and dead loads will need to be resisted and pile design can be carried out using conventional soil mechanics methods. These can be found in BS 8004[48] and in standard textbooks on foundation engineering (for example Tomlinson[44]). Elsewhere, piling may be chosen to limit differential settlements or facilitate construction. In these circumstances it is usually sufficient to take the piles down into a competent bearing stratum. In all cases a knowledge of the soil profile is required to ensure that the bearing stratum is of adequate thickness and is not underlain by compressible material (see Section 4.8).

The designer should ensure that there is no danger of the foundation being undermined. Loss of support might be caused, for example, by a general lowering of the beach (see Section 4.9) or by excessive seepage of water beneath the seawall leading to a piping failure.

6.5 Design of vertical walls

Vertical seawalls can be designed using the standard procedures for conventional retaining walls. In general, the design should follow the recommendations of BS 6349[47].

6.5.1 Modes of failure

Gravity walls and RC cantilever walls can be considered together in stability terms as they share common geotechnical modes of failure. These walls derive their stability largely from self-weight, although in the case of cantilever walls the majority of the weight is actually provided by the soil which rests on the wall base. Tied walls are considered separately because of their rather different modes of failure.

Figure 6.21 shows the four major types of failure which can affect gravity and RC cantilever walls. Failure by overturning occurs when the overturning moment due to the applied loads exceeds the restoring moment due to the weight of the wall. Sliding takes place when the frictional resistance over the base of the wall, together with the passive resistance at the toe, are insufficient to withstand the applied loads. Bearing capacity failure occurs when the contact pressure beneath the toe of the wall exceeds the bearing capacity of the foundation soil. Deep-seated rotational slips can happen in poor ground and represent a slope type failure. In addition, cantilever walls can suffer structural failure from overstressing of the stem.

Figure 6.22 shows the four principal ways in which a tied wall can fail. Rotation of the wall about the tie takes place when there is inadequate passive resistance at the toe. Rupture of the tie rods or overstressing of the wall material are structural modes of failure and are often precipitated by corrosion. Deep-seated rotational slips can occur as described above for gravity walls.

The soil on the seaward side of the wall in the passive region plays a very important role in the stability of the wall. Loss of material from this area for whatever reason can lead in turn to one of the above modes of failure.

(a) Overturning

(b) Sliding

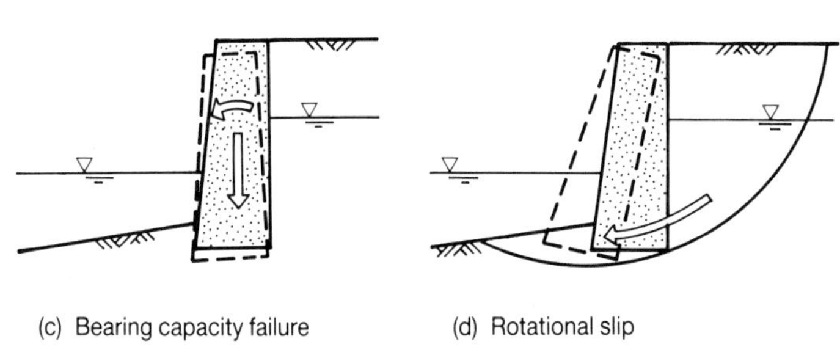

(c) Bearing capacity failure

(d) Rotational slip

Figure 6.21 Modes of failure of gravity walls

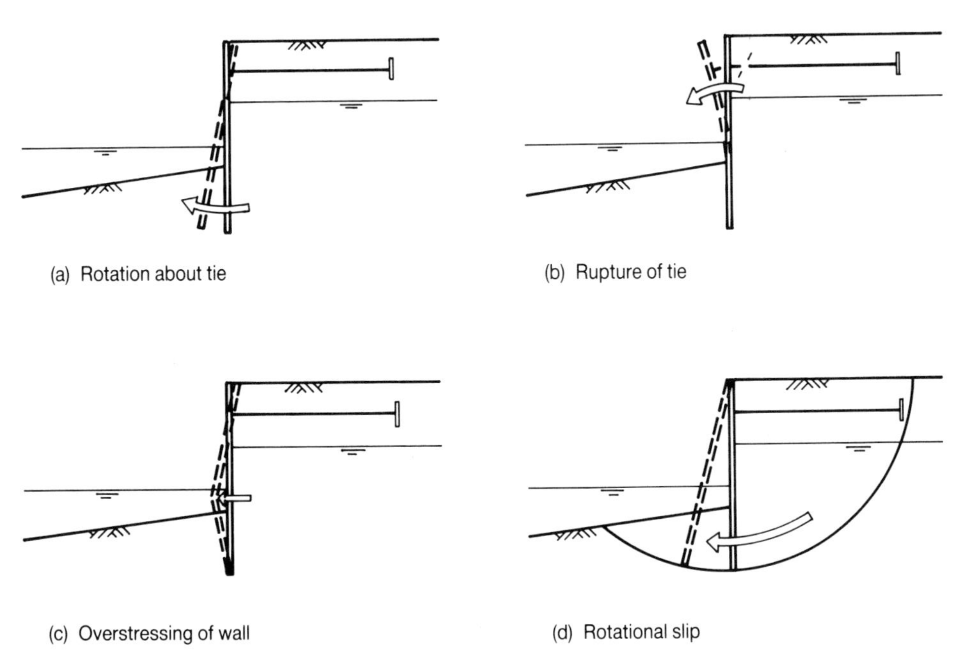

(a) Rotation about tie

(b) Rupture of tie

(c) Overstressing of wall

(d) Rotational slip

Figure 6.22 Modes of failure of tied walls

6.5.2 Analysis

The starting point in analysing the stability of vertical walls is the prediction of the soil and water pressures which will act upon them. When considering overall stability, active conditions can usually be assumed on the retained side of the wall, unless the wall is being designed to act as a restraining structure (see Section 6.2.1). In the case of RC cantilever walls, active pressures are taken on a vertical plane through the heel of the wall. In the design of a cantilever wall stem, substantially higher pressures are adopted to allow for compaction stresses within the soil acting on a wall which is essentially unyielding. Passive pressures on the seaward side are calculated in the usual way, but great care needs to be taken to adopt a realistic lowest beach level. When measuring earth pressure coefficients, values should be adopted which take account of any sloping ground surfaces.

The water pressures acting on a wall are often higher than the soil pressures, and care should be taken to choose appropriate values. Groundwater levels will vary seasonally and fluctuate with the tide. On a falling tide there will be a lag between the groundwater level behind the wall and the sea level in front of the wall. The height of the tidal lag will depend on the nature of the retained soil, the porosity of the wall, and the effectiveness of the drainage system behind the wall. Recommendations regarding differential water levels are given in BS 6349[47].

Overtopping can result in a build-up of water pressure behind the wall and this can be a major consideration in design. The extent to which it affects wall stability depends on the amount of overtopping, the permeability of the decking, and the rate at which the excess water can be discharged.

The stability of gravity walls should be checked under the most adverse combinations of tidal lag, groundwater seepage and uplift. These conditions can result in a reduced resistance to sliding and overturning, or a reduction in passive resistance.

Stability against overturning is usually assessed by checking that the resultant force acting on the base of the wall lies within the middle third. This requirement theoretically prevents any tension occurring beneath the base. If the wall is founded on permeable material, the middle-third rule should be satisfied by the resultant force in effective stress terms, using the worst assumptions regarding water pressure distribution.

The stability of tied walls should be checked under the most adverse groundwater and seepage conditions. Where the wall penetrates cohesive soils, short-term stability should be assessed in total stress terms using undrained shear strength parameters. Long-term stability should be assessed in effective stress terms, particularly when lower beach levels are being allowed for in the future.

Deep-seated rotational stability for all types of wall can be assessed using the methods outlined in Section 6.2.2.

6.5.3 Foundations

Gravity walls should generally be founded on a suitable stratum of soil or rock, and guidance can be found in BS8004 on the allowable bearing pressures to adopt. Where granular strata occur beneath the wall, an adequate groundwater cut-off should be provided to prevent seepage leading to piping or a bearing capacity failure.

Where piles are required to facilitate construction or limit differential settlements, they should be taken down into a competent bearing stratum. The penetration of sheet piles is normally determined by stability requirements and the need to provide adequate passive resistance. Where they need to carry significant vertical loads, they should be treated as bearing piles and taken down into a competent bearing stratum. In all cases a knowledge of the soil profile is required to ensure that the bearing stratum is of adequate thickness and is not underlain by compressible material (see Section 4.8).

The construction of vertical walls often results in a considerable net loading of the ground. Estimates of consolidation settlement should be made so that a settlement allowance can be built into the design crest level of the wall.

6.6 Design of crest (see Section 5.6)

In terms of design the crest can be considered as one of three broad types. The first, wave walls and wave return walls, placed at the immediate crest of the wall (i.e. not set back) will require to resist wave loads. The second, splash walls, are set back and are required to withstand a short-term 'hydrostatic' head to prevent water flowing onto the land behind and other live loads such as vehicle impact. The third type, deckings and slabs, are basically facings to the fill material beneath. They should be designed to resist the erosive forces imparted by wave run-up and overtopping, as well as other live loads due to vehicles and people. This resistance to overtopping is very important in consideration of the back face, the erosion of which led to many breaches in the 1953 floods.

6.6.1 Wave walls and wave return walls

The governing load will, to a large extent, be wave forces, although the designer should consider carefully the possibility of other significant load cases such as vehicle impact. The performance of a wave return wall will, in terms of its success in restricting any overtopping, also be a function of its shape. No definitive rules exist for the dimensioning of curved wave walls. They should be designed so that the wave is deflected smoothly seawards and should be of sufficiently large proportions so that they are not swamped by large waves.

6.6.2 Splash walls and flood walls

Splash walls and flood walls are set back from the top of the face of the seawall. They should be designed to resist a full hydrostatic head up to the top of the wall. Depending on the frequency and severity of overtopping of the seawall in front of the flood wall or splash wall the engineer may consider designing the wall to resist a horizontal jet of water travelling at a velocity equal to that of the breaking wave. The flood walls and splash walls will also need to resist other live loads such as vehicle impact, or, if they act as retaining walls, soil pressure.

6.6.3 Deckings, slabs and revetments

Deckings, slabs and revetments are required to resist some or all of the following:

- The erosive force of overtopping waves both on the top and the back face of the wall;
- The impact of falling water which has been thrown vertically into the air by a vertical or sloping seawall or wave wall;
- Overtopping water from flowing into the core of the wall.

Again, no definitive method for design is available, largely due to inadequate definition of hydraulic loads. When considering seawalls whose purpose is to protect from flooding overtopping is, by good design, likely to be rare. In this case a grass slope reinforced with a geotextile can be used or, at greater cost, lightweight open concrete blocks or open-stone asphalt which allow vegetation to become established. These should be designed to resist a horizontal water velocity equal to that of a breaking wave, in accordance with CIRIA recommendations[36]. When on the top of a flood defence used for regular access (perhaps a footpath) these may not be sufficiently durable. A surface dressing of gravel or hoggin maybe more appropriate.

Where the purpose of the seawall is to prevent erosion or when it is an urban area with a promenade, overtopping may well be much more frequent and the crest will need to be more durable. Horizontal deck slabs should be designed to withstand vehicle loadings and a check should be made on the effect of water (from waves thrown into the air) falling onto the decking. Model studies are necessary to define the loads with confidence but the engineer may well be able to make an initial assessment on the basis of other sites in similarly exposed locations. As an upper case he may consider the load imposed by a downwards vertical jet acting on the deck, whose velocity is equal to the horizontal velocity of a breaking wave. The engineer will need to consider carefully the extent of support that he can rely on from the underlying fill.

6.7 Design of toe (see Section 5.5)

6.7.1 Modes of failure

In structural terms the main purpose of the toe is to prevent undermining of the body of the wall. Toe stability is essential since failure of the toe will generally lead to overall failure of the wall. Under the most adverse conditions it should prevent soil from being removed from the base of the body of the wall. The two most significant modes of failure are:

- Geotechnical instability when the beach is drawn down;
- Lack of resistance to wave action in severe weather when the beach is drawn down.

Extreme low beach levels for design purposes are considered in Section 4.9.

6.7.2 Types of structure

Steel sheet-piled toe

These should be designed in a similar fashion to vertical, anchored, walls, taking due account of any load applied down the slope onto the toe by the slope protection system. The steel sheet-piled toe should resist wave action adequately, with wave loads being taken by the retained soil.

Concrete apron

Considerations similar to those for a concrete sloping wall (see Section 6.4.2) apply. As the apron is probably of a much shallower slope, the wave forces are likely to be somewhat smaller unless waves are likely to break directly onto the toe. Detailed consideration of this aspect requires model studies.

Rubble or rip-rap toe

The toe should be soil 'tight' and the sizing of underlayers should be in accordance with that for slopes (Section 6.2.4). Unless the toe is well below the troughs of wave action it is likely to require rock of a size similar to that on the slope. For rubble at the toe of a vertical wall, work by Brebner is presented in the *SPM* which gives design guidance on rubble size in terms of wave height.

To ensure that the wall is not undermined the toe can either be excavated as an extension to the slope forming the main body of the wall or be a falling apron. The former case should extend and require excavation down to design lowest beach level. In the latter, the rock is placed as a horizontal apron on the existing beach. The horizontal extent of such a toe is defined on the basis of the structure slope (or stable soil slope) and the design lowest beach level.

Asphaltic falling apron

Falling aprons can be constructed of sand mastic or grouted stone. The sizing and nature of the toe layer is described in reference 49, although the horizontal extent of the apron should be determined as for rubble (see above).

6.8 Design for construction and maintenance

This section examines the practical constraints that exist in constructing and subsequently maintaining works on the coast in terms of their influence on design. Both new construction and the renovation or upgrading of existing defences require careful design and planning, and the majority of the comments in this section apply equally to both.

The foreshore is a hostile place to carry out construction work (see Plate 9). Seawalls may therefore be costly or the quality will suffer if design and construction techniques are not related to each other and to the conditions that will be encountered during construction. The engineer should ensure that the structure will be stable during the proposed construction sequence, take account of stresses likely to be induced in the structure during construction, and consider the effect that construction methods may have on long-term durability and hence on future maintenance requirements. The use of an experienced workforce to construct the works is very important in this respect.

It is important to recognize ease and economy of construction and maintenance as major functional requirements. The design should be based on concepts which are realistically achievable in the particular location and at the particular time. The level and type of maintenance should be thoroughly assessed during design so that they can be taken into account in selecting the most appropriate design.

Although the factors are clearly interrelated, it is convenient to discuss the principles involved in each under separate headings before examining some of the different construction techniques that can be adopted.

6.8.1 Tidal construction

Many of the problems of working in a tidal environment are related to the amount of time available for *in-situ* construction. To some extent, all seawalls are subject to these constraints, but the degree to which they are relevant in design is dependent on:

- The levels of high and low water relative to the seawall;
- Beach profile and type;
- The toe and crest levels of the specific wall.

In general, the four cases shown in Figure 6.23 encompass all the main tidal variations associated with seawalls giving rise to the extreme situations of access, available working time and working conditions.

The available working time can vary from zero to 24 hours per day. The predicted tidal window in which work can be carried out is often affected by adverse surge and wind conditions. Although the tidal window can become longer because of favourable surge and wind conditions, programmed cycles of work cannot be made sufficiently flexible to take full advantage of the time gained. Unlike land-based operations, construction works in a tidal environment that remain incomplete during the high water period cannot always be continued during the next low tide cycle. In some instances damage to the partially completed work has to be removed before construction can recommence, and in many cases the complete sequence of work has to be restarted.

Design should therefore recognize the limited quantity and quality of work that can be constructed during a tidal window. Often, the works are designed for construction

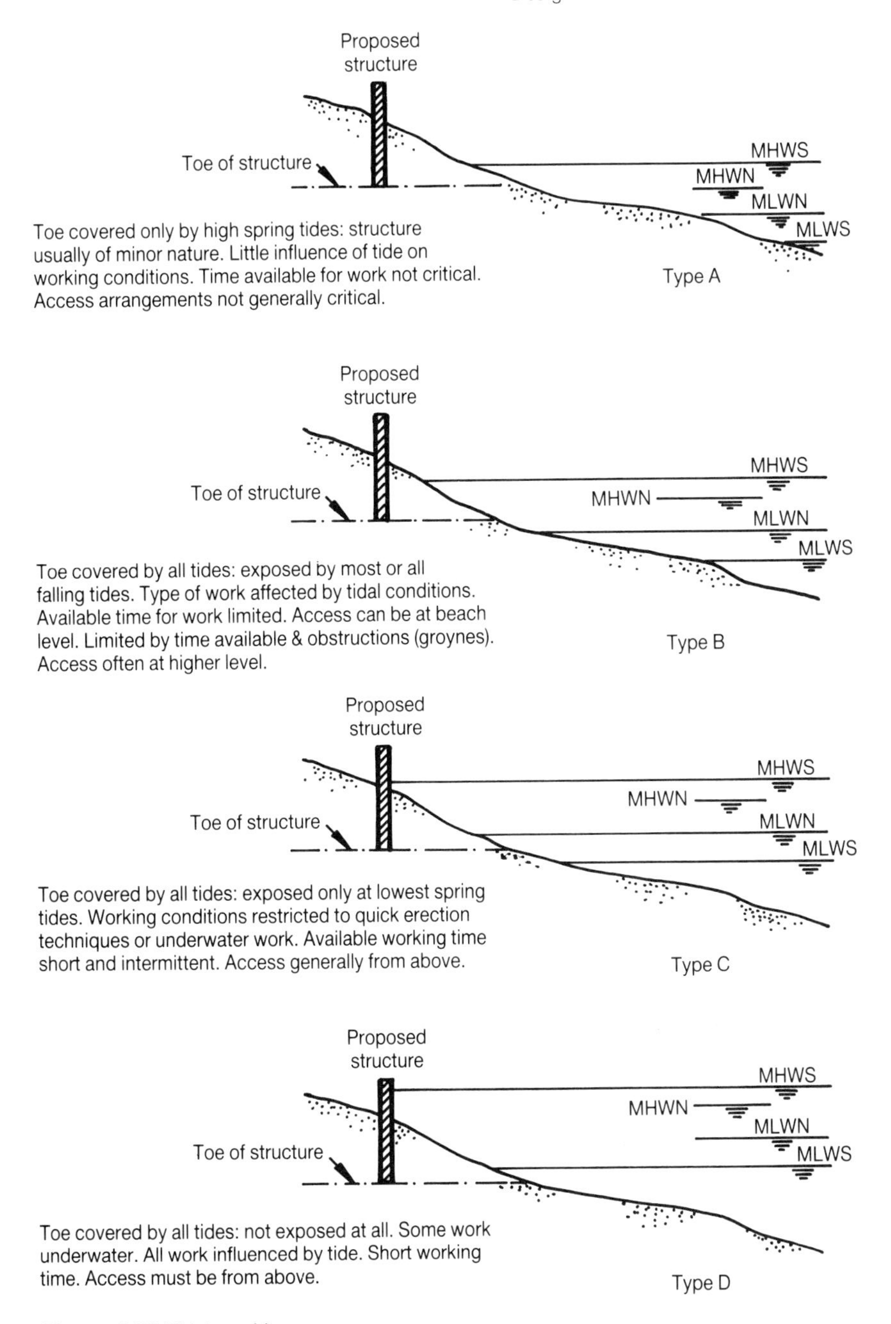

Figure 6.23 Tidal working

in stages which are limited to lengths and heights that can be completed in the time available and/or designed for construction methods permitting quick on-site erection.

In so doing, the way the structure works and transfers load has to be examined to ensure that in both temporary and permanent conditions, stability is maintained and joints can be adequately designed. In all cases simplification of construction details is essential so that speed in preparation and carrying out the work can be achieved without impairing the quality of the structure. Where working time is limited the number of different construction operations that have to be carried out during the tidal window should be minimized.

A major factor is the timing and duration of excavation. Although excavations in hard rock take time, it is not always necessary for the construction to be completed during the same low-tide period. Conversely, in situations where the beach is mobile, excavations cannot be left open for the complete tidal cycle unless extensive and expensive temporary supports such as cofferdams can be provided. The control of ground and tidal water also has an effect on the working cycle both in terms of the time spent on excavation work and in its effect on the construction itself.

The quality of work that can be achieved in the tidal cycle at a particular location has an influence on the choices of construction and material types specified in the design (see also Chapter 7). Where underwater work has to be carried out, for example, the designer's confidence in the quality of foundation that can be achieved should influence the values of allowable bearing pressure adopted and hence the size of footing specified. Factors involved in the design of concrete for underwater work are described in Section 7.3.

6.8.2 Seasonal factors

Almost all civil engineering work in the UK is affected to some extent by the seasons. Work in the coastal zone is adversely influenced to a greater extent than other civil engineering projects, and the following discussion examines the aspects that are specific to maritime construction.

Generally, the result of seasonal influences is to exaggerate the effect of tidal working or to bring construction into conflict with tourism. In the first case, design may be able to minimize the results of limitations in working time. In the second, if major seasonal phasing becomes the only solution, then the designer must allow for and provide the necessary safeguards to the semi-completed project at each stage of its life (see also Section 6.8.9).

Summer working

From a purely engineering point of view, it would be better if all work on seawalls were carried out during the summer months.

- Construction would be easier;
- The quality of finished work is likely to be better;
- There is less delay due to storm conditions;

- There is less risk of damage to either partially completed work or to sections of coastline where the old defences have been removed to make way for the new.

Where construction is required at the level of the lowest tides and when underwater work is impractical or undesirable, the best period of the year is at the autumn and spring equinoxes. On rural sites, summer working will usually be preferred. On town frontages, summer work may be prohibited to avoid interference with tourism. When summer working is allowed the designer should note the following areas in which the design principles adopted can radically affect the work:

- Roads in busy coastal areas, such as the popular tourist resorts, can be heavily congested. The methods of construction envisaged in design should therefore avoid being reliant on continuous regular supplies of materials. Alternative delivery methods such as sea transport should be investigated for the supply of large quantities of heavy materials such as rock armour or large pre-cast sections.
- Every effort must be made to ensure the safety of the general public, especially at sites involving the use of promenades or public beaches. The designer may be able to minimize the risk by ensuring that the sequence of work can be completed in relatively short lengths.
- Types of construction which require the use of noisy plant should be avoided, especially if the work has to be carried out at extreme low water in parts of the country where low water spring tides occur during unsociable hours (see Figure 6.24).
- The effect of sun and wind on large areas of exposed *in-situ* concrete in aprons and promenades is especially harmful during the construction process. In particular, the drying effect of the wind under conditions of low humidity causes rapid loss of moisture from setting concrete even when the sun is not shining. Additional reinforcement to combat shrinkage may be included, although it is better if the loss of moisture during setting is prevented. Adequate measures to protect the structure from the wind in the form of windbreaks, curing compounds, covers to partially set work, or a combination of all three should be specified.

Winter working

When work is to be carried out during the winter the engineer is less inhibited by difficulties in access through a town, tourism and public safety, but has a greater responsibility for ensuring that the works can be constructed to the quality required in the time available. The major considerations that he should be aware of are as follows:

- There is a limitation in daylight working hours especially at extreme low waters (see Figure 6.24). On extreme tides, low water can occur either early in the morning and evening or around noon in different parts of the country. Although times of low water vary from day to day, low water spring tides reach their lowest level at approximately the same time of day in any specific location. Clearly, the number of

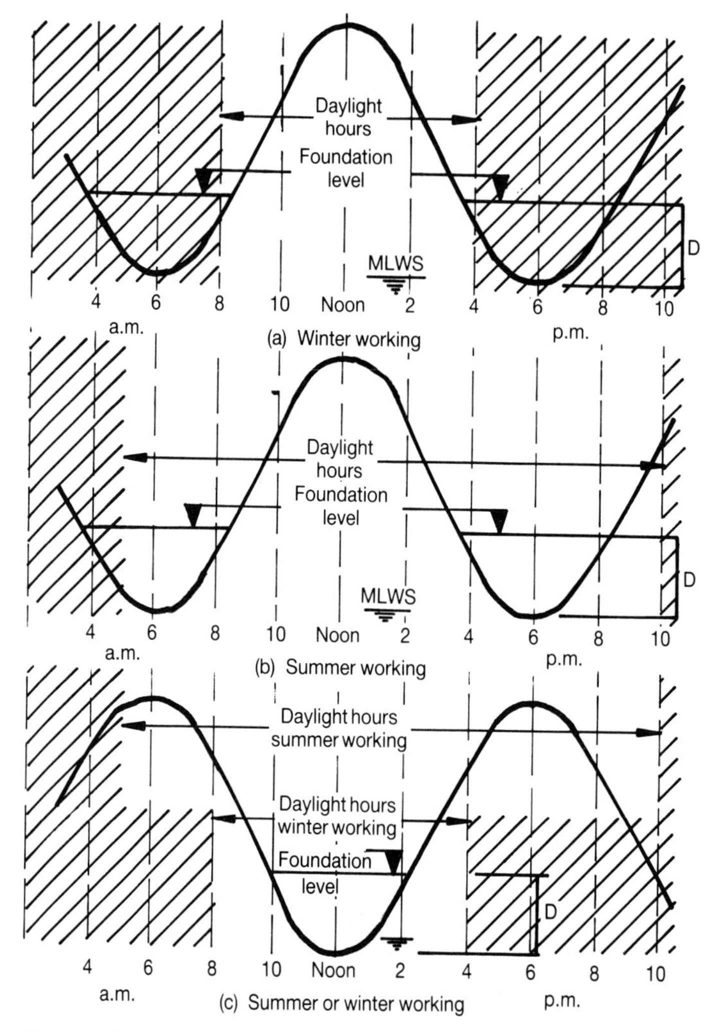

Figure 6.24 Spring tide cycle

daylight hours available for low tide working during the winter in a situation such as the south-east of England may be minimal. This construction constraint may be overcome by the use of pre-cast units, construction methods that can be carried out from a higher level, or by designing for underwater work. If these are not possible, the designer may be forced to reschedule the work to a more acceptable period of the year (see also Section 6.8.9).

- Part of the problem of having to work early in the morning and evening during the winter is the influence of the cold on the quality of work that can be produced. Construction in timber, steel or natural rock may not in themselves be badly affected, but the engineer should treat work involving the use of bituminous or cementitious materials with a degree of caution. Asphaltic revetments, for example, will be subject to large temperature gradients during placing. *In-situ* concrete work is likely to crack and the designer will be well advised to provide greater numbers of smaller-diameter bars together with contraction joints and/or crack raisers at closer intervals than would be adopted for work during the summer.

- Breakdowns, due to cold, at the concrete batching plant are also common, so that the facility to be able to insert stop ends in concrete pours without adversely affecting the structural ability or aesthetics of the wall is essential. Setting time and curing are clearly affected by low temperatures, and the engineer should take notice of the likelihood of a slow initial increase of strength. This is especially relevant when the wall may be subjected to forces from wave action early in its life or even when the initial set is still taking place. Generally, the specification should fix limits within which special concreting measures can be applied, and a limit at which concreting will cease. In addition, the formwork specification should give extended striking times and may give design criteria for the strength of the formwork itself.
- The risk of damage during storm conditions both to the new work, which may be partially completed, and to lengths of unprotected coastline is high during the winter. The consequential risk of flooding or damage to land behind the defences is therefore increased, and is further compounded by the increased probability of occurrence of surges. Therefore, the design should, as far as possible, seek to minimize the risk or, at the least, reduce the amount of damage that may be done during winter storms. Ideally, no reduction in defence standard will be allowed and new work will be designed to be independent of or incorporate the old (see Section 5.7). If this is not practical, the engineer must specify that the length of old defence removed at any time is the minimum required to allow construction of the new, and must design the new wall so that it can be built in the smallest possible number of operations.

Even where good practices have been adopted, sudden deterioration of weather conditions, especially at weekends, can cause severe problems. Safety measures including the backfilling of excavations when storm conditions are predicted, and/or the provision of materials stockpiled on site to be available at short notice to fill excavations or stem any breach, are recommended.

Where the partially completed work may be subject to wave and storm conditions early in its life, the engineer may incorporate temporary support works which may be built into the final structure (see Section 6.8.4) or he may design the partially completed sections with reduced allowable stresses. In some instances the risk of damage during construction is relatively low compared with the expense of ensuring that the partially completed works provide an appropriate level of protection for all conditions. In such a case the cost of occasional damage and reconstruction may be acceptable, but would have to be specified as part of the contract.

In other cases, the consequences of damage by severe wave attack during partially completed stages of construction may be so serious that the engineer will have to consider summer working only. If a rock revetment has to be built during the winter the placing of the primary armour should be tightly specified and controlled to minimize the time for which the underlayer and core are exposed.

Seasonal changes

A key factor which may adversely influence either summer or winter working is the changes that take place in beach levels during the year. The engineer should use beach profile and other data (see Section 4.9) to assess:

- Changes that may take place between the time of his survey and the construction, which can produce major alterations in the extent and cost of the work;
- Changes liable to occur during the construction period.

In terms of designing for construction the designer may be able to ensure, if other commercial pressures are not overriding, that beach excavations take place during a time when the beach is low or, at least, when it is relatively stable. In other instances, reclamation or fill material behind a defence may be retained more easily and at less cost when the beach is high.

In any of the above cases the engineer should ensure that not only the final works but also all partially completed structures will be stable even when beach levels are at their lowest possible level. The effect of increased wave height reaching the structure should be examined. Conversely, if a change results in the raising of beach levels the designer should consider the effect of run-up on the complete system of defences.

6.8.3 Stages of construction

The stages of work are dependent on the specific site conditions, and are concerned principally with providing a sensible working pattern to permit completion of the project safely in an uninterrupted sequence. Although the construction sequence envisaged by the engineer may be amended, it is essential that the design is based on a 'buildable' series of stages that are compatible with each other and with the overall concept. To avoid errors, especially with regard to the design of partially completed stages of work, the engineer should communicate accurately and clearly any design requirements affecting methods of working and stages of construction.

For seawall projects the major considerations to be examined in determining the stages of construction are:

- The effects of tidal working;
- Seasonal influences generally allied to tidal working;
- Access requirements;
- Design limits on the sequence of operations;
- The maintenance of adequate levels of defence during construction;
- The design of partially completed stages of work.

Construction above the influence of the sea is normally quicker and easier than work in the tidal or intertidal zone. This is particularly valid during winter periods when storms and extreme surges are relatively common. Therefore, stages of construction designed to raise the level of the main works above the high water level prior to completion to the finished crest level are often preferred.

To ensure the structural integrity of the finished defence, the engineer will have to consider design limits that need to be imposed on the sequence of construction. Generally, these criteria dictate the timing of construction stages but not necessarily their order. Examples include specifying the striking times of formwork, or the number of days required for cementitious or bituminous materials to gain sufficient strength before the next operation can be carried out. Where the subsequent operation involves the imposition of load on the structure from plant, stressing, jacking, or from other parts of the structure the design requirements may be onerous but are clearly an essential consideration.

The sequence of operations may be determined by external restrictions or by the need to retain an effective defence system throughout the construction. It may be necessary for certain sections of the work to be completed within given times governed by seasons or access dates, etc. In other instances the proposed work may be replacement, renovation or upgrading of a damaged or inadequate seawall that necessitates the demolition of some elements of the old prior to the construction of the new (see also Section 5.7). This can result in a period with no defences and the engineer will have to determine an acceptable distance or time for demolition to precede construction. The distance will be dependent on several criteria such as the sequence of construction, type of construction, ground conditions, the time of year and the need and feasibility of providing temporary defences if severe conditions should occur.

The length of work and the speed with which it must be completed affect both the sequence of construction and the type of structure that can be designed. Where a long length of defence in concrete is involved and relatively simple sections are appropriate, the rapid erection of precast units can minimize the unprotected distance and hence the risk.

It may be unacceptable for any break in defences to occur, in which case the position and shape of the new work may have to be aligned so that it provides an overlap with the old before demolition takes place.

In some cases, major savings in cost and reduction in risk can be achieved by incorporating the existing wall into the new structure. Where this is possible, temporary or even permanent support for the new is often provided by the old. Where partial removal of the existing works is necessary, a reasonably accurate assessment of the extent of each type of operation may be made during design investigations. However, where the hidden aspects of the existing works are uncertain, construction cannot be predicted accurately in advance, and if the works are being undertaken by contract, the engineer should consider carefully a suitable form of contract (see Section 5.7.3).

The order in which stages of construction are carried out should be determined by those on site to suit their programme and resources. However, the engineer will often have to specify restrictions and limits based on the design of partially completed sections of work. A wall that is subsequently to be backfilled may not be sufficiently stable against wave forces until the backfilling is completed. Often a lower stage of wall, constructed to raise working levels to above the high water mark, will need to be backfilled and consolidated before higher levels of construction are added. Similarly, the designer should determine the sequence of backfillings and tie bar fixings for a sheet-piled structure, to avoid overstressing. In some cases, *in-situ* concrete work cannot be backfilled until sufficient time for gain of strength has elapsed. The engineer will then consider alternative ways of providing temporary support, but may be forced to accept the risk of damage during construction. He may be able to minimize the risk by specifying the time of year in which construction is to take place, or may be able to convert the *in-situ* design to a pre-cast one.

It is of considerable benefit to the construction sequence if the designer is able to standardize as much as possible. This permits continuity and interchangeability of units which will expedite construction.

6.8.4 The incorporation of temporary works into permanent works

Three forms of temporary work can be defined as follows:

1. Major elements of temporary work not forming part of the permanent structure, which can be removed on completion of the works, but which require significant design by the engineer for the main structure;
2. Temporary works which are designed as part of the main structure and which are built into the permanent works;
3. Temporary works designed by those carrying out the construction to facilitate their chosen construction procedure.

Form (3) is not considered in detail here since it generally forms part of the post-design considerations. However, they will affect the construction and the engineer should give due consideration to their effect on the design and the possible consequences of their adoption.

Temporary works, not forming part of the permanent structure, along the complete length of a coastal defence are not usually cost-effective. For example, if it were necessary to provide a heavy cofferdam along several kilometres of frontage to construct the foundations of a seawall, it is likely that a smaller and lighter form of construction, possibly with a sheet-piled toe to form an integral part of the main structure, would be more economical. Exceptions are isolated structures, possibly for an outfall, a temporary access, or to cope with particularly poor ground conditions at a single location within a long length of defences.

Temporary works built into the defence and designed as part of the works are often used in seawalls. They are chosen in the light of the stages of construction envisaged and of the problems associated with tidal working. Frequently they act as temporary support to partially completed sections of the defence, but since they are built into the final work they can often result in savings in materials. The types of temporary works that are built-in include various forms of supporting structures, ties, struts, etc. void formers of lightweight materials, permanent formwork of sheet piles or precast concrete planking, bulkheads and intermediate breastworks to retain armour stone.

Some elements of the work may have more than one purpose. As an example, bulkheads can be used to separate backfilled areas under a promenade or apron to permit construction to proceed in manageable-sized bays, and at the same time are often designed to prevent undermining of the previous day's work. In the final construction they can minimize the consequence of any loss of fill material, or they can also be used as an integral structural element.

The prevention of undermining of the work both during and after construction is important (see Section 5.5). As part of the design studies the engineer should establish, and counter, the effects of the temporary or partly constructed works on the coastal processes (e.g. increased wave reflections from partially completed bulkheads or toe piling – see Section 4.9). The engineer should estimate the loads which will be applied to the elements both in the partially constructed and in the completed state.

6.8.5 Access

Early in the design, thought needs to be given to access for construction, the public and subsequent maintenance. Ideally, all three can be combined, but this is not always possible, and on long lengths of seawall several access points may be necessary. The extremes of conditions facing the constructor and designer vary from built-up resort towns to rural areas, and from low-lying floodplains to eroding high cliffs. Essentially, the problems fall into three categories:

- Access to the site location through the hinterland;
- Access to the site itself;
- Access along the site.

Access to the site location

In rural areas above floodplain level some improvements to existing roads, access tracks across fields and wayleaves may have to be negotiated, but it is unlikely that any limitation on the type of seawall will be necessary. In busy urban areas, especially during the tourist season, access for heavy plant and large prefabricated sections may be impractical (see Section 6.8.2).

Access to the site

In many cases access through the hinterland and access to the site are one and the same. The exceptions are:

- Where access is across a low-lying floodplain of limited bearing capacity. The scheme may then have to include the design of an access road, which may be of considerable length and is likely to be costly;
- Where access is from the top of high cliffs. The engineer should consider the type of work proposed, its purpose, whether access by the public will be needed, the long-term maintenance requirements, and how access along the works will be provided. Access from high (often eroding) cliffs is expensive to construct, and there will often be only one for each project. Such accesses can be made permanent, and may be turned into features for public use once the works are completed. Alternatively,

access can be provided by craneage or hoists over the clifftop, and in some cases designs have incorporated a combination of both.

Access along the site

Access along the site is crucial to the construction techniques and to the sequence of operations. Impediments to free movement can be caused by one or more factors, including rocky foreshores, soft foreshores, obstructions such as groynes, and the tide itself. The work envisaged should be compatible with the method of gaining access along the defences during construction. In some cases this will result in a different type or shape of defence than that which could have been provided had access been easier.

In the example quoted earlier of the soft low-lying floodplain, access along the site can be provided by continuing the access road along the line of the works either as the crest of the defence or at a temporary lower level which can eventually form part of the tidal embankment.

An example of the change in defence shape that can cater for the need to provide access along the toe of high eroding cliffs is shown in Figure 6.25. In this example the rocky foreshore combined with the limited time available for construction, as a result of tidal levels and the length of the works, create major difficulties in the construction of either a simple rock bund (a) or a simple revetment (b). It may then be necessary to give consideration to the type of structure shown in (c) or (d), which incorporate access above the tidal influence along the works.

Access from the sea should not be overlooked. Access from the land may still be required, for men and possibly plant, but if significant quantities of raw materials or prefabricated units are needed, sea access can be viable. If it is to be considered, the relative levels of foreshore, tide, and working area, and the risk of delays or damage during storms should be estimated and evaluated in advance.

Where construction access is to be provided through or along unstable cliffs, slides or rockfalls may impede access. Safety considerations may impose a constraint on the position adopted for the works.

6.8.6 Availability and cost of materials

Local availability of construction materials should be part of the design considerations. A knowledge of the local sources of materials (quarries, beaches, etc.), is essential and the engineer should study several alternatives, including ones involving the importation of materials, before a final design is selected.

When considering the materials to be used, transportation costs must be borne in mind in terms of the overall economics of the project. Transportation by sea can be

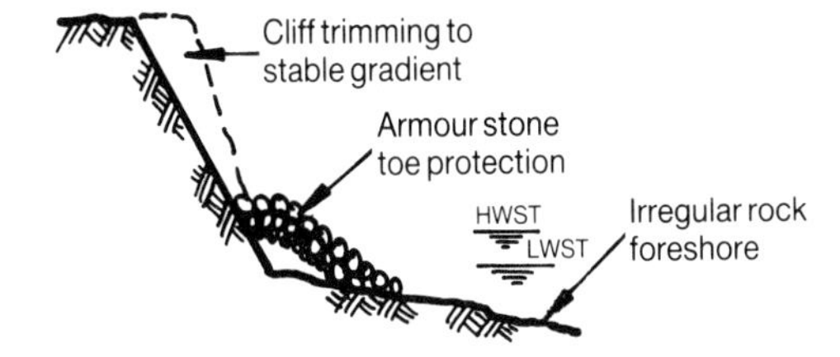

(a) Protection as rock bund

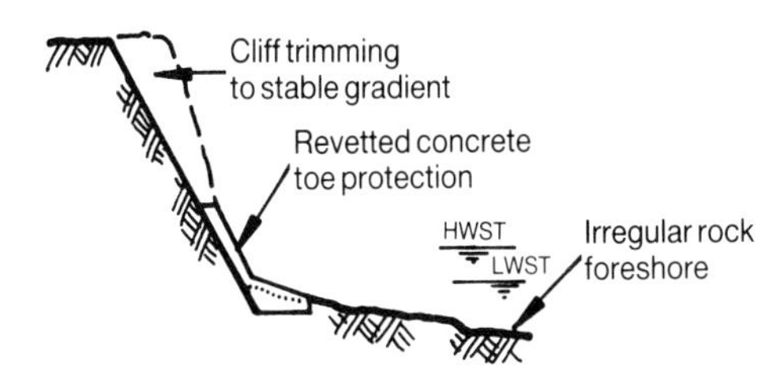

(b) Revetted toe protection

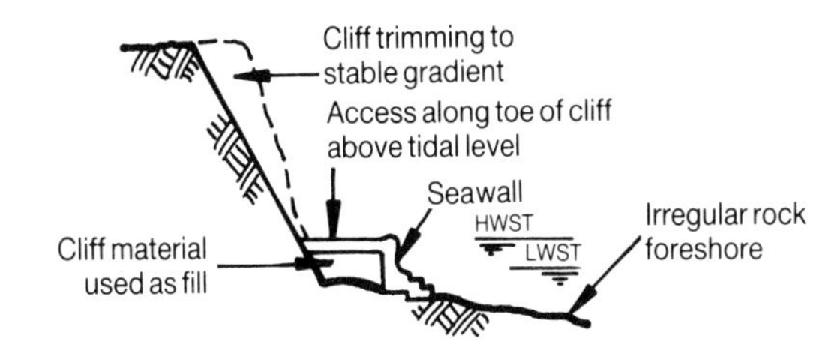

(c) Seawall with filled access deck

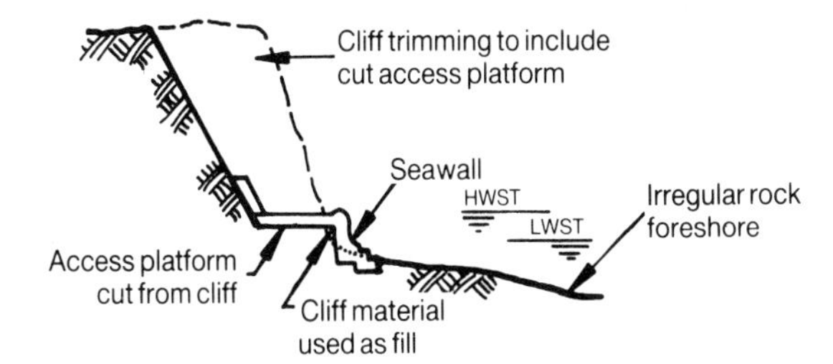

(d) Seawall with cut access deck

Figure 6.25 Access along the site

both advantageous and cost-effective, and, particularly in the case of rock armour, overseas sources may prove useful.

An advantage with the use of local materials is that of long-term availability, which may be crucial for maintenance. A good understanding of the locality may also help the engineer in locating sources of waste products (such as fly ash from a power station) which he may be able to incorporate economically into his design.

6.8.7 Planning and environmental constraints

The planning and environmental constraints involved in seawall design have been described in Chapter 3. The primary constraints of concern during construction, rather than those of the completed works, involve disturbance or disruption to people, plants and animals. They include noise, odour, dust, vibration, as well as longer-term pollution. On the coast, interference with tourism is often a potentially serious problem (see Section 6.8.2).

To some extent, the engineer can impose controls on the construction methods to minimize nuisance, but in the extreme he may be forced to consider alternative construction methods affecting the type of design adopted.

6.8.8 Phasing (see also Section 2.3)

The four usual reasons for phasing the works are:

- To avoid interference with other seasonal activities;
- To take advantage of natural coastal processes and so minimize overall project costs;
- To observe the effectiveness of a pilot scheme;
- To suit the available flow of cash.

Taking advantage of the changes brought about by the coastal processes (i.e. excavating when the beach is low) has been mentioned in Section 6.8.2. Often these are seasonal, but they may be of much longer duration in, for example, the situation of an eroding coastline, where progressive improvements as the need arises can be a useful design concept.

Phasing may also be necessary to avoid interference with seasonal tourism, but whatever the reason, the effect on design is similar in principle. First, a suitable physical termination point should be chosen which is adequate for the conditions that it is likely to encounter. In so doing the engineer should consider the detrimental effect that such a termination may have on adjacent defences and on coastal processes. There have been cases where the cost and effects of end works are so serious as to call into question the advisability of using phases. Second, he should ensure that suitable provision is made in the work for continuation at a later date. (A 'T' pile with an exposed clutch in sheet piling, for example.) Third, he should ensure that the quantity of work that remains in each phase is adequate for economic implementation of the chosen construction method. If it is not, mobilization costs will be disproportionately high. In some situations there may be no alternative, but in others a different form of construction may prove more cost-effective and worth examination.

6.8.9 Construction plant and methods

It is not the purpose of this book to give details of plant and methods of working used in seawall construction. However, the engineer should have a good basic knowledge of the options available, the advantages and disadvantages of each, and the problems that are encountered in practice. Even with a good understanding of site practice it is not possible at the design stage to solve all the problems that may be encountered during construction. Where a project is sufficiently large, the experience gained on the site can often be incorporated into the design of later stages so that construction methods can be refined as the works proceed.

With all plant, the major criteria to be examined in the design are:

- The overall size of the plant and the power available, so that access and working space can be assessed;
- The dead and working weight of the plant;
- The outreach at which the plant can work efficiently;
- The speed of working, to ensure that bay lengths can be constructed within the period available.

It is recommended that the engineer reviews his design with the following three criteria in mind to see if improvements can be made:

1. Construction plant needed;
2. Methods of working;
3. Convenience in construction of the design details.

The type and size of plant required may have an effect on the works or on existing works. The size of crane required, for example, to achieve the placing of armour stone at the toe of a revetment may be much heavier than the stone size suggests, due to the length of outreach needed. If such a crane has to be placed on an existing promenade, the deck must be robust enough to support it. Where ground conditions at the beach are too soft to support heavy concrete trucks, pumped concrete may be considered; the engineer should establish a location from which it can easily be dispatched and choose a grade of concrete suitable.

Careful consideration of the types of materials specified and the methods of application is of considerable benefit at the design stage. The use of pumping to control groundwater and the inclusion of suitable drainage during construction may be essential. Where materials such as expansion joint filler and sealants have to be applied in wet conditions, the choice of material and the method adopted for its application are crucial.

Simplicity in design detailing is of paramount importance in ensuring that construction problems are minimized (see Section 6.9).

6.8.10 Specific maintenance considerations

Perhaps the most important point to appreciate is the extent to which the basic type of wall elements will define the sort of maintenance commitment that is required. Well-designed concrete slopes and vertical walls are likely to require limited maintenance except at joints, as are steel sheet piles (even though their life may be limited by corrosion and abrasion where not encased or otherwise protected). Rock armour, rip-rap and many concrete armour units may require maintenance (the addition of new material) from time to time and particularly after very severe weather. Flexible armoured revetment systems, pitched stone and asphaltic systems, as described in Section 5.4, rely on continuity for their strength. Once damaged (if, for example, one unit breaks or the asphalt is locally cracked) rapid collapse is possible. This clearly indicates the need for regular inspection and rapid maintenance in response to damage reports.

The engineer should also be very aware that there is always a risk of the design conditions being exceeded. Inspection following severe weather is important and good maintenance is inextricably reliant on good inspection. The ability of the client to carry out inspection and the subsequent maintenance is an important element of the choice of potential seawall options.

In order to evaluate the options and to allow him a valid assessment of scheme costs, the engineer should prepare maintenance schedules and on this basis estimate their costs (see also Section 8.1).

Detailed design

Seawall components which are likely to require repair or replacement at some future date should, where possible, be detailed or selected in such a way as to facilitate replacement or repair. This is discussed in Section 6.9.

Access for maintenance

Provision for future access for maintenance is necessary and may include:

- Plant access across the wall to the foreshore either for access to the seaward side of the wall or to beach-control structures;
- Plant access along or to the rear of the wall;
- Access to seawall components, including joints, manholes for drainage, etc.

Considerations of access are generally covered in Section 6.9.8.

Stockpiling

In cases where special materials are used or where the supply of certain materials such as heavy rock involves substantial mobilization costs, the engineer should consider the likely needs for maintenance and whether there is a justification for stockpiling of such materials during or at the end of construction.

6.9 Detailing

Good detailing forms an important and integral part of successful design and strongly influences:

- Construction time;
- Cost;
- Hydraulic performance;
- Maintenance;
- Life of structure;
- Appearance.

Most importantly, poor detailing can precipitate a short life and often makes maintenance difficult. The effect of good detailing should be to enhance the performance, life and appearance of the structure and simplify construction in the most practical and cost-effective manner.

In general, recommendations contained in the British Standard Code of Practice 6349[47] for the design and detailing of maritime structures will be applicable to seawalls. Aspects of design which relate specifically to construction and maintenance are dealt with in Section 6.8.

6.9.1 Damage limitation

An important element of detailed design will be consideration of damage limitation. The engineer should aim to ensure that any local damage is confined and not allowed to spread to other areas. This may be approached first by identifying the possible causes of damage and then by detecting the different modes of failure that might take place within any one form of construction. Having identified the cause and effect of damage it is possible to incorporate such damage-limitation measures as can be justified by the function and requirements laid down for the wall.

Long lengths of sloping walls and revetments may be protected by dividing up into short bays by transverse bulkhead beams or cut-off walls. For wide aprons cross bulkheads may be included. Steel piling, *in-situ* or precast concrete, timber piling or planking can be used for this purpose.

6.9.2 General points of detailing

Provision for settlement and flexibility

The detailer should ensure that any lateral or vertical movements can be accommodated without detriment to the performance or life of the structure. Settlement or differential movement may occur through variable loading, unstable ground conditions or changes in beach levels. On non-porous walls movements due to impact loading from breaking waves may have to be considered.

Settlement and thermal movements may be determined by calculation, but for most other conditions the engineer will have to rely on his own judgement and experience based on the behaviour of similar structures. Most structures can tolerate some uniform settlement and problems that arise generally result from differential movements. An early assessment of the likely magnitude to be accommodated will influence the form of construction to be selected. The choice of fill material can have a considerable impact on the need for flexibility in any structure built on it.

If flexible and rigid construction are combined, special care must be taken when detailing the interface to ensure that only those loads for which the structure has been designed can be transferred between the structural components. Anchorages to piled walls or breastworks located in ground conditions where settlement may occur should be detailed to allow flexure of the tie (see Section 6.9.5).

Small differential movements between rigid components or structures including pre-cast concrete units can be accommodated by careful detailing using:

- Slotted holes;
- Hinged joints;
- Compressible packings and bearings;
- Flexible ties;
- Articulated joints;

and specific joint characteristics are shown in Section 6.9.5.

Forms of flexible construction commonly used include:

Type	*Guide to allowable settlement*
rock armour random armour units	in excess of 300 mm
rip-rap cribwork gabions grass	up to 150 mm
blockwork grouted mattresses asphalt	less than 75 mm

Corrosion and abrasion

The nature and form of degradation by abrasion are presented in Section 7.2.3 and chemical attack or corrosion in Section 7.2.4. Rates of loss of material from exposed faces are given in Section 7.3 for most materials of construction relative to their use in different weathering zones. In particular, means by which durability of concrete can be achieved are set out in Section 7.3.3.

Steelwork

The corrosion of steel may be reduced by the provision of a protective coating, and such systems may be classified as:

- Organic coatings such as paints and wrappings;
- Metallic coating such as hot-dipped galvanizing with or without an organic top coating;
- Plastic coatings with or without metallic undercoat;
- Cathodic protection;
- Concrete cappings or encasements;
- Bare steel with an appropriate corrosion loss allowance.

Applied organic coatings can seldom offer long-term protection in severe coastal environments. In heavily populated or holiday resorts, function, appearance and environmental considerations may dictate that exposed surfaces are treated for cosmetic reasons. Where protective coatings are applied prior to construction, such as painting to steel sheet piles, it is often difficult, if not impossible, to ensure the coating is not damaged during construction. This can severely limit the effectiveness of corrosion resistance. Given regular maintenance and repainting, the life of such structures may be considerably extended but at a significant cost. For further details of materials and their application, BS 5493[50] should be consulted.

Plastic coatings applied to galvanized steel are commonly used for protecting handrailing and wire mesh used for the construction of flexible mattresses. They can provide a high level of protection against corrosion but are easily damaged by abrasion caused by wave action. In areas of severe corrosion the encasement of steelwork and, in particular, steel piles in plain or reinforced concrete may be justified and will provide a permanent and largely maintenance-free protection. There are few examples of cathodic protection being applied to control corrosion in seawalls.

As the approximate rate of loss of steel for various levels of exposure can be predetermined it will frequently be found that the optimum and least troublesome solution to the problem of corrosion will be to use bare steel and increase the thickness of the critical sections to compensate for long-term losses. Guidance is given in Section 7.3.4.

The need for protection against electrolytic action should always be considered where dissimilar metals are in contact. Insulating gaskets, sleeves and washers or waterproof wrapping tapes should be provided between the interfaces of all contact surfaces.

The durability of steel sheet piles and their effective life are likely to be determined by corrosion and abrasion. A low-modulus pile with a uniform thickness can often be utilized in areas such as toe walls and cut-offs, where strength may not be a critical factor, to provide extended life. However, large increases in thickness to offset local metal loss may not be cost-effective. Alternative options are sacrificial cladding, concrete encasement and capping.

Local well-defined regions of wear can sometimes be more economically dealt with by the provision of external cladding. This can either be applied as protection to the face of new piles or as a means of reinforcing older or worn piles. Methods may include thickening with welded steel plates, cladding with sacrificial vertical or horizontal timbers or partial encasement in concrete. Figures 6.26 and 6.27 show details of such cladding and encasement.

Where wastage occurs over a large area or throughout the length of the wall the encasement of the exposed pile face in reinforced concrete may be considered. If incorporated within the wall design savings on pile costs may be achieved. All encasements should be extended for a short distance below the lowest water or anticipated beach level.

The tops of toe piling can be quickly worn away by an abrasive beach with serious consequences to the stability of the wall and should be encased in concrete or protected by a replaceable timber or precast capping.

Steel ties and bolts are often designed to low stresses to allow for redistribution of loads and the effects of corrosion avoiding reliance on additional protective measures. The ends of tie rods and turn buckles will suffer most and will benefit from wrapping with a petroleum-coated fibre tape or encasement in concrete. In corrosive ground conditions bars may be wrapped throughout their length and given added protection against mechanical damage during backfilling or from abrasion by overwrapping with a bituminous tape.

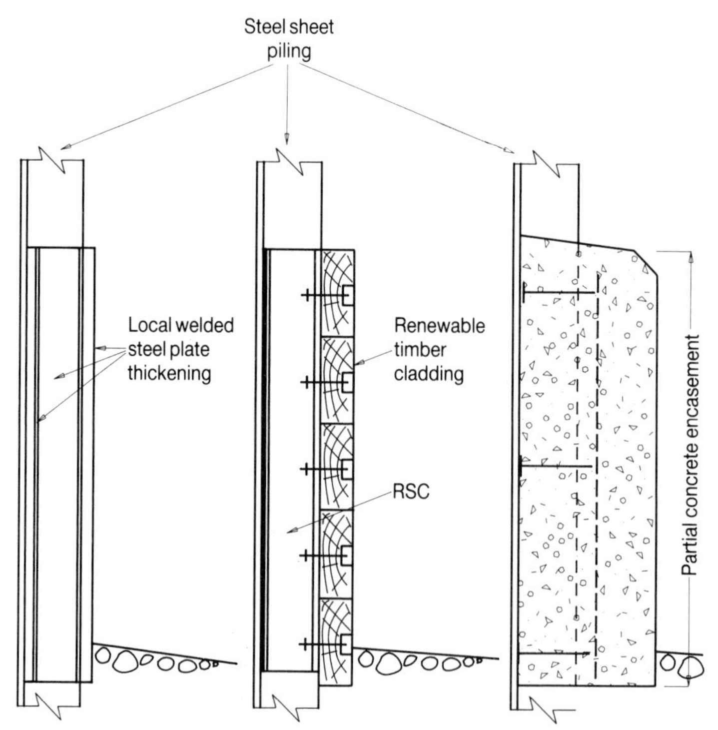

Figure 6.26 Protection against abrasion – sacrificial cladding

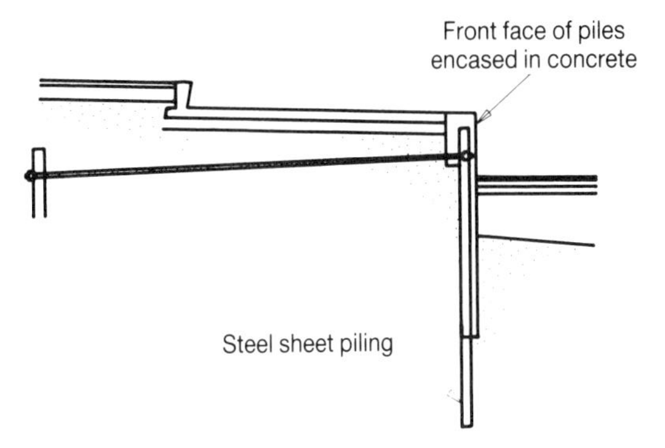

Figure 6.27 Protection against abrasion – concrete facing

Concrete

During curing, vertical surfaces may be protected against scouring by delaying removal of the forms of construction of temporary bund walls to prevent encroachment by the waves. The use of pre-cast panels as permanent forms should be considered where damage is likely to constitute a serious problem (Figure 6.28). Sloping surfaces of fresh concrete may be protected against wash-out or scrubbing from beach material by the provision of top forms or cover plates or by a thick covering of sand applied as soon as the concrete has attained sufficient strength to support it. Where serious damage is likely to occur the use of pre-cast concrete slabs or stepwork should be considered or temporary cofferdams provided to protect the works from wave action.

On vertical walls and aprons subject to moderate abrasion the addition of concrete in the form of extra cover to reinforcement or sacrificial cladding will often be the most cost-effective solution. The required thickening of concrete will depend largely on the anticipated severity of the erosion but also on the structural importance of the concrete and may vary from a few millimetres up to 300 mm. Only in the most hostile locations where access for maintenance would be difficult or prohibitive on grounds of cost would the extreme value apply (see Section 6.9.3). In areas where very severe abrasion might be experienced a more economical form of protection may be provided by cladding the concrete with sacrificial timber, a masonry facing or simply allowing for future refacing with concrete.

In environmentally sensitive locations the additional cost of providing a masonry facing to the wall may be justified. This can be in the form of *in-situ* blocks or setts with concrete backing, or preformed faced panels with reinforced concrete backing. (see Figures 6.28 and 6.29).

Masonry can be built up in small lifts to act as a permanent form for the backing concrete or as a facing tied back to the new concrete. The abrasion resistance of a masonry facing as a whole will be increased by the use of minimum joint widths and a high-strength mortar or fine-bedding concrete.

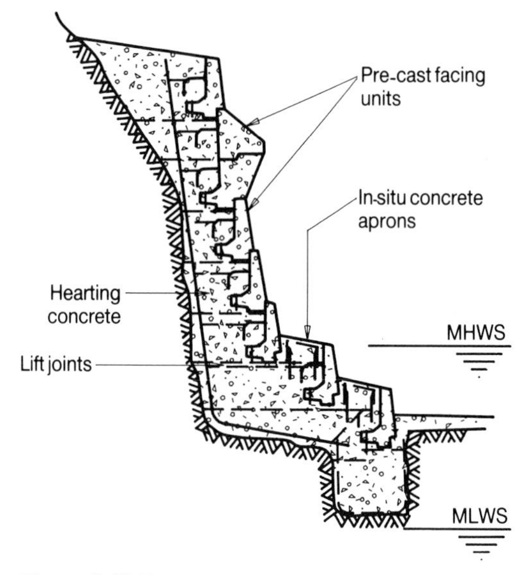

Figure 6.28 Pre-cast concrete facing units

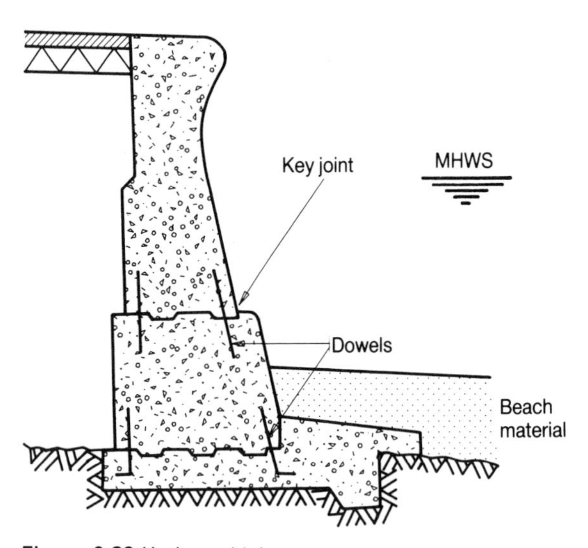

Figure 6.29 Horizontal joints

6.9.3 Concrete and reinforcement

Failure of mass or reinforced concrete walls can result from overstressing as a consequence of gradual degradation of elements forming some part of the structure. Displacement cracking and spalling can occur through local overstressing due to poor detailing which in turn may impair the performance of the wall as well as cause disfiguration or constitute a public nuisance.

The geometry of the various structural components may be altered throughout the life of the seawall as a result of abrasion, corrosion and decay. By careful detailing, the avoidance of small sections, unnecessary embellishments and local stress raisers, care in the choice of materials and use of low stresses in components liable to undergo degradation, the engineer should produce a design where the life of the wall is not determined solely by the residual strength of a single component that cannot be easily replaced or strengthened.

Where practical within the limits imposed by tides and other construction factors, the body and other main elements of reinforced or mass concrete walls should be constructed in the largest possible units so as to distribute and dissipate wave-induced stresses over the greatest possible area.

Reinforcement should be detailed so that the concrete can be easily placed and effectively compacted. Detailers who ignore this point are sowing the seeds of future trouble and shortening the life of the structure.

In general, a small number of large-diameter bars will require less time to fix than a greater number of smaller bars and will be likely to provide a stronger, more robust cage less liable to damage by wave action if fixing and concreting are not completed in one tide. Wider spacing of reinforcing bars will also enable formwork and reinforcement to be more easily cleaned if contaminated by seaweed and beach material and permit easier access for large-diameter vibrators, enabling the concrete to be rapidly and thoroughly compacted before coverage by the incoming tide. In selecting the ratio between bar size and spacing care should be taken to ensure that surface cracking does not exceed the acceptance level.

Steel reinforcement to form laps or starter bars, which has to be left projecting in tidal waters, is liable to damage during construction. The length of projecting bars should be restricted as far as possible to the minimum lap length required to develop the design load or bond strength in the bar at that location. The risk of damage at joints in exposed positions can be reduced by providing separate short lengths of larger-diameter dowel or lap bars. Where bars are to be left projecting in very hostile conditions for a considerable time, as in the case of a length of toe beam which is to be completed before the construction of the body of the main wall, the use of threaded bars and couplers may be considered worthwhile. Careful supervision will be required of each bar when reconnecting reinforcement to ensure that threads are undamaged and bars are fully engaged within the coupler.

The use of high-yield, plain or twisted mesh reinforcement enables the rapid placement of reinforcement in deckings, ramps, slabs, splashbacks and sloping revetments. For slabs with a single layer of reinforcement it is usual to position the mesh in the top of the slab to protect the corners and edges, which are the most vulnerable areas likely to suffer damage from wave impact, movement of heavy plant and vehicular loading. Wastage of mesh reinforcement is reduced where slab dimensions can be related to the sheet sizes in which mesh is supplied. The mesh should be accurately positioned and securely held in place in accordance with accepted methods of good practice against disturbance by external forces.

Mesh reinforcement may also be used with advantage in lightly reinforced vertical or sloping walls. In particular, where long lengths of repetitive construction are required, considerable savings in construction time may be achieved. Reinforcing mesh is, however, easily damaged and difficult to clean and its use should be avoided in tidal locations where reinforcement cannot be fixed and concreted in a single tide.

The key between existing structures and new concrete encasements or facings can be improved by dowelling. A suitable pouring grade or capsulated resin grout may be used for this purpose. If vertical or inclined holes can be provided a cement grout may be more cost-effective where a large number of dowels are to be provided and there is little risk of disturbance before the encasement has cured.

The corrosion of steel reinforcement to concrete is discussed in Section 7.2.4. The quality and depth of cover is critical to the life of the structure. BS 6349 Part 1[47] recommends a minimum cover of 50 mm. Under conditions of extreme exposure, such as severe freezing, local contamination by waste solids or minor surface abrasion, it may be necessary to increase the cover to 60 or 75 mm (see also Section 6.9.2). Where there is any possibility that the thickness of the concrete cover could be significantly reduced locally or randomly over the face of the wall or other sections by abrasion then the concrete cover should be increased by an appropriate amount.

Where additional cover is provided to compensate for future abrasion or as extra protection against penetration of moisture or corrosive salts, extra care must be taken in detailing the reinforcement, as the increase in cover may result in larger crack width at the surface.

Unsightly staining and cracking may be produced in upstand and parapet walls cast along the top of large rigid walls. This is as a result of the differential shrinkage induced by the edge restraint provided between the new concrete and existing section. The basic pattern of cracking is dependent on the amount of reinforcement provided, and if the critical reinforcement ratio is achieved the widths of the primary cracks are controlled, although finer secondary cracks may be induced. The size and spacing of these cracks depends on the amount of distribution reinforcement provided.

The visual effect of seawalls and back walls is often spoilt by the appearance shortly after construction of small rust spots on the face of the concrete. This problem can be avoided by close supervision, the use of stainless steel tying wire or proprietary non-ferrous reinforcing clips.

It is quite impractical to form and retain sharp edges or corners on concrete slabs or structures. Substantial chamfers are essential to avoid a ragged appearance.

6.9.4 Piling

Bearing piles

Where natural ground conditions are incapable of supporting the whole or part of the proposed structure within the allowable design tolerance, bearing piles may have to be provided to support separate structural elements such as toe beams, bulkheads, crest walls, etc. or to provide the foundations for the complete seawall (see Section 6.5.3). Use of preformed driven piling has the added advantage that unforeseen variations in soil conditions are revealed as the pile is installed, enabling corrective measures such as lengthening, shortening or the provision of additional piles to be implemented on-site. The piles may be inspected for soundness before driving so any potential defects may be rectified or the pile may be rejected. The main disadvantage of this type of pile is that the length is decided in advance of the start of work and subsequent variations to the original length may result in wasted surplus lengths or the need for special extension pieces which can delay construction. Where the engineer has insufficient knowledge or experience of pile behaviour in the area or of the installation of the pile type in similar ground conditions, the driving of test piles may be justified. The use of bored piles in waterside locations is not generally recommended, as the ingress of water to the pile excavation can cause serious structural defects.

In the case of pile caps and capping beams the engineer should make allowance for physical ground conditions as well as the exposure of the site and available working window for tidal operations. Over-rigorous specification of final tolerances for pile position and shaft verticality may significantly reduce the rate of piling, increasing construction time and the cost of the works when a wider tolerance could perhaps have been accommodated within the design at little or no extra cost.

The following minimum tolerances are suggested as a guide for single piles:

- Pile head 75 mm;
- Shaft verticality 1:80.

For piles driven into boulder clay, cobbled beaches and dense gravels a wider tolerance may be found necessary.

Sheet piling

Seawall types are described in Chapter 5 and the use of sheet piling for complete walls, toe construction and crest formation is discussed. Design information is provided in Sections 4.8, 6.1 and 6.5. The materials are discussed in Section 7.3 where design stresses are given.

When detailing steel sheet piling, the manufacturers' handbooks are essential guides to the geometry of the many and varied sections available. Walings, capping beams and anchorages required by the design have to be detailed to suit the pile section chosen. Some ingenuity is needed to plan the detail such that modular spacings dictated by the pile section fit into the overall layout which meets the fundamental requirements. Joints for flexibility are discussed in Section 6.9.5 and fixings in Section 6.9.6.

Timber sheet piles can be provided for use in marine works, in high-strength hardwood timbers resistant to both abrasion and attack by marine borers (see Section 7.3.5).

Sheeters are readily available in sections of 2 in × 9 in to 3 in × 12 in and can be supplied either with plain edges or tongued and grooved to reduce leaching of fine material and give added stability.

Concrete sheet piles can be provided in reinforced or prestressed concrete but are now seldom used in the UK as they are generally uneconomic compared to alternative piling materials. They are not affected by marine borers, require less maintenance than steel piles, but are liable to damage during driving, heavy to handle and difficult to seal against loss of fines.

In locations subject to heavy abrasion all sheet piles may deteriorate rapidly, and consideration should be given to the relative merits of providing increased pile thickness, encasing the exposed faces of steel in concrete or providing a timber cladding.

The appearance of steel piles is likely to be improved and the risk of injury to members of the public reduced by protecting the top of the piles with a concrete coping or a steel or timber cap. This also offers the potential for providing structural continuity from pile to pile.

6.9.5 Joints

Two fundamentally different types of joint are used in a seawall:

- Construction joints designed for minimal discontinuity;
- Movement joints to accommodate:
  inner change, i.e. expansion and contraction,
  flexure, i.e. angular change,
  lateral or vertical relative movement,
  vibration,
  some combination of these.

The manner in which the joints are made will vary considerably with the materials in use. As joints are potential points of weakness, only the minimum number needed should be used[51].

Construction joints in concrete

The structural integrity of a concrete wall can be maintained at a construction joint through the continuity of reinforcement and bonding of the concrete surfaces along the contact interface. In this case, no allowance is made for relative movement between adjacent faces at the joint. The number of construction joints provided should be kept to the minimum necessary for the efficient execution of the works, but the detailer should also consider whether additional joints may be needed for the safe construction of toe walls or foundations where construction may be impaired by sudden changes in the sea state.

Care will be required in the preparation and detailing of construction joints, to ensure that the freshly placed concrete forms a tight bond with the previously placed concrete[52]. The bonding at joints will be increased through aggregate interlock if the surface of freshly placed concrete is lightly roughened to expose the coarse aggregate. The prepared concrete surface should be thoroughly cleaned with fresh water immediately prior to the placing of fresh concrete. Particular care should be taken when placing new concrete close to a joint to ensure that the mix has an adequate fines content and is capable of being fully compacted without loss of grout through leakage or leaching by wave action. Further general guidance is to be found in BS 8110[52].

Where horizontal construction joints have to be provided between vertical lifts the risk of early age thermal cracking due to restraint along the bonded joint will be reduced by ensuring the shortest possible time interval between consecutive concrete lifts. Resistance to sliding will be increased by the provision of horizontal keyed joints or dowels within the concrete where multiple-lift construction is required. Figure 6.29 shows an example.

Expansion and contraction joints in concrete

The need for frequent expansion joints in seawalls is questionable and these are often omitted altogether from walls regularly exposed to tidal water. The initial shrinkage of the concrete during hydration of the cement will normally be greater than the subsequent expansion of the concrete due to changes in atmospheric temperature, and the concrete itself can withstand quite high compressive stresses. As a result, the need for expansion joints at more frequent intervals than 60 m, or at junctions, changes in direction or between different forms of construction, is seldom likely to be found necessary. Expansion joints are usually provided in thin sections such as deck slabs, splashbacks, parapets and back walls, although these will seldom be required at centres less than 20 m.

Expansion joints may only remain effective as long as they are sealed. Should the sealant be removed, stones may quickly become wedged in the joints, preventing movement or causing spalling of the concrete along the joint, and making resealing difficult without first enlarging the seal rebate.

Sealed expansion joints subjected to water pressure (tending to force the sealant into the wall) should be supported by a suitable filler board. Where sealed joints may also be subjected to back pressure such as at low tide, the seal should also be continued down the back of the wall. It is seldom necessary to provide a completely waterproof joint in seawalls, but where required, as in the case of free-standing wave walls or where leakage might overload a pump drainage system, joints should be sealed on both faces. If necessary, a water bar can be incorporated within the joint but this will greatly complicate the stop-end shuttering. Suitable expansion joint fillers are formed of non-absorbent, rot-resistant materials which will not react nor interfere with the bonding of the selected sealant.

Where lateral movement may occur the detailing of keyed expansion joints becomes cumbersome and the provision of a sliding dowelled joint is likely to provide a better option (Figure 6.30).

Whereas the need for frequent expansion joints in seawalls is questionable, the provision of contraction joints at regular intervals is necessary to accommodate shrinkage and thermal movements. In determining the interval between joints the engineer should consider that, at one extreme, thermal cracking may be restricted by providing suitable joints at close intervals with the need for little or no additional crack-control reinforcement. At the other extreme, continuous construction can be

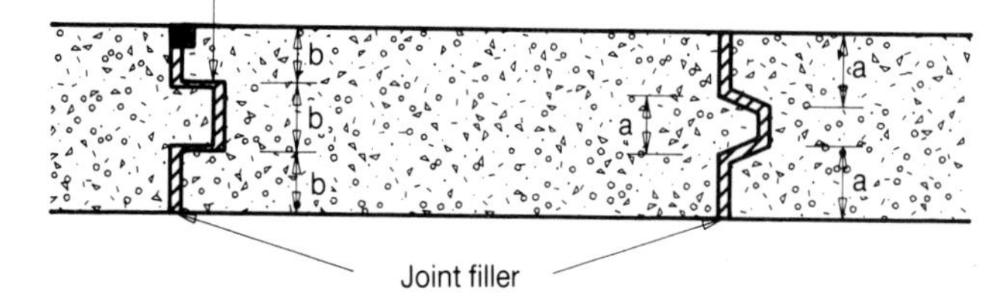

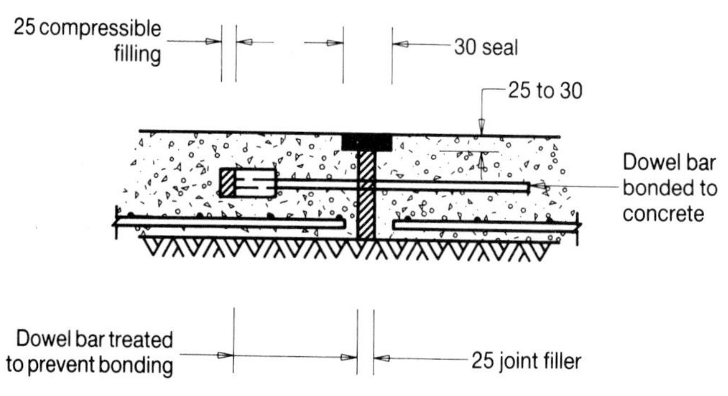

Figure 6.30 Expansion joint in RC slab

carried out with contraction joints provided at infrequent intervals and thermal movements contained by the provision of additional crack-control reinforcement. In practice the optimum solution will seldom be provided by either of these options. Joint spacing is likely to be determined by practical considerations such as size of temporary forms and limitations imposed by tidal conditions or for reasons of economy.

Provision for crack control is then made accordingly. A bay length of 5–6 m is frequently adopted for vertical walls although walls have been constructed in single bay lengths of 9 m with few problems. Vertical or horizontal contraction joints can be plain but the engineer should consider carefully the need to key the joint to provide additional shear resistance. A debonding agent should be applied to the surface before fresh concrete is placed against it.

The frequency and need for movement joints in large areas of decking will normally be influenced by the nature and quality of the sub-grade, type of surface finish, loading and ambient temperature during the construction period, in addition to the effects of thermal movement within the concrete. The sealing of deck joints should prevent downwards percolation of surface water or wave splash into the sub-grade where this could prejudice wall stability (Figure 6.31).

Vertical contraction joints can be left unsealed where water seepage would not be detrimental to the performance of the wall. Concrete is often less well compacted in

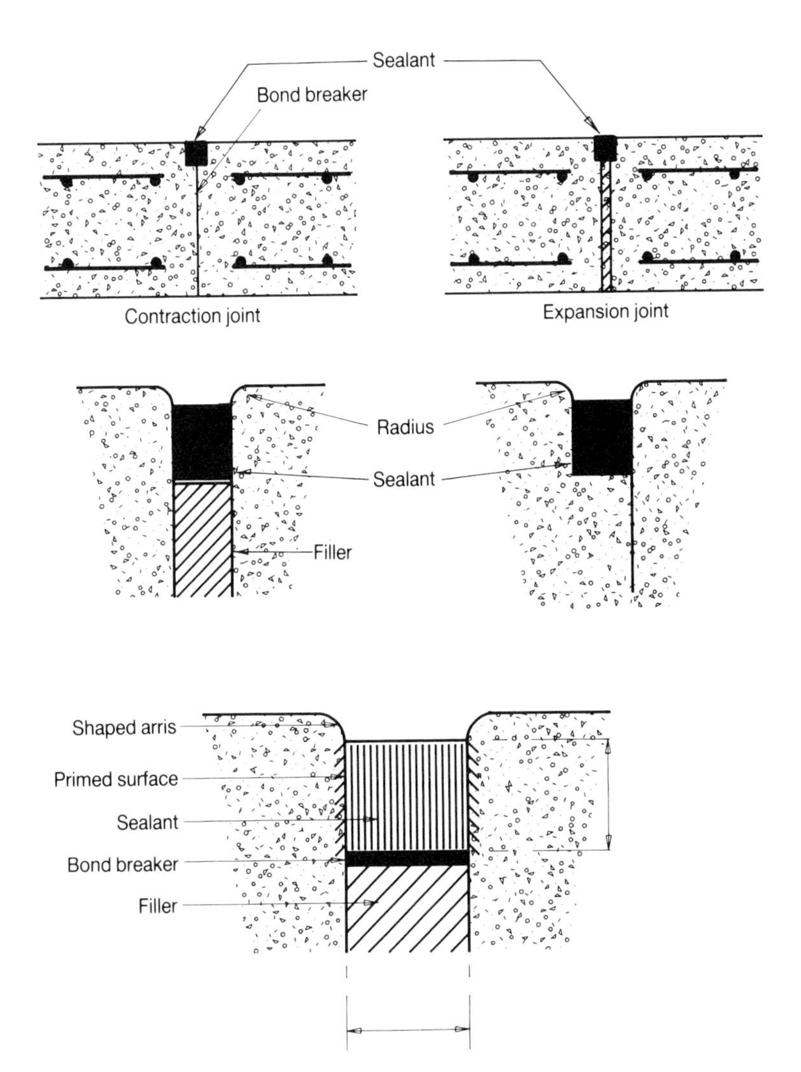

Figure 6.31 Sealed deck joints

arrisses than elsewhere and grout loss may occur if shutters are not properly sealed so that sharp edges tend to become rapidly worn and rounded. As rounded arrisses are difficult to form in vertical joints, edges should be chamfered and if a sealant is provided this should be set well back from the face to reduce the risk of damage through abrasion (Figure 6.32).

Maintenance costs will be reduced by detailing joints where possible to avoid the need for sealed joints in tidal zones or locations subject to severe abrasion. Where sealed joints are required, sealing components are either bitumen based or elastomeric and all require the use of a suitable primer which should be applied to *dry* concrete. Bitumen-based sealants are inexpensive and tend to be soft with only moderate resistance to erosion and damage by ultra-violet light. Their life may be extended by

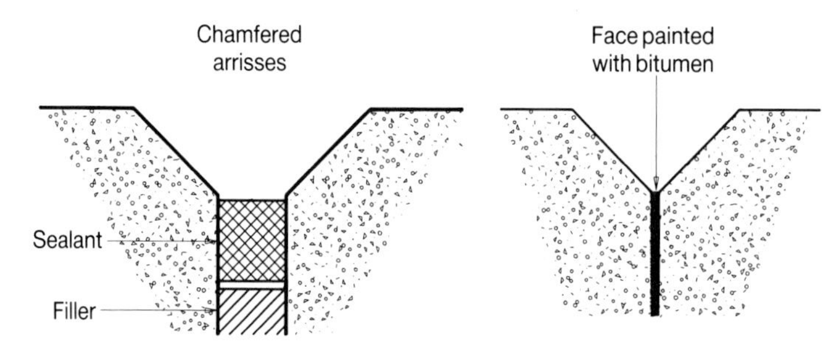

Figure 6.32 Sealed vertical joints

application of a rubber bitumen cover strip, which is easily repaired or replaced. Elastomeric sealers tend to be tough, provide a high degree of adhesion and good resistance to ultra-violet light, retaining their extensibility over a long period. These may be classified under three separate groups:

- Polysulphide polymer-based sealants: strong and durable but with a long curing period and liable to damage if immersed before full curing has taken place;
- Epoxy-based resin sealants: harder and can offer a high degree of resistance to abrasion, particularly suitable for sealing low movement and contraction joints but relatively expensive;
- Polyurethane polymer-based sealant: strong and durable with good resistance to biodegradation and abrasion and can be provided with an accelerating catalyst to promote a fast cure which is often useful in tidal applications.

The properties of proprietary sealants are dependent on their specific formulation as well as their broad generic type. Before recommending use of a particular sealant the engineer should ensure that there is satisfactory evidence that it will perform adequately. That evidence should preferably be used in similar environments elsewhere.

Where it is essential to provide a sealed joint in difficult or exposed conditions the detailer may also consider the use of preformed compressible sealing or capping strips fixed by adhesive or cast into the concrete (Figure 6.33).

The detailer should ensure when making provision for sealed joints within a tidal construction that all stages of the sealant operation, including curing of the sealant prior to tidal submersion, are capable of being completed within the available time. Whatever sealing system is used it is most important that the guidance of the manufacturer is obtained as to the suitability of the proposed sealant for the particular joint location and specified purpose.

Suitable sealants for use in marine works are widely available only in black and grey, but this is seldom a cause for concern provided sufficient care is taken when detailing the width and spacing of joint rebates in crest, parapet and back walls or other highly visible features. Chamfers and rebates can sometimes be used to good effect to mask horizontal or vertical construction joints or to create a feature by breaking up a plain concrete surface.

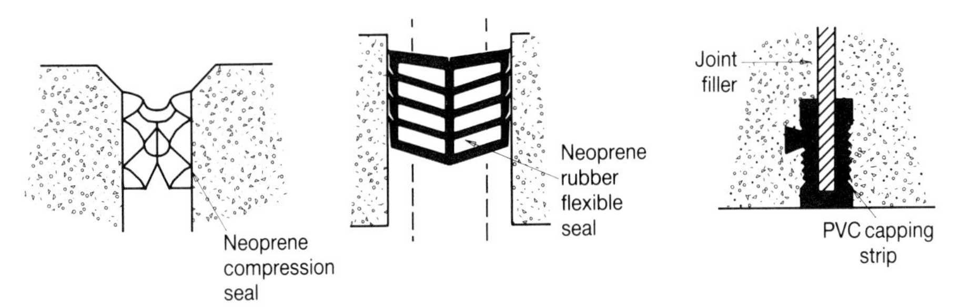

Figure 6.33 Preformed sealing or capping strips

Other joints

Vertical cantilever or anchored sheet-piled walls can be continuously constructed over any length without the need for joints other than those formed by the pile interlock. Joints in steel walings may be designed to carry shear or bending stresses; standard waling details can be obtained from the BSC or other piling handbooks. Joints may be omitted in low-level or underwater piled structures to facilitate construction and walings designed as short discontinuous beams.

Settlement of filling behind anchored walls and breastworks due to consolidation, recompaction of fill by wave impact or loss of fines through leaching, will induce bending in the tie bars, increasing the stress with a possibility of yield or failure occurring where bending is severe. The effects of bending may be reduced or eliminated by introducing pin couplers, rocker plates or spherical seatings to take up flexural movement (Figure 6.34).

6.9.6 Fixings (Table 6.8)

The overall aim of the detailer should be to produce fixings that are:

- Capable of transferring the design load;
- Simple to produce;
- Capable of being rapidly installed under prevailing site conditions;
- Robust and durable;
- Capable of replacement (if required).

Economies in the design of fixings are likely to be small compared with the overall cost of construction and are seldom justified in a marine environment. Failure of a single fixing or connection could lead to progressive overall failure. Methods of fixing include:

- Bolting;
- Welding;
- Screwing/spiking.

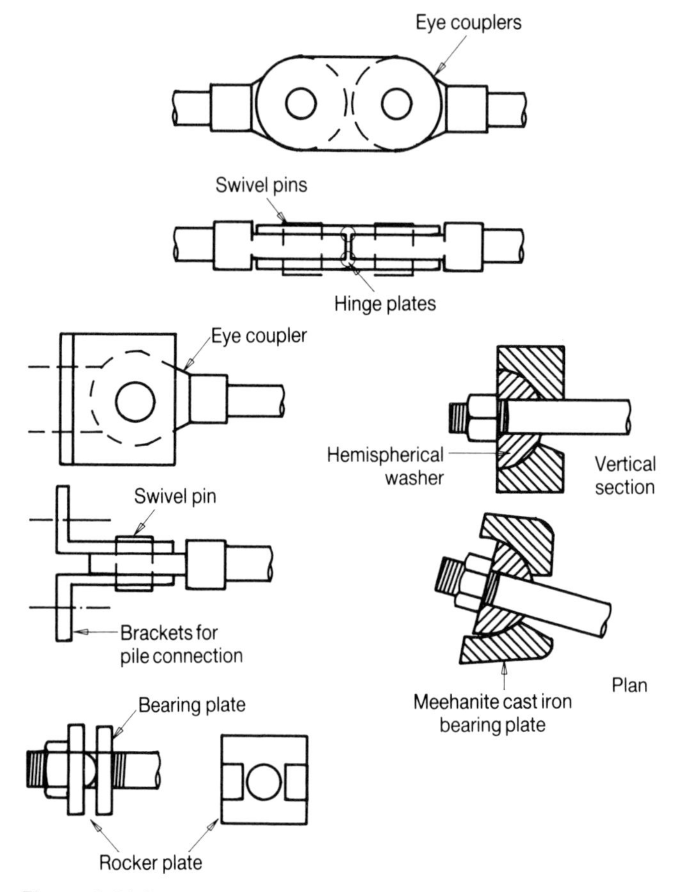

Figure 6.34 Connections in tie bars

Table 6.8 Bolted connections

Bolt and anchor types	*Typical uses*
Black bolts	General fixings steel and timber
Threaded rebar	Cast-in anchors, foundations and screw rods
Indented foundation bolts resin or cement grouted	Suitable for use with wall fixings
Screw sockets	Cast-in anchors
Self-drill	Mechanical wedge or expanding[a]
Expanding bolts	Action suitable for temporary and permanent site fixings including wall mountings[a]
Wedge anchors and stud anchors	Mechanical and cast in place
Eye bolts and U bolts	Fixings for handling and lifting
Tie rods	Cross ties, bracings, toe and wall anchors
Rock anchors	Post-tension, high-yield bars for holding down and tie backs with mechanical or grouted anchorage
Ground anchors	Grouted high-yield cables for holding down and tie back

[a]Use galvanized or stainless steel for permanent fixings.

Bolting

The detailer should adopt a generous approach in determining bolt diameters and keep the number of bolts to the minimum required for the proper function of the connection. Bolts of less than 20 mm diameter are generally considered unsuitable for use in structural connections in exposed positions. For more detailed information on fixings in steelwork reference should be made to BS 449[58].

Bolted connections in flexible structures such as cribwork which are subject to regular wave-induced sway or vibration are liable to become slack and worn and under extreme conditions bolts can drop out, causing the loss of a member or severe damage to the structure. This may be largely avoided by the use of double-lock or self-locking nuts or by spot welding nuts after tightening.

Steelwork fabrication should include drilling of the bolt holes. Burnt holes should, in general, only be used for temporary works but where approved for permanent construction should be cut to size using a suitable template. The diameter of prebored bolt holes in timbers is best determined by trial drilling and should be such that when driven home the bolt forms a tight fit.

Caution should be exercised in considering the use of exposed stainless bolts. The lack of corrosion renders them easily removed, either by vandals or by naturally working loose, unless they are locked tight. Proprietary anti-theft nuts may be considered.

The replacement of permanent fixings cast into concrete or grouted into preformed holes can be difficult and costly. Consideration should be given to the use of heavier sections, corrosion-resistant materials, or external protection.

There is a wide range of special and proprietary bolts available in mild steel and corrosion-resistant materials suitable for both general use and special fixings. Resin grouts with high bond strength are available in either pouring or capsule grades, enabling horizontal and vertical anchor fixings to be formed in tidal locations.

Welding

Welded joints for structural steel components are commonly used in maritime construction often in conjunction with bolted connections. Manual metal-arc processes are generally adopted for this purpose and carried out in accordance with the requirements of BS 6322[53] or 5135[54].

A significant part of the time and cost in forming a welded connection is that of the joint preparation. Where possible, welded fixings should be detailed to enable fabrication to be carried out under controlled conditions within weatherproof workshops. Fillet welds will generally require least preparation. The welding of hardened or carbon manganese steels including bullhead rails should only be undertaken in strictly controlled conditions. Oxyacetylene gas welding is generally only used for temporary fixings. A generous approach should be adopted in the choice of weld size for site welds. Site-welded fixings close to low water or within locations subject to tidal swell may result in delay to the construction programme.

Screws and spikes

Square-headed gimlet-pointed coachscrews are available in diameters up to 25 mm and lengths to 400 mm and are suitable for temporary or permanent fixing of planking, cladding or fixings of secondary importance. Timbers are predrilled to prevent splitting, the diameter of the hole being determined by experiment to suit the timber. Coachscrews can be quickly and safely positioned using air-operated drills and screw wrenches. Heavy-gauge brass screws may be used for ancillary non-structural fixings in timber such as guard rails, seats, information boards, etc.

Square-section spikes are used for permanent fixing of timber deckings or for temporary works. Pilot holes are predrilled and counterbored to enable the head of the spike to be driven home flush with the finished surface. Coachscrews and spikes are normally provided galvanized when used in timber construction.

6.9.7 Drainage

It is uncommon for a seawall, the adjacent foundations and subsoil to be either fully free draining or totally impermeable. The design should ensure adequate provision for surface water and subsurface drainage within and through the seawall to enable it and its component parts to function effectively.

Pressure relief to seawalls

Due consideration should be given to the placement, configuration and detailing of the drains so as to ensure that the system is capable of removing the volume of water at the required rate while minimizing disturbance to the surrounding area.

Non-porous walls constructed on natural shingle or gravel beaches will normally require little additional provision for drainage other than protection against the leaching out of fines. Excess water will tend to be rapidly dissipated and drain through the backfill and sub-base. Walls founded on clay or rock or those provided with deep continuous toe walls that penetrate to impermeable strata and interrupt the natural drainage path beneath the wall are potentially liable to suffer from the effects of a build-up of hydrostatic pressure. Where a change in water level occurs, as in the case of tidal fluctuations, the function of the drainage system should be to minimize the differential pressure head to reduce loading on the back of the wall.

The simplest and most commonly adopted systems to control and dissipate water pressure are provided by means of open-ended weep pipes. A single row of holes positioned close to the base of the wall may appear to provide the optimum solution, but in practice such holes can easily become covered or blocked. On sites where beach levels are liable to fluctuate, two or more levels of weep pipes may be provided. Care should be taken over the vertical and horizontal spacing to avoid setting up a large differential head on a falling tide. Unguarded weep pipes will enable seawater driven by tides and wave action to pass into the backfill as well as allow water to drain out, and carefully constructed filters are needed to ensure that fine particles are not carried away with the discharge. Pipes of 75–100 mm diameter are frequently used, the size being decided more by the nature of the beach material than their capacity for hydraulic discharge. Spacing of outlets will normally be determined by the nature and permeability of the backfill, but a spacing of less than 2 m is seldom justified.

The provision of flap valves is recommended where the location of weep pipes is subject to inundation by ordinary tides or the seawall is particularly sensitive to trapped water. In operation, flap valves may be propped open by debris or vandalism, but, on balance, they do reduce inflow. The minimum practical size is probably 100 mm and double-hung valves are to be preferred on the grounds of reliability.

In low-permeability soils where the build-up of water head is likely to be slow and due to natural seepage and dissipation of pore-water pressures, water levels may be controlled by the provision of low-level drainage systems placed within the backfill. These may consist of porous or open-jointed pipe collecting drains laid to falls between inspection chambers. Discharge can be through gravity outlets or by means of pumps.

Inspection chambers can be conveniently constructed to any depth to suit site requirements using pre-cast box or ring sections. The provision of heavy-duty lockable covers will prevent lifting through back pressure generated by sudden fluctuations in water level or their unauthorized removal. For ease of access, chambers should have a minimum internal dimension of 1050 mm and be provided with built-in ladders or step irons. Regularly spaced chambers along the back of the wall will not only facilitate maintenance of the drainage systems but enable changes in water level to be conveniently and accurately monitored.

Drainage systems

The drainage of low-lying land or a floodplain will require ditches, dykes, etc., discharging to tidal outfalls at the seawall. When computing discharge flows and consequent storage levels, due allowance should be made for extended tide lock during the periods of high surge tides. The risk of the seawall being overtopped should be assessed and provision made for the evacuation of floodwater in the light of this risk. The capacity of an outfall and the storage available should be such that any differential water load applied to the seawall is tolerable.

Tidal outlets provided with flap valves can be affected by flotsam, a build-up of molluscs, changes in beach level or vandalism. The discharge capacity can be significantly reduced or backflow can take place. Outfall sluices need to be readily accessible for maintenance and protected from debris by bare grills or by housing within chambers. If entry, by children or adults, into the outfalls is possible, then outfalls become a potential hazard to the public.

The run-off from graded cliffs can be collected in longitudinal intercepting drains and piped to suitable outfalls. There is a wide variety of techniques available for sub-surface drainage of clay slopes, including systems incorporating piped rubble drains and secondary herringbone drains. The dewatering of deep-seated strata may require the use of specialist measures such as sand drains or pumped well systems.

Vegetation can be used to improve the stability of slopes but the root systems of unsuitable trees or shrubs will quickly choke any shallow drains in their vicinity. Grass or similar vegetation will tend to bind the surface of clay cliffs or back slopes and reduce the siltation of drains by material eroded from the surface.

All surface-drainage systems tend to have their effectiveness reduced by fine sediment, sand, shingle or litter, the degradation being greater where the flow is intermittent. The choice of size or pipe diameter should be generous; where practical, pipes should be laid to self-cleansing falls and grit traps provided. The provision for maintenance should be positive and may be expensive relative to the construction costs of the system. Even with routine maintenance it may not be possible to guarantee the effective life beyond some 25 years. Provision for renewal may be necessary where the system is essential to the long-term stability of the seawall and the area served.

6.9.3 Permanent access and safety provisions

The functional requirements, developed as discussed in Chapters 3 and 5, will determine the nature of access requirements to, along and across the seawall. Detailing the design will require established needs to be met with minimal impact on the hydraulic and structural performance of the seawall, and in a safe manner. Minimum access needs are likely to be for maintenance and repair of storm damage. More generally, safe access provision should be made for amenity and leisure activities, commercial operations and environmental needs of the area. The nature of the access will vary to meet the requirements of heavy plant, boats, pedestrians, etc.

Access

Openings formed in splash or flood walls for access may be closed off by means of stop logs, sliding, hinged or lifting flood gates. The clear width of openings should be sufficient to allow access for emergency services and maintenance plant. The number of openings should be kept to the absolute minimum, as each opening represents a potential weakness in the defence system.

Where access ways are normally left open and unguarded, provision should be made nearby for the secure storage of all materials necessary to effect a full closure. Hinged or sliding gates may be provided as single or pairs of gates and are generally fabricated in steel or steel and timber. Substantial pillars may be required to support the weight of wide or heavy hinged gates. Alternatively, additional support can be provided by means of a wheel or rollers under the opening edge.

Where space permits ramps should be considered as an alternative to temporary closures. These will provide permanent access without interfering with the integrity of the wall and require little maintenance. Ramp access for wheelchairs should be considered where access would otherwise be prohibited.

The inclusion of at least one beach-access ramp in each section of frontage is likely to be necessary for ease of future maintenance and access for emergency services. Ramps with a width of not less than 4 m and slope not steeper than 1 in 6 are likely to be considered acceptable for most purposes where there are no special access requirements.

Where only vertical or stepped access is available over kerb or flood walls or between tiered decks and promenades, light access ramps should be included for use of wheelchairs at a slope of not more than 1 in 12. Sides of ramps should be guarded and orientated with safety in mind.

Lengths of potentially tide-locked beach without a means of exit should be avoided. Steps should extend down to the lowest anticipated beach level where wide or frequent fluctuations in level are likely to occur. Steps should have a tread width of not less than 250 mm and a riser of not more than 200 m. Where possible, a non-slip surface should be provided and treads laid to self-draining falls. Long flights of steps of more than 12 risers without intermediate landings should be avoided. Steps and stairwells should be protected by means of guard-rails supported on robust uprights. Where possible, sloping rails should be fixed on brackets secured to the face of the wall (Figure 6.35).

Risers not exceeding 300 mm in stepped aprons and slopes flatter than 1 in 3 on plain surfaces may generally be considered acceptable for emergency access. Where space permits, ramps and steps should be set within the line of the seawall, orientated parallel to the wall and be positioned so that the slope faces away from the direction of the predominant storm waves to reduce the effect of local run-up. Inset ramps and stairwells should always be fully guarded with balustrading or safety rails.

Safety

Where members of the public enter, provision for their safety should be made. Prohibition of entry on its own is rarely sufficient. On high seawalls and on walls subject to wave wash and spray, in areas accessible to the public, the decking access

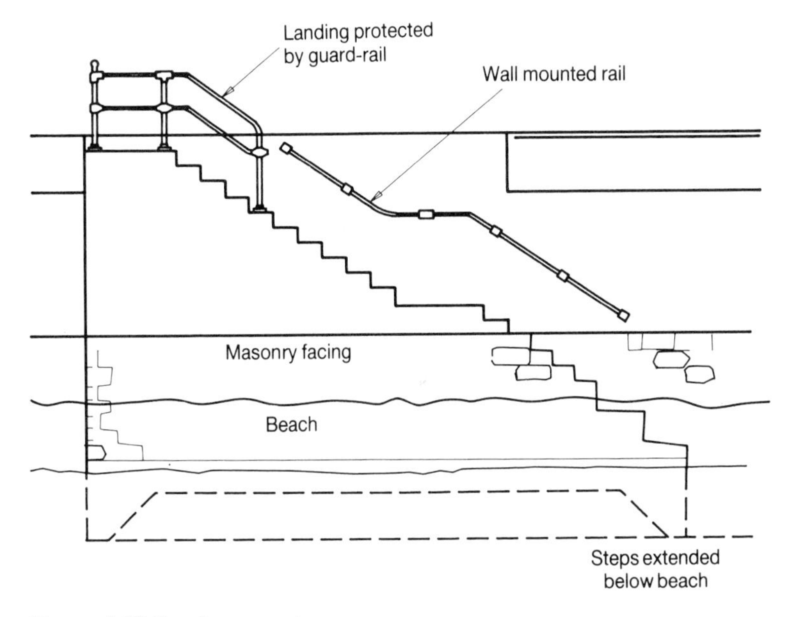

Figure 6.35 Beach access steps

steps and ramps should be protected by guard-rails to maintain public safety. Various proprietary systems and designs suitable for use in the marine environment are available in a variety of materials, including aluminium alloys, galvanized steel, stainless steel and cast iron. Two- or three-rail systems are considered suitable for most applications with a minimum top rail height of 1060 mm. In exposed locations rails may have to be checked for wave loading in addition to prescribed loading under BS 6399, Table 4[55] or, where vandalism is likely to be a serious problem, designed for additional destructive forces. The use of infill panels or close-slatted panels should be avoided on walls liable to overtopping by wave wash.

Where the crest of a high wall is carried up above the level of the deck to reduce overtopping or splash, consideration should also be given to safety aspects, including:

- Minimum height to avoid tripping (not less than 600 mm);
- Use of crest as a seat;
- Misuse of the top of wall by the unwary.

Most of these problems can be overcome by either shaping the crown of the wall or the incorporation of a single longitudinal rail within the crest (Figure 6.36).

Smooth float finishes to concrete surfaces may become slippery and should be avoided in areas subject to pedestrian and vehicular traffic. Low-level decking, ramps and step treads may quickly become contaminated by algae, lichen or other marine organisms, making surfaces hazardous to walk on. Surfaces above high water will not generally become contaminated if properly drained.

Medium/coarse tamped, brushed or wood float finishes can be provided to improve adhesion, but surfaces subject to abrasion are likely to become smooth within a relatively short time while generally remaining free from organic contamination. Very coarse tamp finishes should be avoided as they are uncomfortable to walk on and the troughs will retain moisture, encouraging growth of contaminating organisms and icing during cold weather.

Decking and paved surfaces subject to overtopping or spray should be laid to falls to ensure rapid draining without being dangerous to walk on. Falls of less than 1 in 30 or steeper than 1 in 20 should generally be avoided.

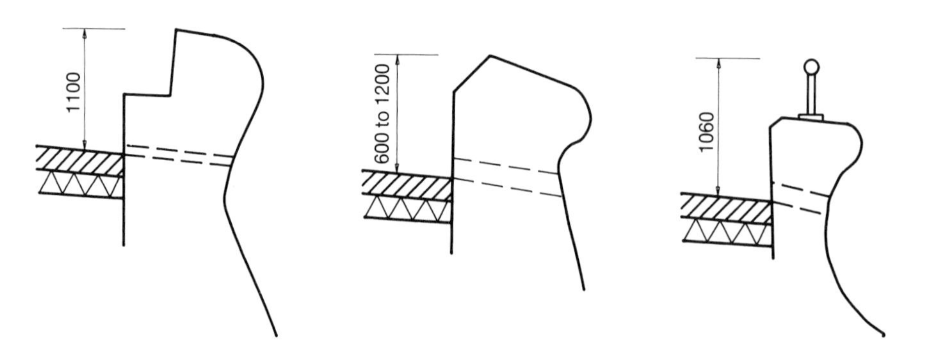

Figure 6.36 Seawall crest details

Flexible sloping walls of large random placed rock armour, random placed concrete units or pattern placed hollow concrete armour units form a potentially hazardous environment. The lower units may become slippery and coated in weed. The crevices and voids may be large enough to obscure a trapped or injured child from view. Access to such slopes should be discouraged and safe alternative access to any adjacent beaches provided.

Steel toe piling, piles in low-level crib construction or breastworks which are submerged at high water will constitute a danger to bathers on public beaches. Where abrasive conditions exist, exposed tops of steel piles may be rapidly worn to a jagged or razor sharp edge. Such potential dangers should be avoided by capping the piling with timber or concrete.

Where public access is provided for along a seawall at the foot of steep or high cliffs, consideration will need to be given to the condition of the cliff face and the risk of sudden falls, or the risk of stones becoming dislodged from the face by natural weathering, sea spray or birds. Detailed inspection and trimming of a large area of rockface or partial encasement or rock bolting to secure the face against minor falls may be effective but the cost may be high.

Where space is available to the rear of the seawall and major cliff falls are not anticipated, a measure of protection can be provided by containing falling debris behind flexible mesh fencing constructed along the rear of the decking at the foot of the cliff.

6.9.9 Appearances and finishes

Visual intrusion

Visual intrusion is a possible major impact of a seawall, and the engineer should consider carefully the appearance of the structure he is designing. Long lengths of straight, vertical concrete or piled walls, sloping aprons and revetments or wide expanses of plain decking tend to be uninteresting and intrusive and should be avoided where possible. The introduction of curves and offset lines for back walls produces a less severe effect where visual impact is important but may not always be possible to achieve. High vertical walls take on a more robust and natural appearance when faced in rock. The inclusion of split-level decks or sloping or stepped splash walls in place of wide plain surfaces provides a more compact appearance. Berms or sections of stepped wall, introduced into long lengths of sloping construction where justified on grounds of hydraulic performance, often improve the overall appearance. Symmetry and plainness of long lengths of wall may also be broken up by the careful location of ramps, steps or built-in amenity features such as seats or shelters.

Patterns and moulds for existing cast iron stanchions and balustrading are sometimes available locally. The inclusion of traditional ironwork along the top of a wall can be used to maintain continuity or to create a point of pleasing visual interest.

Features which may be incorporated to improve the aesthetic effect of the wall include:

- Profiled walls;
- Cappings and copes;
- Preformed panels and facings;
- Ornamental finishes.

Masonry is a material frequently used for enhancing the appearance of concrete walls, albeit at a cost, often in conjunction with its abrasion-resistant properties. This may be incorporated into the form of partial or full facing in both vertical and sloping walls. Dressed or specially shaped copings, nosings, kerbs or treads can be used to good effect to create functional as well as aesthetically pleasing results. It does, however, require specialist skilled labour, which is often difficult to obtain and costly. Timber can be less obtrusive than concrete or steel in many instances.

The appearance of continuous interlocking steel sheet piling in the construction of a crest wall will be improved by the inclusion of a prominent concrete or timber capping, but regular painting of the exposed steel surfaces with bitumastic may be required to maintain an acceptable appearance. High piled walls in prominent visible locations can, where necessary, be encased. Hot-rolled asphalt is suitable in many situations as an alternative surfacing material to concrete for large areas and will reduce surface glare. Asphalt is available in green and red in addition to traditional black, and tar spray and chip surfaces can be used to give a pleasing effect.

Finishes to concrete

The concrete finishes available to the engineer will depend on how the surface is created, e.g.:

- Cast against shuttering – near-vertical faces;
- Cast without shuttering – near-horizontal faces;
- Modified after casting.

Unwrought, rough or selected sawn timbers can be used in the shuttering to produce a textured or special board-marked finish or simply to form a rough key for bonding facing materials. Foamed polystyrene, polyurethene and PVC sheets or inserts can be used as linings to produce profiled or sculptured surface finishes where a highly ornamental effect is required. Rubber sheeting is also sometimes used as a lining to produce textured or profiled surfaces.

The type of finish to be applied to concrete decks, promenades, sloping aprons, walls and other unshuttered plain slabs will depend on the type of traffic they have to carry, area of bay or surface, level of abrasion, slope, speed of construction and aesthetic importance. The finishing treatment is not applied to the surface until the concrete has been fully compacted, screeded to level and obtained the degree of set necessary to receive the required finish. Suitable finishes include:

- Tamped;
- Float;

- Brush;
- Patterned print.

Fine to medium tamped or ribbed finishes are commonly applied to decks, promenades and ramps used by pedestrians and occasional vehicular traffic to increase slip resistance to surfaces that may become regularly wetted or dusted with fine sand. Corrugations should be rounded and not peaked or plucked. Coarse tamped finishes are not comfortable to walk on but are sometimes provided on steep sloping surfaces such as boat ramps or low-level surfaces used for access that may become coated in weed or algae. Tamped surfaces will quickly lose their effectiveness if subject to regular washing with sand and shingle.

A smooth uniform finish can be applied to small unshuttered level or sloping surfaces by means of hand or machine floats. To obtain an even consistency it will be necessary to delay the finishing operation until the concrete has sufficiently hardened to enable the surface to be worked without laitence being formed. For surfaces subject to coverage by the tide, sufficient time should be allowed for the concrete to attain the required degree of set, and for the completion of the finishing operation before the surface is submerged. For low-level work or surfaces liable to abrasion it will usually only be necessary to provide a trowelled or float finish to ensure a dense close-knit surface. For larger areas or where there is insufficient time to produce hand float finish the surface can be trowelled with a steel power float and then uniformly brushed with a stiff bristle broom to remove any float marks and produce an even combed effect.

The appearance of a flat, smooth surface can be given added interest and its non-slip characteristics improved where tamped or float finishes are unacceptable by the application of a patterned or footprint roller to the prepared concrete surface. Uniform battened or indented surfaces can be produced over large areas or provided to create local features or bordered panels. For concrete work white or grey cements normally produce the most natural effect. Colouring agents are available but are expensive and seldom used as uniform colour matching is difficult to maintain and colours are liable to fade. A wide and interesting choice of colour, shade and blend can be obtained by the careful selection of suitable aggregates and the removal of the outer mortar matrix to expose the aggregate surface. Where uniformity of colour is important materials should be obtained from a single reliable source and be free from impurities which cause staining when exposed to atmospheric weathering.

Finishes to other structural materials

Rock, concrete armour units or revetments, steel sheet piling, gabions, etc. provide very little opportunity for significant change in appearance at the detailing stage of seawall design.

Seawalls are likely to attract the attention of vandals and serious damage or disfiguration can be caused. By careful detailing it is possible to discourage vandalism and limit the effect and extent of damage. Plain smooth surfaces are more likely to be contaminated by graffiti than rough or textured surfaces, but the effects are more easily removed. Accumulated litter and timber seats in bays and re-entrants can be the source of fire damage to concrete surfaces. The use of concrete seats or stout timber slats securely fixed to concrete forms is likely to deter all but the most determined vandals.

Timber planks may be removed from breastworks for firewood or resale unless bolts are securely tightened. Nuts may have to be spot welded in difficult locations. Loose materials for repairs and maintenance should not be retained on-site unless stored in a secure compound. The modern vandal and pilferer is now often equipped with saws and spanners in addition to brute force, and there have been recorded incidents of long lengths of tubular handrail having been removed. Cast-in stanchions and the secure fixing of rails to each upright will help to deter would-be thieves. Loose rocks should, where possible, be of a sufficient size that will discourage their removal.

Vegetation to soil slopes

It is generally possible to re-establish interesting coastal flora on banks, graded cliffs and reclaimed areas within a relatively short time after completion of construction works by means of a careful programme of seeding, turfing and planting to coincide with the most suitable growing seasons. However, changes in the local ecology can be brought about by the introduction of new species of flora in grass seed, turf or by planting of shrubs not commonly associated with the area. In areas sensitive to ecological change it may be prudent to only use soils collected from the immediate vicinity and seed mixtures carefully selected to avoid contamination of the natural flora. Naturalist groups may recommend that trimmed and graded areas are left rough after construction to allow the area to recolonize naturally, but the merits of such a process will require in each case careful consideration in the light of further disturbance or instability likely to be caused by weathering and spray and the possible need for even shallower slopes.

The grassing of sea banks, crests, back slopes, reclaimed or filled areas, graded cliffs, etc., adjacent to or forming part of the seawall, can be used to bind the surface against wind erosion and provide limited resistance to scouring in areas subject to occasional inundation as well as to produce a pleasing and natural environment. Great care must be exercised over the selection of the seed mix and consultation with a reputable local seedsman as to what mixtures flourish best in the area is often a useful first step to the establishment of a successful grass cover. Grass may be sown by hand over small areas or by mechanical or hydraulic seeding methods over large areas. Hydraulic seeding methods incorporating a mulch are particularly suitable for steep slopes such as graded cliffs where access is difficult for normal seeding methods and ground conditions are exposed to drying and eroding winds. The resistance of seeded slopes to disturbance by wind and rain may be improved by incorporating geotextiles or geogrids into the surface layer, but there is little supporting technical information available at present on the various manufacturers' claims for these materials.

On horizontal berms or slopes subject to occasional coverage by the tide and light wave action scour resistance can be increased by the use of perforated concrete revetment blocks, the voids in which are filled with topsoil and seeded to produce a natural grass appearance when fully established.

In open rural areas sea banks may be liable to damage by grazing animals, including sheep, cattle and horses, or by uncontrolled pedestrian traffic, and temporary or permanent fencing may have to be considered.

The appearance of large plain or graded grassed areas can be made more interesting by landscaping where this can be achieved within the criteria governing stability or by interplanting with groups of shrubs. There are many shrubs which will grow well in a coastal environment and which are capable of tolerating various levels of exposure to wind, salt spray, drying and various soil conditions. Tyhurst[57] lists both the grasses and the shrubs grown successfully on the south coast. The shrubs include tamarix, escollonia and hippophae on the lower slopes with sallow, birch, poplar and holm oak on the upper ones. Elsewhere, gorse, blackthorn, hawthorn and bramble have been used. However, no particular species is likely to be universally acceptable, and a review of the indigenous shrubs local to the seawall is essential as a basis for a successful choice.

Planting of vigorous shrubs such as buckthorn will assist in the stabilization of slopes or dunes but can in time become invasive and dominate an area. On regraded or sandy coastlines the planting of marram grass (*Ammophila areneria*) is commonly practised to stabilize sandhills and back slopes which might otherwise be denuded by wind erosion. Shoots of marram grasses can be plucked and gathered locally where growth is prolific to produce a cheap and effective natural cover. Sea holly, sandwort, spurge and sea bindweed may also be found in stable sandy environments and can be sown or left to colonize naturally. On exposed sites natural or graded surfaces may have to be given temporary protection by kidding or pegging down a brushwood cover in conjunction with a planting programme. Marram grasses are easily damaged by foot traffic and fenced footpaths may have to be provided to control pedestrian access through dune areas.

Unless the special requirements of establishing shrubs and vegetation at each coastal site are fully understood and catered for, heavy losses will occur. Where possible, stock should be obtained from local sources so that it is already adapted to a coastal environment. Firm planting, staking, the provision of shelter from wind and avoidance of a dry root system will help young plants to become quickly established. Further information on use of vegetation in seawalls is contained in Coppin and Richards[36].

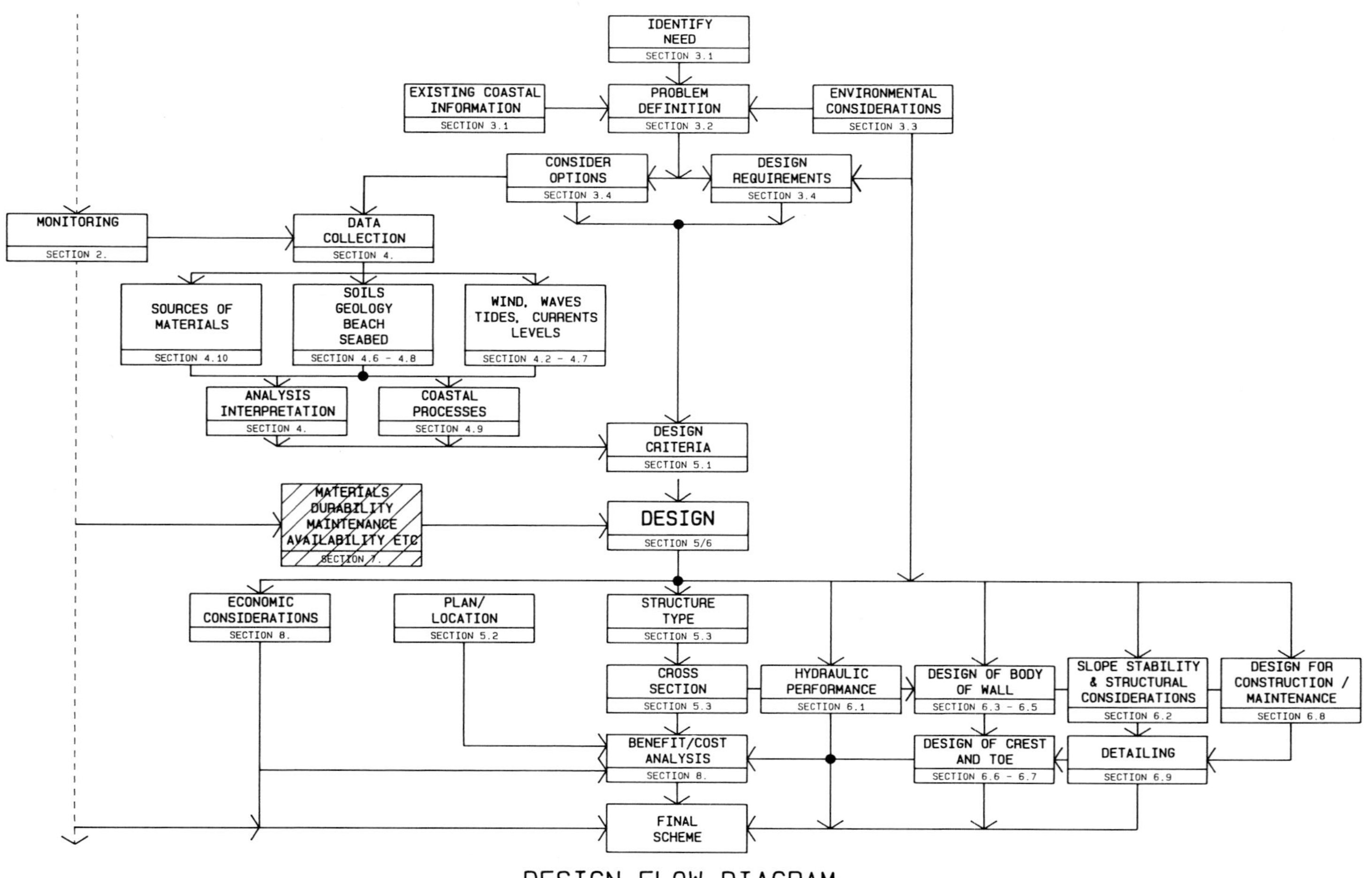

DESIGN FLOW DIAGRAM

7 Materials

The establishment of functional requirements for the seawall and the choice of suitable options for design have been outlined in previous chapters. The choice of materials will be a relevant consideration in the identification of options at each stage and subsequently in making a choice as to the preferred option. The engineer should choose materials that are:

- Suitably durable;
- Environmentally acceptable;
- Economical in use.

To support these considerations, this chapter concentrates particularly on strength and durability.

Section 7.1 discusses the overall aspects of the evaluation and selection of materials. Environmental aspects of different materials are discussed in Sections 3.3 and 5.4–5.4.6, and economy in the design is referred to as appropriate in Chapters 2, 3, 5 and 6.

Section 7.2 discusses the nature of the degradation suffered by the different materials and the zones in which the seawall is subject to the most severe conditions. The effects of abrasion, corrosion, biological attack, etc. are described as a basis for relating the choice of materials to the design life of the structure.

At the detailed design stage, the engineer will need to consider materials in more detailed terms and the physical properties of each will be relevant. Section 7.3 describes the characteristics of materials that are in general use and provides information to support the design process.

7.1 General considerations

The availability of suitable materials can be very site-specific and exercise a strong influence on the choice of solution to the problems posed by hydraulic and structural considerations. In addition, cost of material supply, ease of working and working life are relevant to the cost-effectiveness of the chosen form of construction. Environmental considerations, including appearance, should influence the form of structure and the materials used will have a great impact.

The characteristics of conventional materials when used in seawalls, are generally well researched and extensively reported. Markets for supply are well established and provide good initial information on costs.

In choosing the most appropriate materials, forward projections as to working life and acceptable maintenance commitments are required. If replacement or partial renewal at some future date is contemplated then the engineer should be satisfied that there will be continuity of supply, as well as on practical matters such as access, the ongoing capability of the client organization to manage such work and the impact on the environment of these maintenance activities.

The structural performance of conventional materials is generally well documented. Structures should be proportioned to suit anticipated loads and the design stresses. Care is needed to ensure that proportions are appropriate to the most critical stress and that the design stresses chosen are appropriate to both the material and its environment. Some materials are more capable of sustaining higher stresses caused by short-term or impact loading than those caused by long-term loading. For economic design this advantage should be utilized.

7.2 Required characteristics of materials

Seawalls, and the materials that comprise them, must survive in a hostile environment. They must resist abrasion, chemical attack, corrosion, marine borers and vandalism. Durability of materials, and especially loss by abrasion, is very site-specific. There are few stretches of coastline in the UK which do not have existing structures in the vicinity. Such structures represent a practical means of assessing locally the scale of abrasive activity.

Information on age and specification can be obtained from records or may be derived from inspection. Comparative influences of hydraulic circumstances and foreshore conditions can be readily observed. The engineer will then have a measure of the performance of different materials in conditions comparable with those envisaged. Fundamentally unsuitable materials can be discarded.

Figure 7.1 shows three broad categories of requirements for the materials to be used in seawalls. The nature of these requirements is reviewed in Sections 7.2.1 to 7.2.6 and the degree to which various materials meet the needs stated is outlined in Sections 7.3.1 to 7.3.9.

7.2.1 Strength

Ultimate and recommended working stresses are well documented for conventional materials. Section 7.3 includes physical characteristics in general and suggested stresses in particular for the materials listed.

Strength data are generally based on testing samples, and care needs to be exercised to ensure that the strength characteristics assumed are properly representative of the

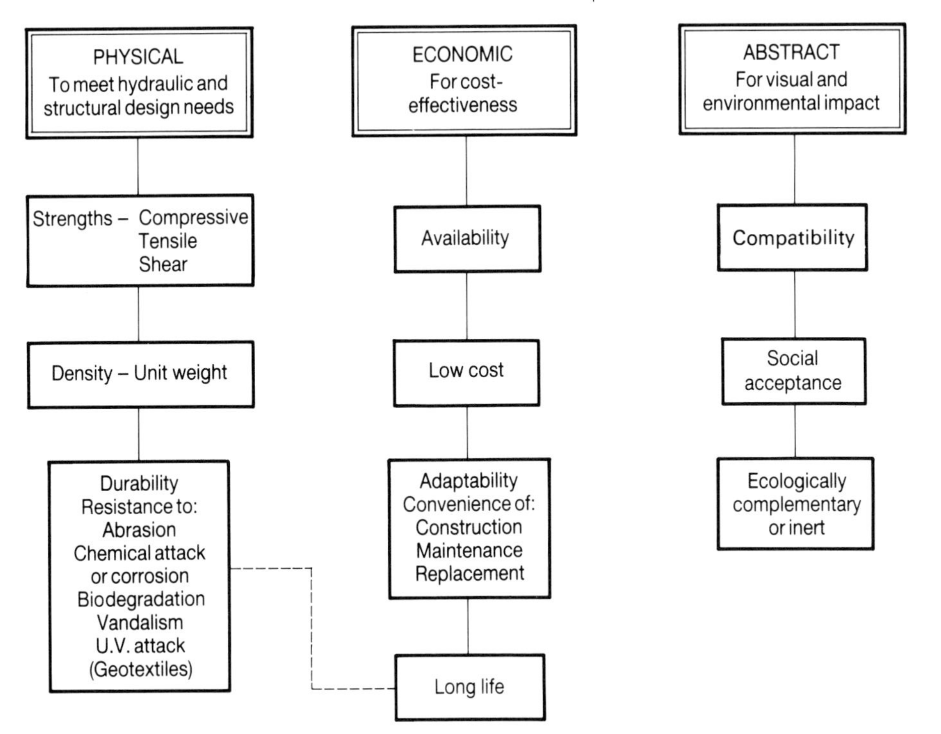

Figure 7.1 Materials of construction – characteristics required

materials and their application. This is especially relevant to seawall components where the environment may change the geometry of the structure or the nature of the materials. Examples are the reduction in section by abrasion or corrosion, the reduced effectiveness of some timber species following immersion in seawater, change in unit shape of rock with weathering, etc.

Where mechanical characteristics for particular materials are given in Section 7.3, both ultimate and working stresses are quoted to give the designer freedom to analyse by assuming the final state or to study the initial state at reduced permissible stresses. In using material from tables in Section 7.3 it is important to choose the figures appropriate to the analysis being undertaken.

7.2.2 Durability

The general description, durability, is taken to include resistance to the climate, abrasion by foreshore material, chemical attack/corrosion and biodegradation by bacteria, worms or molluscs. Figure 7.2 is a diagrammatic representation of a seawall and foreshore which shows the limits of waves and tides, a representative time distribution for water level and four zones used to describe the differing environments encountered around the crest, body and toe of a seawall. It will be seen that the tidal characteristics determine the cumulative time for a given water level and that this is

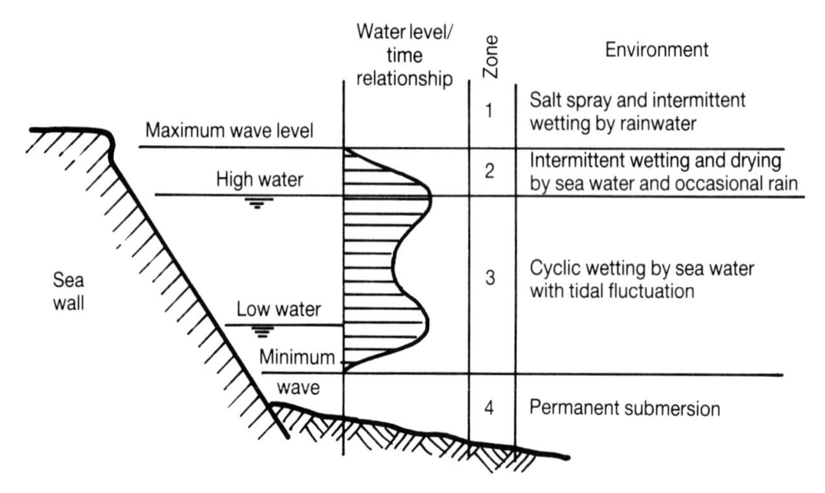

Figure 7.2 The weathering zones of a seawall

usually greatest near high and low water. The seawall above highest wave level is in zone 1 and receives wind-blown salt spray plus rain and exposure to the sun and drying winds. It is an environment conducive to corrosion and chemical attack. The face of the seawall between highest wave level and high water, zone 2, is intermittently wetted by both seawater and rainwater, which is conducive to both chloride penetration and corrosion. The cyclic wetting and drying of the seawall between high water and the lowest wave level in zone 3 provides conditions for chloride penetration, corrosion and abrasion by foreshore materials moved by wave or tidal currents. Permanent submersion of the seawall in zone 4 inhibits corrosion and normally produces only limited abrasion. Zones 2 and 3 are sometimes referred to collectively as the splash zone.

The manner in which abrasion, chemical attack/corrosion and biodegradation reduces durability varies both with the location in the seawall and with the type of material considered. The components are also interactive. However, it is convenient to consider them separately with appropriate reference to location and material where particularly relevant.

7.2.3 Resistance to abrasion

A seawall on a sand or shingle foreshore will be subject to abrasion by particles of the foreshore carried by tide and wave currents and driven into contact with the wall. If the material size is large enough to resist motion no abrasion will occur, but the larger the particles carried, the greater will be the rate of abrasion. This concept is illustrated and quantified to a degree in Figure 7.3.

The four main zones of wave and water attack on a seawall are shown in Figure 7.2. The crest of a seawall in zone 1 will suffer minor abrasion from windborne particles which may damage paint or plastic but is of little consequence to the structural materials of the wall. Similarly, in zone 2 the added wetting and drying may cause

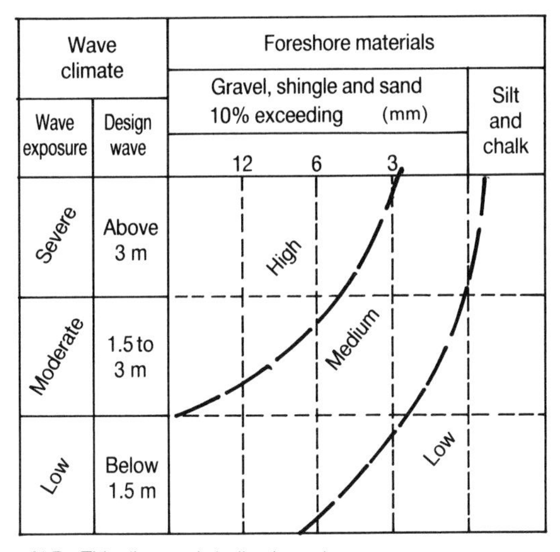

N.B. This diagram is indicative only

Figure 7.3 Abrasion forces

some weathering but structural damage is not expected from abrasion. The full abrasive effects on the wall are likely to be in zone 3 and concentrated at a level just above or around highest beach level. While there will be some abrasion in zone 4, the zone of permanent submersion, it will not approach the intensity of that in zone 3. The long-term effect of abrasion to the body of a seawall in zone 3 will depend on the water movement experienced and the nature of the foreshore. High rates of abrasion resulting from waves over 3 m high and a shingle foreshore can be expected to scour away the face of concrete to expose the large aggregate in a few months. The surface removal beyond this stage will be much slower provided:

- The coarse aggregate used is as hard as the beach shingle;
- The fine aggregate used is the minimum needed to ensure a dense concrete;
- The cement/aggregate ratio is adequate;
- The water/cement ratio is the minimum to facilitate placing and compaction of the concrete;
- The concrete has been fully compacted.

Concrete mix design for areas of high abrasion risk is dealt with in Section 7.3.3.

Large rock used in zone 3 and subjected to high levels of abrasion will be smoothed by the removal of sharp edges in a short time. However, subsequent loss from the rounded profiles will be very much slower, being of little consequence to stability provided that the rock used is harder than the foreshore materials and the mass of individual units is adequate to prevent movement by waves.

High rates of abrasion can be expected to remove the corners of dense hardwoods located in zone 3 in as little as one year. The effect on plain surfaces is slower but may be a few millimetres each year.

It is impractical to separate loss from steel faces due to abrasion from that caused by corrosion. The combined effect on localized areas of steel placed in zone 3 and subjected to high rates of abrasion is a loss of up to one millimetre each year. Often abrasion of steel occurs in patches without any obvious reason why local attack should be more extreme than general reduction.

Abrasion losses to materials in zone 3, subjected to medium abrasion forces (because of either reduced wave action, smaller stone or both), are likely to be less than half the extreme figures quoted. Losses in areas of low abrasion can normally be ignored unless materials are below normal standards.

7.2.4 Resistance to chemical attack and corrosion

The chemistry of seawater and its temperature range are relevant to the chemistry of degradation. The salinity of the sea surrounding the UK is approximately 34 g total salt/litre and the variation is quite small. Minimum seashore temperatures are such that heavy ice formation is not expected, but maximum temperatures are difficult to assess as they depend on orientation and local effects. However, the range of temperature is likely to be low by world standards.

Reinforced concrete

Seawater salts will react with constituents of concrete at rates limited by the temperate climate. In the presence of oxygen and water, steel will corrode. Where steel embedded in concrete corrodes, the corrosion products will cause expansive forces which will burst the concrete.

The processes of chemical attack and corrosion are briefly described below and rates of degradation are assessed. Factors which increase the rate of degradation and actions which might be used to slow it are reviewed. Further details as to constituents and working practices are given in Section 7.3.

Seawater attack on reinforced concrete in seawalls occurs in three stages:

- The reduction of the chemical protection given to reinforcement by the concrete surrounding it (loss of passivity);
- Oxidation of the reinforcement and generation of expansive forces within the concrete (rusting);
- Spalling away of the concrete cover to the reinforcement and accelerated corrosion.

Visible spalling, the third stage, is an indication of a substantial problem which is likely to lead ultimately to failure. The stages described above are discussed in more detail below.

Initially, the reinforcement is protected by a combination of chemical reactions on the surface of the steel and the barrier provided by the concrete cover. Fresh concrete is very alkaline with pH values ranging from 12.6 to 13.5 and at these pH levels the electrochemical reactions of the corrosion processes are inhibited. Chlorides from seawater penetrate the concrete during the life of the structure and reduce its alkalinity. The rate ingress of the chloride is controlled by the thickness of the concrete cover and the permeability of the concrete. These factors also determine the rate of diffusion of oxygen and moisture which are also necessary for corrosion to occur.

Corrosion of reinforcement in a concrete seawall is usually as a result of chloride attack. However, an alternative process, known as carbonation, should be mentioned. Carbonation is the effect of atmospheric carbon dioxide reacting with the alkaline materials in concrete to reduce the alkalinity and allow corrosion to commence. The onset of corrosion does not take place until the carbon dioxide diffuses through the concrete cover. Corrosion will then only occur when sufficient moisture is present. Carbonation appears to be largely inhibited in a seawall environment by the presence of the chlorides.

Once the alkaline environment is destroyed by the ingress of chlorides the metal ions react in the presence of oxygen and water to form ferrous or ferric oxides. The oxides occupy considerably more volume than that of the steel destroyed and exert internal expansive forces large enough to spall off the concrete cover.

By the time the concrete cover is spalled away, the bond between concrete and steel is much reduced and the reinforced concrete is no longer an effective composite material. The reinforcement is even more vulnerable to corrosion, as it is exposed to a ready supply of oxygen and water with the result that the process is accelerated.

The penetration of chlorides into concrete will reduce alkalinity and eventually make the maintenance of passivity impossible. Recent results from the Concrete in the Oceans programme reported by Leeming[3] indicate that in the splash zone:

- Chloride will penetrate cover of 25 to 75 mm to reach the reinforcement in ten years;
- Chloride reaches the reinforcing steel down cracks as small as 0.1 mm at the surface early in the design life of the structure, and this is the forerunner of corrosion to the steel;
- Moist curing of green concrete in the absence of chlorides reduces chloride penetration relative to that for air-cured concrete;
- Curing with seawater increases the rate of penetration;
- The addition of some 20% pulverized fuel ash reduces penetration of chlorides.

This work suggests that mass concrete should be used in preference to reinforced concrete within zones 2 and 3 wherever this is a practical proposition. It further indicates that where reinforcement is provided all possible steps should be taken to minimize surface cracking, and that workmanship in placing concrete should be such as will ensure no defects in the cover to the reinforcement. Curing should be moist and free from chlorides.

While the penetration of chlorides will lead to loss of chemical protection of reinforcement from corrosion this stage is by no means the end of structural integrity of a seawall. If the reinforcement is in close contact with the cement paste, then the diffusion of oxygen proceeds very slowly and rust formation is inhibited. Given concrete with complete absence of avoidable defects, then the life expectancy is very long. The use of materials and the construction process should be such as will come as close as possible to the creation of defect-free concrete. Section 7.3.2 discusses the materials and workmanship necessary to achieve this.

Iron and steel

Steel sheet piling, plates and bolts may be considered as a group, even though bolts may be used to connect timber or other materials. A proportion of the surfaces is likely to be exposed and corrosion accelerated by the salinity of the environment. The removal of inhibiting corrosion products by water or windborne sand ensures that corrosion is virtually continuous and at the maximum rate for the material.

The loss by corrosion alone, from one face of steel sheet piling, has been reported by British Steel as up to 0.15 mm/year in zones 2 and 3. The maximum corrosion losses were observed at mean low water and just above mean high water, while losses at mid-tide were only about one third of the maximum. The addition of copper to mild steel appears to have little effect on the rate of corrosion.

Surface treatment to exposed iron, be it galvanizing, painting or coating with some other inert substance, is only of value in preventing corrosion attack for an early limited period in the life of the structure and is discussed in Section 6.5.2.

7.2.5 Resistance to biological degradation

Of the materials commonly used in seawalls only timber is susceptible to animal attack or decay. The figures in Section 5.4 show the more common applications.

Signs of infestation by gribble (*Limnoria* sp.) or shipworm (*Teredo* sp.) should be sought during reconnaissance of the site and in adjacent areas. Gribble attacks the surface of exposed timber predominantly below mean tide, initially penetrating up to about 10 mm. The resulting ragged surfaces are most noticeable above low water, probably because water movement and abrasion emphasize the effects of attack, leaving a typically stringy surface. Teredo shows little evidence of entry but is capable of destruction from within the timber over a few years. Evidence of infestation is only visible where surfaces have been abraded or broken away.

The small animals known commonly as gribble are crustaceans resembling wood lice and are of a similar size. Individual burrows are about 2 mm in diameter and the multiplicity of holes produces an appearance of a very open-textured surface. Gribble breed within the timber, the young commencing boring from the parent burrows. New infestation probably results from dispersion by tidal movements, but the animal is capable of swimming short distances.

Teredo enters suitable timbers after a free-swimming larval stage, the point of entry being less than 0.50 mm in diameter. The burrow is progressively enlarged, generally heading along the grain, and may become up to 500 mm long in tunnels 10 mm in diameter. The tunnels are lined with a white calcareous deposit.

The distribution of gribble and teredo has been surveyed by the Timber Research and Development Association, who found that gribble infestation either existed or was capable of existing anywhere on the UK coastline. Teredo infestation was much less severe and more dependent on local circumstances of water temperature, salinity, pollution, etc. Various observations have indicated that both gribble and teredo thrive in a clean environment warmed by cooling water discharges and that their activity is stimulated by the warmth. The absence of teredo and reduced activity of gribble adjacent to industrial areas suggests that pollution inhibits their existence.

Some timbers, mostly exotic hardwoods, show a very high resistance to animal attack which borders on immunity. Timber species likely to be used in seawalls generally have been classified into groups varying from non-durable to very durable, and some of these are tabulated in Section 7.3.5. The very durable class of timber can be relied on to survive in an effective condition for more than 20 years, and examples are known in which 100 years has been exceeded.

In a marine environment decay is rarely a problem, as salt water acts as a preservative and salt deposition inhibits fungal decay. Only when salt deposits are completely washed away by rainwater is the risk of decay a cause for concern. Timber driven as sheet piles is also free from decay provided it is continuously in contact with the ground, as there is insufficient oxygen available to support decay fungi. The areas of concern to the engineer are reduced to ground surfaces remote from salt water spray and possibly some high-level horizontal surfaces where rainwater might accumulate. Generally, those timbers resistant to marine borers are also resistant to decay. Minor pockets conducive to fungal decay are then catered for.

The application of preservatives to timbers used for seawalls is usually impractical. The dense species used to resist abrasion and provide high strength do not allow preservatives to penetrate to a sufficient depth. Preservative application is enhanced as moisture content is lowered and it is impractical to reduce the moisture content of the large sections required. Preservative treatment forms a shell which, if breached, is ineffective. It is not a practical proposition to create and maintain the integrity of the shell in the hostile environment of the seashore.

7.2.6 Availability

The availability of suitable local materials can have a far-reaching effect on the design of a seawall. However, the matter is very site-specific and only limited general guidance can be given.

Natural materials occurring locally in quantity and quality, required for construction and future maintenance, can avoid potential delays and unnecessary haulage costs. However, prices can be influenced by foreseen demand and a review of possible sources that goes beyond the obvious is recommended. Quarries for suitable rock, aggregate pits, waste product and byproducts of local industry are best explored using trade associations and directories followed by visits to promising sources. Cement, steel and timber are products that show little fluctuation in supply and cost, but delivery times should be sought in the light of the quantities involved. Imported materials may be subject to EC regulation. The storage available at the construction site will be relevant to the use of materials in intermittent supply and the possibility of pre-ordering to avoid initial delay.

Discussion with other client organizations or engineers in the area will introduce the substantial benefit of experience. Design for construction is considered in Section 6.8 and reference is made to the influence of availability and cost of materials in Section 6.8.6.

7.3 Characteristics of materials in use

7.3.1 General practice

It will be seen from the figures in Sections 5.4, 5.5 and 5.6 that the crests of larger walls are commonly, but not exclusively, concrete. The facing of the body of the wall is usually rock or concrete, but timber, steel and asphalt can be used in support or to retain the facings. The walls generally have toe piling to ensure support is not progressively washed away if the beach level falls and this may be steel or timber. Other materials are used to serve ancillary functions. Materials likely to be favoured in some part of seawall construction are reviewed individually below, but it should be recognized that they are rarely used in isolation.

7.3.2 Stone for armouring and protective works

The UK climate is regarded as temperate and the practices recommended are specific to those circumstances. This book is concerned with seawalls, but breakwater practice is drawn on as relevant, although it is usually related to more severe wave conditions.

The design of protection systems for seawalls is described in Chapter 5 and Sections 6.3–6.5. It will be seen that armouring or pitching with nominally single-size rock blocks is a suitable system for revetments in moderate to severe wave climates. Alternatively, rip-rap – having a wider range of block sizes and random placed – may be chosen for less severe conditions. Dressed rock for masonry faces to vertical walls requires the same attributes as rock used for armouring, but additionally it should be suitable for preparing to the shapes and finishes required.

The basic geological characteristics of igneous, metamorphic and sedimentary rocks are shown in Table 7.1, which is based on work by Fookes and Poole[1]. Although igneous rock is to be preferred, suitable stone can be found from the metamorphic and sedimentary rocks described.

Rock placed as armouring to the sloping face of a seawall will inevitably suffer some degradation, but with appropriate design and choice of material, such changes as occur within the life of a wall are quite tolerable. Such surface losses will alter the initial interlock, friction and weight of individual stones but within the limits of the design assumptions.

The degradation is essentially physical, the processes being spalling, fracture and abrasion. Solution loss can become a problem with poorer-quality rocks, particularly in warmer climates. The spalling of surface layers is most commonly associated with salt attack, alteration of minerals and expansion of clay minerals. The splitting of blocks into large sections will occur with handling during construction or with wave action sufficient to move the blocks if there are incipient planes of weakness within the rock chosen. Abrasion will take place as a result of adjacent blocks rubbing when moved by extreme wave action but, more commonly, by wave action carrying foreshore particles into the exposed faces.

Single-size stone will be required for pitching or armouring and the nominal size should be chosen by the engineer with reference to expected wave conditions (Section 6.2). Generally, a prismoidal shape of individual stones should be preferred with maximum dimension rarely exceeding twice the minimum dimension and never exceeding three times. Weathered outcrops may indicate the form that quarried stones are likely to take and Figure 7.4 illustrates the forms and terms used to describe them. The engineer should be cautious in estimating the output of armour stone from a quarry as it will often involve blasting techniques different from those normally used by the operator. Often the yield is less than 5% of total output. When assessing the possible output, the engineer would be well advised to consult a suitably experienced engineering geologist.

The characteristics of rock available may be assessed for use as protection using the tests specified in BS 812[13]. Those regarded as particularly relevant are:

Apparent relative density	min 2.6
Water absorption	n.e. 2½–3%
Aggregate impact value	n.e. 25–30%
Soundness – magnesium sulphate	n.e. 12–18%
Abrasion value	n.e. 15%

The more stringent values arise from recommendations by Allsop *et al.*[2] following research on the stability of rubble breakwaters. An additional test for fracture toughness is also suggested and a suitable limiting value of 0.7 $MN/m^{3/2}$ is given.

The limiting values suggested are for protection placed between high and low water levels, and some fall in quality might be tolerated outside these zones if separation of rock qualities can be guaranteed. Within the zone the more severe criteria might be adopted where future maintenance is expected to be difficult or expensive because of access or other problems. Soundness is probably the most useful single indicator, but impact value and density should not be overlooked. The test procedures are well documented but the tests are not ideal, as they have been developed for use on aggregates.

The engineering characteristics found in common rocks together with notes of performance to be expected in breakwaters is shown in Table 7.2 taken from Fookes and Poole. Single stones are normally specified by weight with upper and lower limits, being 75% and 125% of the nominal weight as specified by the design.

The choice of rock for rip-rap, filter stone and core materials should be based on the criteria used to assess armouring but modified to recognize the less severe wave and tide climate. The grading should be wider both to allow the material to fulfil its purpose and to allow economic production.

Rip-rap should be specified by a size range of $0.13W(50)$ to $4.0W(50)$, where $W(50)$

Table 7.1 Simple geological characteristics of common rocks

Igneous rocks: strong rocks with interlocking crystals

Rock type name	*Typical grain size range (mm)*	*Visible voids*	*Relative weathered state*	*Typical joint spacing (m)*	*Typical fragment shapes*	*Typical distribution*
Granite	20–2	Common: small or microscopic	Fresh to moderate	0.5–10	Equant	Mountain and shield areas: extensive
Diorite	3–1	Rare	Slight to moderate	0.2–10	Equant	Localized areas
Gabbro	5–2	Very rare	Fresh to highly	0.5–10	Equant	Mountain areas: localized
Rhyolite	Grains not visible to unaided eye	Rare	Fresh to slight	0.1–2	Equant Prolate Tabular	Localized areas
Andesite	Grains not visible to unaided eye	Rare: small and large	Slight to moderate	0.2–2	Tabular Prolate	Extensive sheets
Basalt	Grains not visible to unaided eye	Common: large and small	Fresh to highly	0.2–5	Tabular Prolate Equant	Extensive sheets
Serpentinite	Grains not visible to unaided eye	None	Slight to highly	0.05–1	Equant	Mountain areas: localized

Metamorphic rocks: crystals usually interlocking but grain orientation common

Rock type name	*Typical grain size range (mm)*	*Texture*	*Relative weathered state*	*Typical joint spacing (m)*	*Typical fragment shapes*	*Typical distribution*
Slate	0.01	Narrow size range: orientated	Fresh	0.002–0.1	Tabular	Localized areas

Phyllite	0.5–0.1	Narrow size range: orientated grains	Fresh to moderate	0.01–0.2	Tabular bladed	Extensive areas
Schist	5–0.5	Narrow size range: orientated grains	Fresh to moderate	0.01–1	Tabular bladed	Extensive areas
Gneiss	5–0.5	Wide size range	Fresh to moderate	0.5–10	Equant	Extensive areas
Marble	3–0.1	Narrow size range	Fresh	1–10	Equant areas	Localized

Sedimentary rocks: bedded rocks with grains cemented by interstitial material

Rock type name	*Typical grain size range (mm)*	*Visible voids*	*Texture*	*Relative weathered state*	*Interbedded or associated rocks*	*Typical joint spacing (m)*	*Typical fragment shapes*	*Typical distribution*
Quartzite	2–0.2	Very rare	Narrow size range	Fresh	Sandstones Siltstones Shales	0.1–5	Equant tabular	Localized areas
Sandstone	2–0.06	Uncommon but usually	Narrow and wide size range	Fresh to moderate	Siltstones Shales	0.1–10	Equant tabular	Extensive areas
Siltstone	0.06–0.002	Very rare	Narrow size range	Fresh to moderate	Sandstones Shales Limestones	0.05–1	Tabular	Extensive areas
Shale	<0.002	Very rare	Narrow size range	Fresh to highly	Sandstones Siltstones Limestones	0.005–0.01	Very tabular	Extensive areas
Limestone	2–0.01	Common, large and small	Narrow size ranges or fragmental	Fresh	Maris shales	0.5–1	Equant tabular	Extensive areas
Chalks	<0.01	Rare	Narrow size range	Fresh to moderate	Limestones Maris	0.1–2	Tabular equant	Extensive areas

Figure 7.4 Idealized sketches of commonly produced shapes on the erosion of rock outcrops

is the median size in tonnes. Filter material grading can be specified by stone size in tonnes at which 0, 15, 50, 85 and 100% is smaller. If the material is small, then specific gravity and the percentage passing five sieve sizes is more practical.

Having determined a suitable grading for the purpose of meeting the design requirements, care should be taken in placing to avoid segregation of the large and small fractions. Material tipped without thought from the top of a sloping face inevitably produces layers with different grading characteristics at the top and the bottom of the slope and invites progressive failure. It may be necessary to place graded material by skip or grab to ensure that the completed layer is uniform as required by the design.

In choosing core material for a seawall, economic features are likely to be dominant because of the volume required. While there are limits, a core can be formed of almost any readily available material subject to the choice of appropriate core dimensions, the use of correct handling and compaction techniques, the provision of necessary drainage blankets and filters, provision for settlement, adequate protective works, etc. If a choice of materials for a seawall core is available, then economic and aesthetic assessment allowing for structural proportions, ease of construction, special works, etc. are likely to determine the preferred option.

The supply of rock for revetment armouring, pitching or rip-rap, will be a substantial part of the material costs for a seawall using these materials. A shortfall in the rate of supply will increase construction time with inherent risks to part-finished work. Enquiries as to sources of supply for the quality of rock required are necessary before the design is finalized. Because of the high cost of haulage, it is tempting to look at the nearest source of suitable rock regardless of whether or not it is being quarried. However, in the UK this is likely to be abortive, as planning authorities will

Table 7.2 Simple engineering characteristics of common rocks and notes on performance

	Rock[a]	Seismic velocity (KMJs)	Bulk[b] density (mg/m^2) approximates to oven-dried SG	Water absorption (BS 812)	ACV[e] (BS 812)	Dry unaxial compressive strength (MN/m^2)	Notes
Sedimentary	Quartzite	6.0–6.2[c]	2.4–2.8	0.1–2.0	8.0–25.0	150.0–300.0	Usually good armour and core
	Sandstone	1.4–5.0	2.1–2.7	1.0–15.0	15.0–35.0	10.0–170.0	Often good armour and core
	Siltstone	[d]	2.1–2.3		15.0–35.0	5.0–100.0	May be good core
	Shale	2.3–4.7	2.0–2.5	1.0–10.0		5.0–100.0	Occasionally may be suited for core
	Limestone	2.8–6.4	2.2–2.6	0.2–5.0	12.0–40.0	30.0–250.0	Usually good armour and core but soft types suspect
	Chalks	1.7–4.2	1.8–2.3	2.0–30.0	30.0–50.0	5.0– 75.00	May be suitable core
Igneous	Granite	5.0–6.0	2.5–2.8	0.2–2.0	10.0–25.0	100.0–250.0	Usually good armour and core, beware weathered rock
	Diorite	5.8–6.4	2.7–3.05		12.0–30.0	150.0–300.0	Ditto
	Gabbro	6.4–6.6	2.8–3.1	1.0–5.0	8.0–25.0	150.0–300.0	Ditto
	Rhyolite		2.4–2.6	1.0–8.0	16.0–35.0	75.0–200.0	May be suitable core
	Andesite	2.6–5.2	2.2–2.5	0.2–10.0	18.0–40.0	50.0–200.0	May be suitable armour and core
	Basalt	5.4–6.4	2.7–3.0	0.1–2.0	12.0–25.0	150.0–300.0	Often good armour and core, beware weathered rock
	Serpentinite	6.0–6.9	2.7–3.1		14.0–35.0		Often good armour and core
Metamorphic	Slate	2.3–4.7	2.6–2.8		16.0–35.0	100.0–200.0	May be suitable core
	Phyllite			0.5–6.0	22.0–40.0	40.0–150.0	Ditto
	Schist	4.2–5.0		0.4–5.0	20.0–35.0	50.0–150.0	May be suitable armour and core
	Gneiss	3.3–7.5	2.8–3.0	0.5–5.0	14.0–30.0	50.0–200.0	Often good armour and core, beware weathered rock
	Marble	3.7–6.9	2.6–2.7	0.5–2.0	20.0–35.0	100.0–275.0	Often good armour and core

[a] Only fresh and slightly/moderately weathered rock should be considered.
[b] Generally, this will be slightly lower than saturated surface-dried SG (BS 812).
[c] All data given as ranges of typical rock and extremes.
[d] Gaps in table due to insufficient data.
[e] This test performance on aggregate.

resist opening new quarries for a specific job and mobilization costs mitigate against haulage savings. Enquiries from existing quarries against a range of possible options with an indication of quantities and timing will provide more reliable data as to supply and cost of usable rock.

The supply of rock for a seawall is likely to be a short-term, high-rate, peak demand on any source of supply. The engineer should recognize this by choosing a specification that can be met using normal quarrying techniques with minimum waste. Rock armour size bands need to relate to quarry production to the highest practical degree and advice gained from preliminary enquiries, both local and from a suitably experienced engineering geologist, is valuable guidance in this respect.

The supply of rock to suit a construction programme dictated by seasonal climatic conditions will involve substantial storage of material produced over a longer period. Placing a pre-order for production while the tendering procedures are progressing can facilitate supply when rock is needed.

7.3.3 Concrete

Concrete is the most commonly used material in seawall construction. The opportunity to form suitable shapes of a relatively high density having potentially good durability makes it an attractive all-purpose material. Concrete is reasonably economic in most situations, and not too visually intrusive when used with care (see Section 6.5.9). The required properties of the cement, aggregates, reinforcement and water are standardized and documented as described below. While concrete is regarded as a single material, if the characteristics required are to be achieved then the constituents and processes should be correctly chosen. The primary considerations are set out in Figure 7.5.

It is important to recognize that the environment requiring good-quality concrete for durability is also a difficult one in which to create a good product. The wish to limit water/cement ratios cannot be wholly fulfilled or workability will be inadequate to ensure full compaction: tidal conditions may not permit the use of pulverized fuel ash because of the inherent delay to hardening: fresh water curing in the presence of seawater is difficult to achieve, etc. Some compromises may be necessary, but other costs are such that minor savings at the expense of the finished product are rarely economical in the long term.

Constituents

The cements likely to be used for seawalls are:

Ordinary Portland cement to BS12[14]
Rapid-hardening Portland cement to BS12[14]
Portland blast furnace cement to BS 146[15]
Sulphate-resisting Portland cement to BS 4027[16]

The bulk of all works should use ordinary Portland cement with a rapid-hardening variety being an option where specific site conditions warrant the additional cost and

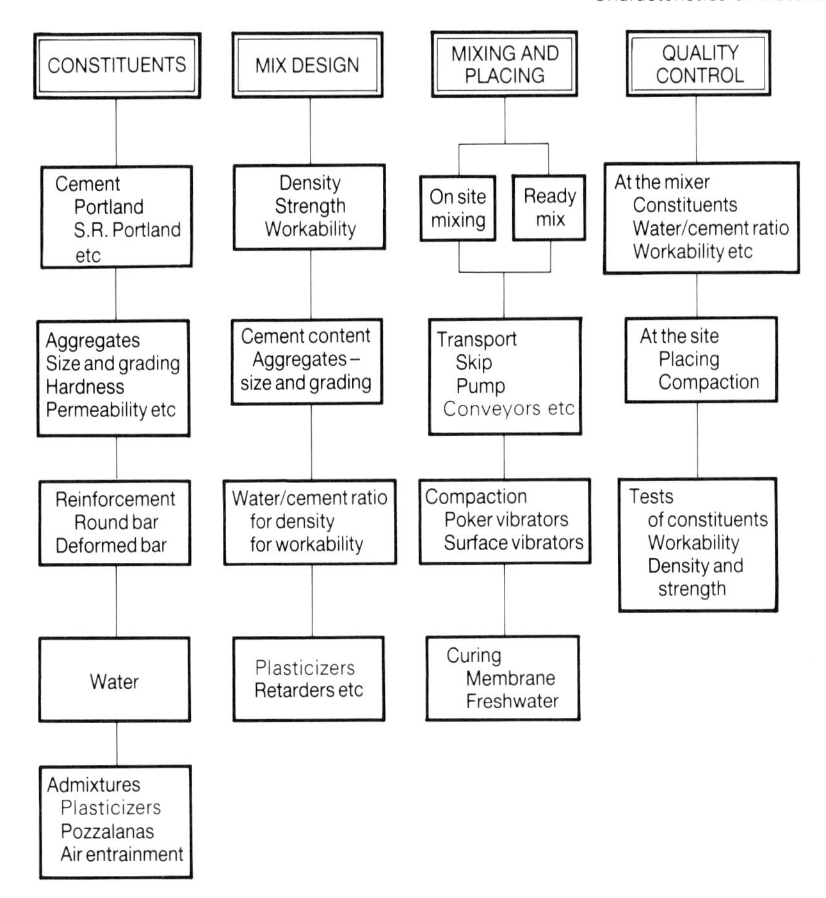

Figure 7.5 Concrete – primary considerations

handling problems. Sulphate-resisting Portland cement may be justified where waters are warmed or polluted by a local discharge, but the basic requirement for a dense product remains unchanged.

An alkali-aggregate reaction is not a problem specific to seawalls and should be avoided by careful choice of aggregate. If some risk remains, then possibility of damage can be lessened by reducing the alkali content of the cement and further guidance may be found in BRE Digest 258[28].

Aggregates should comply with BS 882[17] and be as large as design detail and availability will permit. Of the tests specified by BS, those for soundness and permeability are regarded as being most relevant. If abrasion is of particular concern, then the coarse aggregate should be at least as hard as the material causing abrasion and the fine aggregate reduced to a minimum, consistent with density requirements and workability.

Steel reinforcement should comply with BS 4449, 4482 and 4483[18–20]. Cutting and bending should comply with BS 4466[21]. Immediately before surrounding reinforcement in concrete, it should be clean and free from salt deposits or rust if the required durability is to be achieved.

A further barrier to the corrosion of reinforcement can be provided by surface coating the reinforcing steel before it is surrounded by concrete. Galvanized reinforcing steel has been used in marine structures in the UK at an increased cost of reinforcement, typically in the range 50–100%. Fusion-bonded epoxy coated reinforcement is available in the UK, having been used in other countries for more than a decade. Davies and Harrison[6] report that the cost doubles the price of the reinforcement.

The coating to reinforcement is applied after bending: correction of errors on-site is not recommended. The inevitable minor cuts and scrapes that occur during fixing give rise to concern, as it is felt these may be sufficient to set up a corrosive cell, especially when coated bars are used in conjunction with uncoated reinforcement or tying wire. The manufacturers state that this is not the case.

Stainless steel is available for use as reinforcement typically at a cost of five to ten times the cost of normal reinforcement, depending on the grade chosen. Again, concern has been expressed as to the possibility of electrolytic action taking place if a variety of steels or tying wires is used in one structure. The standard for water-retaining structures (BS 5337[22]) makes reference to the use of coated and stainless steel.

Polypropylene fibres can be added to concrete to increase impact resistance but the addition does not appear to increase resistance to corrosion or improve the strength. High-strength polymer grids have been used to control surface cracking in concrete, their effect being to reduce crack size at the expense of a greater number of cracks.

The water used in the concrete should be free from harmful substances: as a generality, water fit for consumption can be used. Seawater should not be used due to the presence of harmful salts.

Admixtures for purposes of entraining air, improving flow characteristics for pumping, allowing the use of a lower water/cement ratio, delaying settling, etc. should only be used where it can be shown by site tests that the required effect can be achieved without deterioration of concrete or steel reinforcement. Such admixtures should comply with BS 8110[23] with rigid adherence to the limits of chloride ion content. Pozzalanas may be used following site testing to prove compatibility with the cement in use and to demonstrate characteristics obtained.

Mixing and placing

Mix design for reinforced concrete should aim to achieve the necessary durability relevant to the exposure conditions in which the finished product is used. The differing environments and the approximate concrete characteristics are shown in Table 7.3, but it should be recognized that it may not always be practical to vary the mix to suit the location and the most dense concrete may have to be used throughout.

Workability will be limited by the maximum water/cement ratio but should be such as to allow full compaction with the equipment in use. Improved workability can be achieved by choice of aggregates and variations to the grading without detriment to

Table 7.3 Concrete – characteristics

Exposure conditions		*Characteristics of concrete*			
Zone	Environment	Min. density (kg/m^3)	Min. cement (kg/m^3)	Water/cement ratio n.e.	Works cube strength (N/mm^2)
1 and 2	Severe to very severe	2425	350	0.50	40
3	Extreme	2500	400	0.45	40+
4	Moderate	2350	325	0.55	40

the finished product. Natural aggregates showing a tendency to flakiness or elongation should be avoided and trial mixes should be used to determine how workability can benefit from mix or grading adjustments. If necessary, the use of trial mixes can be extended to explore the benefits of commercial plasticizer additives in improved workability.

On-site mixing of concrete has the inherent advantage that supply of constituent materials, batching, added water, etc. are all under direct control and mistakes in grade of concrete, cement used, water/cement ratio, etc. should not happen. However, if a supply from a ready-mix plant is available, it is likely to prove economic, especially if the quantity is relatively small or is distributed over a substantial distance with suitable access. The factors for consideration in using ready-mix are:

- Some loss of immediate control;
- The capacity and reliability of the ready-mix plant;
- The quality of constituent materials in use;
- The nature of the site;
- Economy versus any increase in risk to the product.

If the ready-mix operator will accept an inspector based at the plant, the risk is reduced. Bearing in mind the need for exceptionally defect-free concrete, the engineer may well decide in favour of site-mixed concrete.

Bulk storage and weigh batching of constituent materials are essential, and most modern concrete plant is perfectly capable of achieving the necessary standard in all respects. Transport from mixer to shutter is likely to be by one of the many forms of skip designed for concrete placing but pumps or conveyors may be considered. The nature of seawall construction is such that the wide distribution of relatively small quantities often makes pump or conveyor uneconomical. Additionally, the mix characteristics, especially the low water/cement ratio, make pumping very difficult. The objective during transport should be that of delivering a cohesive mix without segregation of materials to the final position in the works.

Thorough compaction is essential if durability is to be achieved. Poker vibrators are the most suitable form, and the sizes or capacity should be at least adequate and preferably generous. A well-designed mix delivered without segregation needs heavy vibration to ensure compaction. Shutter vibrators may be considered as an adjunct to internal vibration but are unlikely to be sufficient if used alone. Vibrating screed rails improve the finish of open surfaces but should only be used after compaction by poker vibrators and not as a substitute.

All concrete needs time to harden without drying out, but this is of greater importance to reinforced concrete which is to be exposed to salt water than in any other situation. Sprayed-on impermeable membranes are likely to be the most effective method of curing. Surface covering with either impermeable material or damp absorbent material kept wet are alternatives. For Portland cements curing should continue for three to six days, the duration being the shorter in warm humid weather and the longer in cold drying weather. If pfa or similar materials are incorporated into the cement then curing should be extended by 50%.

One of the few differences between mass and reinforced concrete is in the curing. Each needs to be cured in a similar way but mass concrete can tolerate curing in seawater while reinforced concrete should not be allowed contact with seawater until curing is complete.

It is sometimes convenient to place mass concrete underwater. In doing so the concrete is allowed to flow into position from tremie pipes, from pump discharges or occasionally from bottom-opening skips. In each case it is necessary to prevent the concrete falling through the water or constituents washed clean of cement paste will be trapped in the body of the finished concrete. Any consistent compaction is impractical, and the objective is a cohesive mix which flows into place and produces adequate concrete. Basically, the mix should provide much the same attributes as for normally placed concrete in a maritime environment but with cohesion and flow characteristics as paramount additional needs which are usually achieved by a 25% increase in cement content. The substitution of rounded aggregates will further assist the flow needed.

Quality control

The engineer should use thorough quality control of concrete to ensure durability of the finished product. Trial batches provide parameters by which to judge variability.

Cement deliveries should be accompanied by copies of manufacturers' certificates and UK manufacturers have shown that these can be relied upon. Aggregates require a sampling regime at site sufficient to identify trends in quality and grading before unsatisfactory material is incorporated into the works. Problems with water quality are unusual in the UK, but water quantity needs to be carefully monitored by way of workability tests at the mixer. Slump tests are unlikely to provide a suitable measure with the low water/cement ratios in use and compacting factor or other suitable tests should be used. A relationship between water/cement ratio and workability should be derived in advance from trial mixes using the chosen constituents.

Transport is a question of convenience, subject to avoiding segregation which is a matter for visual check. At the seawall and immediately before the concrete is placed, samples should be taken and test cubes made to prove that the density and 28-day strength complies with that required. These cubes should be made, cured and tested to the standardized procedure. Placing concrete and compacting can be subject only to a visual check, but this is of considerable value.

A substantial portion of faults in concrete arise from variations in predetermined practice, often without apparent reason. Supervision is necessary at all times to ensure that the plant is adequate, the methods chosen are adhered to and the required results are being achieved. Remedial work to avoidable faults is expensive and, at best, a poor substitute for a fault-free product. The use of experienced personnel as inspectors is essential and they should be guided to give special attention to:

- Cover to reinforcement;
- Control of mix constituents, especially water;
- Compaction of wet concrete to full density;
- Curing in moist salt-free conditions.

The previous section envisaged concrete being placed *in-situ*. It may, at times, be convenient to place pre-cast units into the seawall either to avoid the need to pour underwater or to facilitate construction generally (see Section 6.8). The overall criteria remain unchanged, but methods can be adapted to take advantage of better conditions during placing the concrete. As an example, small items can be cast on a vibrating table allowing the use of lower water/cement ratios and thus achieving higher densities. Economy in the multiple use of shutters or moulds may compensate for the relatively high cost of placing units in position. Structural design in this case should take account of lifting stresses which may prove to be critical.

Where appropriate, the British Standard for constituent materials has been mentioned in the text. The following British Standards are relevant to the use of concrete in seawalls and should be consulted.

- BS 8110, Structural Use of Concrete[23]
- BS 6349, Maritime Structures[4]
- BS 5328, Specifying Concrete[24]

7.3.4 Steel

The most common use of steel in seawalls (excluding reinforcement to concrete, which is dealt with in Section 7.3.3) is in sheet piling. Steel sheet piling may be driven as the main component of a seawall or used below a concrete wall, often at the toe. Rolled steel sections and steel tie bars may be used in association with sheet piling.

Piling is available in a wide range of sections and in lengths to suit those section strengths. The steel is hot rolled to the required section from weldable grades of steel specified in BS 4360. The choice of section is likely to be dependent upon the rate of material loss by corrosion and abrasion at locations of maximum stress. Table 7.4 shows typical upper rates of steel loss from the exposed face of sheet piling used as a seawall, and it will be seen that the highest rate of loss is some 33 times the lowest. The sheet pile section needed to cater for the forces involved will need to be increased in thickness to cater for the steel loss or a section of greater dimensions substituted. Alternatively, a limit state approach may be used in which the section characteristics for design are reduced to that anticipated at the end of the structure's life.

Table 7.4 Upper rates of steel loss by corrosion and abrasion

Zone and characteristics (see Figure 7.2)	*Abrasion forces (see Figure 7.3)*	*Maximum loss per face exposed (mm/yr)*	*Probable allocation of loss*	
			Corrosion (%)	*Abrasion (%)*
Zone 1 Above highest wave		0.10	100	Neg
Zone 2 Waves at high water		0.30	50	50
Zone 3 Tidal and wave action	High	1.00	15	85
	Medium	0.40	40	60
	Low	0.20	75	25
Zone 4 Submerged		0.03	100	Neg
Below seabed		Neg		

Consideration may be given to the use of a high-yield steel. Morley[7] suggests that high-yield steel designed to mild steel stresses should allow 35% loss of thickness before stresses assume critical values, and that this can be achieved for 8% increase in steel cost. Weather-resistant steels developed for external use inland are not recommended for seawalls as their better resistance to inland atmospheric corrosion is unlikely to be realized in the continuously damp, salt-laden marine environment. Abrasion-resistant steel is being developed and tested but is at present unproven, and needs the use of special welding techniques where fabrication by welding is necessary. Copper-bearing steel has been used in the past but with inconclusive results.

Rolled steel sections used in conjunction with sheet piling and steel plates for timber connections can be treated in much the same way as the piling. Where steel tie rods are used, they are likely to be buried and protective wrapping can be considered (see Section 6.9.2). During the long period in which a seawall is expected to last, there is every possibility of disturbance to buried tie rods with resultant damage to the protective wrappings. The geometry of a round bar is such that loss of area due to corrosion is rapid in the early stages. The geometry and design of a tied wall mean that the tie bars are often the critical component, and experience shows them to be a common cause of failure. The provision of an additional section to that calculated is recommended.

When designing tie bars it should be recognized that the load in the tie cannot be determined with any great degree of accuracy due to the uncertainty of wave induced and soil loading (see Section 6.2.3). It is usual practice to adopt a working stress lower than the value which would be used in most other structural applications. Permissible stresses in tie rods specified in most codes of practice are governed by the nature of the load conditions and are greater in the parent bar than in the threaded section. Tables 7.5 and 7.6 set out the stresses to be used as a proportion of the yield stress.

Table 7.5 Recommended working stresses for steel-sheet piling

Class of works	*BS 4360: 1986 Grade 43A ASTM A328 (Mild Steel)*		*BS 4360 Grade 50A (High Yield Steel)*	
	(kg/mm²)	*(N/mm²)*	*(kg/mm²)*	*(N/mm²)*
Permanent	14.2	140	18.3	180
Temporary	17.8	175	22.9	225

Table 7.6 Design stresses for tie bars: f_y = yield stress

	In threaded length	*In parent bar*
Normal design stresses	$0.5\ f_y$	$0.6\ f_y$
Temporary structures	$0.625\ f_y$	$0.75\ f_y$
Occasional surcharges	$0.67\ f_y$	$0.8\ f_y$

7.3.5 Timber

Timber can be used as a material for the body of a seawall and for sheet piling as toe protection or removable sections to provide access. It is used occasionally as support for stone-filled cribwork.

The criteria to be applied in making the choice of species, in order of importance, are:

- Availability, in sizes and quantity required, supplied to a suitable grading;
- Physical characteristics such as strength (where critical), durability to resist abrasion, workability, etc.;
- Relative economics, of which the supply cost is a large consideration.

Table 7.7 is based on information provided by the Timber Research and Development Association[11] and describes the species likely to be suitable and generally available. However, three of the species listed (Iroko, Keruing and Kapur) are reported to be threatened by overexploitation and their use may be questioned. A suitable alternative species not endangered is Oak. Only Greenheart is managed in such a way that the continued production is seen to be sustainable (at the time of publication of this book). The situation with regard to other species is not clear.

The quality of timber is determined by the grading rules applied in the country of origin. It is important to work to those established grading rules which are well documented and fully understood by the forest workers and operatives in sawmills. Variations in accepted grading rules are a source of potential delay and may lead to uncertainty as to the characteristics of the material supplied. Forward orders, given three to five months in advance, allow very substantial quantities of most of the

Table 7.7 Timber species

Name(s) source	*Character texture grain*	*Density kg/m³ at 15% moisture content*	*Strength category*	*Durability biodegradation*	*Working ease of cutting*
Balau *Shorea* spp. SE Asia	Moderately fine Interlocked	980	Exceptionally high	Durable RMB	Satisfactory
Basralocus Angelique *Dicorynia guianensis* S. America	Medium Usually straight	720	High	Very durable RMB	Satisfactory to difficult
Douglas Fir *Pseudotsuga menziessii* UK, N. America	Uniform – fine to medium	530	Medium CP 112	Moderately durable	Good
Ekki Azobe *Lophira alata* W. Africa	Coarse Usually interlocked	1070	Exceptionally high	Very durable RMB	Satisfactory to difficult
Greenheart *Ocotea rodiaei* Guyana	Fine, even Varies straight to interlocked	1040	Exceptionally high CP 112	Very durable RMB	Satisfactory to difficult
Iroko *Chlorophora excelsa regia* W. Africa	Medium to coarse	660	Medium CP 112	Very durable RMB	Satisfactory
Jarrah *Eucalyptus marginata* W. Australia	Moderately coarse Usually interlocked	820	High CP 112	Very durable RMB	Satisfactory to difficult
Kapur *Dryobalanops* spp. SE Asia	Moderately coarse Straight to shallowly interlocked	770 (variable)	High	Very durable RMB	Satisfactory
Karri *Eucalyptus diversicolor* SW Australia	Moderately coarse Interlocked	900	High CP 112	Durable	Satisfactory to difficult
Keruing Gurjun Yang *Dipterocarpus* spp. SE Asia	Moderately coarse and even Slightly interlocked	740	High CP 112	Moderately durable	Satisfactory to variable
Oak (British) *Quercus* spp. UK	Medium, varies with growth conditions. Usually straight variable	720	Medium CP 112	Durable	Varies
Opepe *Nauclea diderrichii* W. Africa	Coarse Interlocked	750	High CP 112	Very durable RMB	Good

Notes: 1. CP 112 in the Strength column denotes inclusion of the species in the code of practice CP 112, The Structural Use of Timber.
2. RMB in the Durability column denotes resistance to marine borers.

timbers listed to be supplied, but urgent requirements which have to be supplied from stock are inevitably limited. There is no substitute for trade enquiry relating to the specific need.

Most timbers are supplied to dimensions in imperial units: conversion to metric dimensions – where they are used – is based on 25 mm to one inch. For this reason, dimensional data are given in imperial units and data on physical characteristics in both imperial and metric units.

Two species of timber, Greenheart and Basralocus, are available as hewn squares and the use in this form is commended wherever circumstances permit. The nature of hewing at the felling stage is such that the best-quality timber is most suitable and a form of self-selection is introduced. Conversion of a log in this way produces a larger usable unit resulting in better value for money. The effect of the axe and adze is less disruptive to the timber surface than the saw and it is said to have a desirable sealing effect.

Hewn timber is specified by calliper measure to plus or minus 1 inch, at the mid-length. The taper is some 1 inch in 10 feet for Greenheart and rather more for Basralocus. Hewn Greenheart has a much cleaner appearance than hewn Basralocus as the traditional methods used in Guyana are different from those in Surinam. If a sawn surface is required at the head of a pile, hewn timber can be part sawn to a size in the UK in such a way that the saws run out of the timber at the chosen section. Hewn or sawn squares are generally available in sizes from 8 inches to 14 inches or greater for small quantities.

Sawn timber for planking or walings is generally available in 2-, 3-, 4- and 6-inch thicknesses and 6-, 9- or 12-inch widths, the thickness/width ratio being kept below four to advantage. The lengths that can be obtained are a function of the nature of the species shown, the need for economic conversion and transport. A design which utilizes modest lengths effectively will prove economic.

Table 7.8 lists the size availability for timbers in general use and gives an indication of the relative cost of supply. These data should be used with care, as circumstances change and the quantity required will influence availability. The sizes are those to which the timber might be cut before shipment and other sizes can be cut from squares in the UK as required but at additional cost. The table is intended to provide a basis from which a specific enquiry can proceed.

The physical properties of commercially available timbers vary significantly with the species chosen and with the circumstances of use. In the marine environment of the UK the moisture content will remain above 30% (other than very near the surface in dry locations) and shrinkage movement is negligible. The strength properties in use are those of 'green' timber and design parameters must be based on the green characteristics. Evaluation of strength on small dry samples, without adjustment of the results, would be most misleading. The working-strength properties of timber should also take account of naturally occurring defects, the most important of which is slope of the grain relative to the surface of the structural unit.

Tables 7.9 and 7.10 give green ultimate and working stresses for some suitable commercially available timbers. The grade stresses are those recommended for continuous loading and may be increased by 25% for short-term loading or 50% for

Table 7.8 Common sizes of some suitable timbers

Species name(s)	Squares Max. side (in)	Squares Max. length (ft)	Planking and walings Upper and lower sizes (in)	Planking and walings Upper lengths (ft)	Typical ratio of supply cost
Balau	14	35	2 × 6	16	8
			7 × 14	24	
Basralocus	12	40	2 × 6	16	12½
(Angelique)	(Hewn 17)	(60)	6 × 12	35	(Hewn 9½)
Douglas Fir	14	40	2 × 6	10	6
			6 × 12	40	
Ekki	12	24	2 × 6	16	10
(Azobe)			6 × 12	24	
Greenheart	16	50	2 × 6	20	12
	(Hewn 20)	(65)	8 × 16	50	(Hewn 9)
Iroko			Uncertain		
Jarrah	Not standard	—	2 × 6	15	10
			6 × 12	26	
Kapur	Not standard	—	2 × 6	18	7½
			6 × 12	24	
Karri	Not standard	—	2 × 6	15	10
			6 × 12	30	
Keruing	Not standard	—	2 × 6	16	Varies
(Gurjun Yang)			4 × 9	22	
Oak (British)	10 (not normal)	—	2 × 6	12	Varies
			4 × 10	20	
Opepe	14	30	2 × 6	16	9
			7 × 14	20	

1. Dimensions are feet and inches, as trade custom.
2. The list is not exclusive.
3. Limited quantities of larger sizes are available at additional cost.

impact loading. Additional information can be obtained from BS 5756:80, Tropical Hardwoods Graded for Structural Use[26].

Particular species of timber that are resistant to damage by marine borers are indicated in Table 7.7 by the letters RMB in the Durability column. These timbers are suitable for use under conditions of heavy attack by gribble or teredo and they can be expected to be fully effective for at least 20 years.

The manner in which salt deposition inhibits fungal decay has been described in Section 7.2.5. It will be seen that decay will only be of concern if timber is used where salt deposits will be washed away and rainwater allowed to accumulate. Lack of oxygen inhibits decay in buried timber used for sheet piles, etc. Those timbers listed as resistant to marine borers in Table 7.7 are also very durable and their use should ensure a decay-free working life.

The 'green' nature of the timber together with the high densities preferred to resist abrasion make the use of preservatives extremely difficult. The penetration of preservatives (creosote or copper–chrome–arsenate salts) is facilitated by low moisture content and an open-textured species of timber. Green timbers in large sections of dense species are particularly resistant to preservative treatment while being especially chosen for foreshore use. The reliance on preservatives can only be commended in exceptional or unusual circumstances. Where circumstances do permit, use of preservatives should comply with BS 5589: 1978, The Preservation of Timber[27].

Table 7.9 Ultimate stresses in timber: green – ultimate stress

Species name(s)		Bending	Compression parallel to grain	Shear parallel to grain	Density at 30% MC	
Balau	lb/m²	17 500	9090	1980	lb/ft³	56 to 61
	N/mm²	121	62.7	13.7	kg/m³	900 to 980
Basralocus	lb/in²	11 900	6000	1520	lb/ft³	60
(Angelique)	N/mm²	82	41.2	10.5	kg/m³	960
Douglas	lb/in²	7800	3755	1050	lb/ft³	42
Fir	N/mm²	54	25.9	7.2	kg/m³	
Ekki	lb/in²	17 800	9920	2320	lb/ft³	82
(Azobe)	N/mm²	123	68.4	16.0	kg/m³	1314
Greenheart	lb/in²	20 300	9800	2190	lb/ft³	75
	N/mm²	140	67.4	15.1	kg/m³	1202
Iroko					lb/ft³	51
					kg/m³	817
Jarrah	lb/in²	10 400	5390	1500	lb/ft³	63
	N/mm²	72	37.2	10.3	kg/m³	1009
Kapur	lb/in²	12 800	6220	1180	lb/ft³	54
	N/mm²	88	42.9	8.1	kg/m³	865
Karri	lb/in²	11 200	5450	1510	lb/ft³	65
	N/mm²	77	37.6	10.4	kg/m³	1041
Keruing	lb/in²	11 900	6250	1140	lb/ft³	58
(Gurjun Yang)	N/mm²	82	43.1	7.8	kg/m³	929
Oak (British)	lb/in²	8600	4000	1320	lb/ft³	52
	N/mm²	59	27.6	9.1	kg/m³	833
Opepe	lb/in²	13 700	7490	1900	lb/ft³	59
	N/mm²	94	51.6	13.1	kg/m³	945

Table 7.10 Working stresses in timber: green – standard grade working stress

Species name(s)		Bending	Compression Parallel grain	Compression Perpendicular to grain	Shear parallel to grain	Modulus of elasticity
Balau	lb/m²	3210	3060	800	320	2 810 000
	N/mm²	22.1	21.1	5.50	2.22	19 374
Basralocus	lb/m²	2400	1700	580	300	1 812 500
(Angelique)	N/mm²	16.5	11.7	4.00	2.06	12 500
Douglas	lb/m²	1410	1000	230	160	1 493 000
Fir	N/mm²	9.7	6.9	1.59	1.10	10 300
Ekki	lb/m²	3560	3500	1348	460	2 010 000
(Azobe)	N/mm²	24.5	24.1	9.30	3.17	13 900
Greenheart	lb/m²	4100	2600	780	450	2 494 000
	N/mm²	24.1	17.9	538	310	17 200
Iroko						
Jarrah	lb/m²	1800	1500	520	220	1 490 000
	N/mm²	12.4	10.3	3.59	1.52	10 300
Kapur	lb/m²	2200	1960	200	190	1 910 000
	N/mm²	15.2	13.5	13.8	1.31	13 170
Karri	lb/m²	2050	1560	600	230	2 001 000
	N/mm²	14.1	10.7	4.14	1.59	13 800
Keruing	lb/m²	1600	1300	400	220	1 798 000
(Gurjun Yang)	N/mm²	11.0	9.0	2.16	152	12 400
Oak (British)	lb/m²	1500	1000	400	230	1 247 000
	N/mm²	10.3	6.9	2.16	1.59	8 600
Opepe	lb/m²	2400	2100	700	290	1 798 000
	N/mm²	16.5	14.1	4.83	2.00	12 400

7.3.6 Asphalt

The use of natural asphalt to give protection to structures from the effects of water extends from 2000 years ago. Today asphalt is prepared from bitumen, together with mineral-based fillers and aggregates, to produce the required characteristics. A summary is shown in Table 7.11.

The grades of bitumen commercially available are described by hardness as measured by the penetration test. Straight-run bitumen is normally used since bitumen emulsions or cut-back bitumen are only advantageous where greater fluidity is required during placing.

Aggregates used vary from natural sand to large stone – continuous or gap graded to suit the use – and the filler will often be limestone dust, cement or asbestos. Guidelines on the use of bitumen in 'hydraulic engineering' are given in reference 12.

Sand mastic

Sand mastic is designed to be poured hot to fill joints or voids in pitching or blockwork protecting seawall faces. The aggregate is sand and is overfilled with bitumen to assist fluidity when hot. The filler is often cement and, once placed, sand mastic requires no compaction.

When sand mastic is used to fill joints on a sloping face the mix design should produce a material sufficiently fluid to allow hot pouring but not so fluid that it does not remain in place once it has cooled. Site tests may be needed to establish the right mix and slopes of 1 to $1\frac{1}{2}$ can usually be grouted successfully. It is desirable that joints should be dry when filled to allow a bond to form between the concrete or stone and the bitumen.

Table 7.11 The use of asphalt

Asphalt	*Typical constituents*	*Characteristics and use*
Sand mastic	Bitumen, 20/30 to 50/60, 20–40% Filter – limestone, cement or asbestos, 10–15% Aggregate – sand, 40–70%	Flows well when placed hot Impermeable Used to grout stone pitching and blockwork or as a carpet below water
Lean sand asphalt	Bitumen 4–8% Aggregate – sand, 92–96%	Flows adequately when placed hot Not impermeable. Used for underwater protection against scour, as filter layer below open-stone asphalt, or as temporary slope protection
Open-stone asphalt	Sand mastic Single-size stone 25–75 mm	Just pourable when hot Not impermeable Placed to form a wave and scour-resistant revetment
Asphaltic concrete	Bitumen 50/60 to 80/100 6–9% Filter – limestone or cement, 9–13% Aggregate – continuous or gap graded up to 25 mm	Placed and compacted hot to form a durable load bearing surface Impermeable

Sand mastic is effectively impervious and water trapped behind a sealed face will rupture the mastic if the pressure is sufficient. Where water can enter behind the seal, underdrainage should be considered.

Sand mastic can be heated in portable gas-fired equipment close to the point of use and pouring into joints is conventionally carried out manually with special buckets. If the quantity is sufficient and access available, heated tankers can be used.

Lean sand asphalt

This is a relatively inexpensive material often using local supplies of sand and a low bitumen content (of the order of 4%) to serve a different purpose from sand mastic. Mixing requires the use of conventional hot-mix asphalt plant, and transport to site is by lorry, allowing dumping and spreading to provide temporary protection to sloping faces and revetments which, when subsequently covered with a revetment, functions as a filter layer. Lean sand asphalt spreads easily and requires no compaction. The finished product has a high voids ratio and a well-designed mix has the same permeability as the constituent sand. It will resist abrasion in the short term and is easily replaced or made good if damaged but requires prompt attention to avoid progressive failure.

Open-stone asphalt

Hot-mix asphalt plant is used to make a sand mastic to which is added preheated stone to form stone asphalt. The prepared mix is just capable of being poured and can be placed without compaction to form a revetment or revetment protection. Its stability is such that stone asphalt is convenient to use on sloping faces. It should not be placed hot underwater as boiling will damage the binding of the asphalt. It should only be placed underwater in the form of pre-cast mattresses.

The size of stone added to the hot sand mastic is determined by the end usage. As a revetment, the stone can be chosen by reference to local availability and is only limited to that which the plant can handle.

The texture of the finished work is open and permeable. The resistance to wave action and abrasion (depending on stone quality) is such that stone asphalt is suitable for low to moderate exposure.

Asphaltic concrete

Aggregate up to 25 mm, graded sand, a filler and bitumen are hot mixed to create a 'concrete' in which cement is replaced by bitumen once it has cooled. When spread and fully compacted, asphaltic concrete provides a stable surface treatment capable of resisting wave action and carrying traffic. When compared to road use, asphalt concrete for revetments needs a higher content of softer bitumen to assist with spreading and compacting with the lighter plant capable of reaching and working on a seawall site.

The degree to which asphaltic concrete can be used on slopes is limited by the compaction plant necessary. An angular aggregate can be used to reduce the tendency to slide during compaction. Segregation during placing can be limited by the use of continuously graded aggregates. It is desirable that asphaltic concrete should be placed in dry conditions and a thick single layer allows maximum heat retention during compaction.

Asphaltic concrete is a robust impermeable material resistant to wave action and abrasion. The main danger to long life is inadequate subgrades and use by heavy traffic.

7.3.7 Geotextiles

The constituents of geotextiles are polymers in filament or fibre form made up into textiles by weaving or by thermal, mechanical or chemical processes. The most common polymers in general use are polypropylene, polyester, polythene and polyamide.

The durability of polymers when buried in soils is as good as most seawall materials, but they are susceptible to degradation from ultra-violet light and from very aggressive soils (pH more than 11 or less than 3). During construction, exposure to sunlight should not exceed seven days and the pH value of soils should be checked. Also during construction, care is needed to avoid high temperatures (from hot bitumen or other causes) as deterioration commences some 30°C below the melting point of the polymer[9].

Available proprietary products and systems are continually developing. The engineer should always investigate the availability, effectiveness and economy of suitable products on offer against the functional requirements of the design (Figure 7.6).

The variety of geotextiles marketed is helpful provided the products are fully identified. The RILEM Technical Committee on Geotextiles[8] recommends a minimum of six items of information be provided by manufacturers:

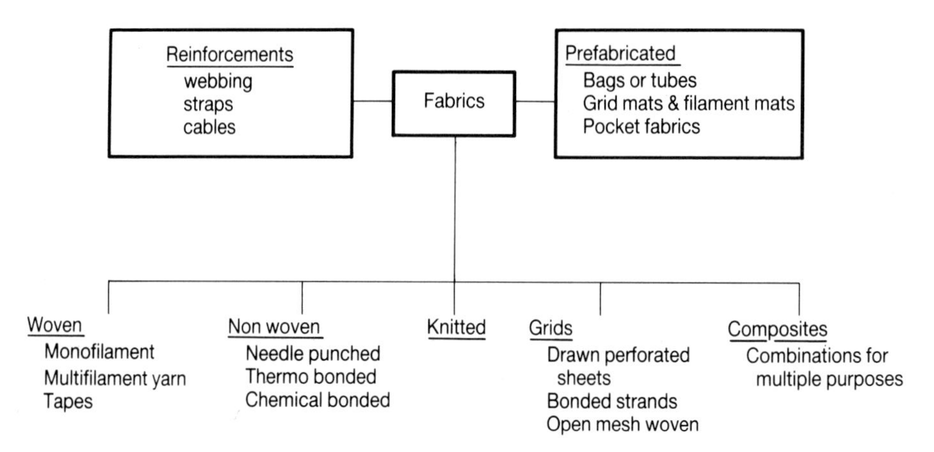

Figure 7.6 Availability of geotextiles

- Trade name;
- Manufacturer;
- Constituents and manufacturing process (type, density of polymer, diameter of fibres or filaments, woven or non-woven, etc.);
- Mass per unit area;
- Nominal thickness;
- Presentation (roll size, etc.).

Obviously, additional information, related to the specific uses intended, is desirable.

The greatest usage of geotextiles is that of particle retention at the interface between different materials used in fill, drainage filters and revetment or armouring. The principal criteria used in making the choice of fabric are the filtration characteristics – permeability for water movement and size of opening to retain smaller material from the adjacent soil. The strength needs to be adequate for service and to enable practical construction methods to be employed. A woven textile has a smaller range of opening size than a comparable non-woven one: woven textiles are strong, but the strength varies with the angle of the applied load relative to the weave. An unwoven textile has a distribution of size of opening which resembles the size distribution of particles in a sand of medium uniformity. However, the textile may be chosen for a very small minimum opening to provide a more tortuous seepage path for water draining through. The strength of unwoven textiles is less than that for woven materials and the modulus of elasticity is greater. The range of textiles is very wide and it is not practical to list details here. Section 6.3.4 shows the design process considerations and manufacturers' literature provides data on the textiles supplied. Figures in Section 5.4 show typical applications.

Geotextiles used as filters are particularly effective when separating granular materials with a grain size in the range 0.06–2 mm and become less effective outside this range. For this reason, use in conjunction with a sand cover is advantageous for fine silt or clay soils. A geotextile may be necessary for soils composed of particles greater than 2 mm.

When a geotextile filter is used for steady-state and one-directional flow, a filter is also built up in the soil adjacent to the fabric. In a seawall subject to wave and tidal action, the direction of water movement reverses at short intervals and a soil filter cannot develop. In making a choice of geotextile filter it is important to distinguish between one-directional and reversing flow situations, as the characteristics required are likely to be different.

The range of fabrics available is very wide and each tends to have specific characteristics. Where no single fabric meets the design requirements, consideration should be given to composite materials in which two textiles are used together to meet the requirements of the site. An example of a composite material is the provision of a coarse-fibre layer on the underside of a membrane to integrate with the soil and reduce downslope migration of the finer particles.

Webbing straps and cables made from geotextiles are used in ground reinforcement in a manner that is not specific to seawalls. Cables and grid geotextiles are used to create systems of interconnected concrete block revetments.

7.3.8 Fill materials

During both preliminary and final design stages, a choice should be made from a range of fill materials for use in a seawall. As the core and other fill requirements often form a high proportion of the total cost, a wide range of materials should be considered.

The possibilities will vary, from weak inexpensive materials that are difficult to use to strong costly ones that are tailored to the site requirements. The range will include:

- Free fill dug from or adjacent to the site;
- Local fill taken from other specific activities;
- General fill arising from building, etc. in the area;
- Fill excavated or quarried for the job;
- Specially prepared material.

The cost of supply, haulage and placing will vary widely for each type of fill considered. The properties of the fill will influence the profile of the seawall, thus varying the quantity required, increasing or decreasing the land needed and having a different environmental impact.

Materials available at the site are all too often soft clay or silt, which can only be used as fill with extreme care. The soil mechanics of the excavated and recompacted fill require extensive testing, both before excavation and during placing, to ensure the properties are appreciated and the limitations catered for. The changes that will occur during the life of the structure from shrinkage on drying or from continued compaction under self-load should be identified and provided for. During construction, the variation in properties must be monitored to ensure tolerable consistency and compliance with the properties assumed in the design. As the likely profile will use additional land relative to that needed for imported fill, either sterilization must be allowed for or provision made for subsequent use, perhaps for a different purpose. It is most important that the effects of taking fill from areas adjacent to the finished wall should be recognized. While the provision of a drainage ditch behind a seawall may have advantages, it can also be a potential weakness in terms of stability (see Section 6.3.2).

Despite the difficulty of construction using soft materials dug on-site, there are long stretches of seawall in the UK built in this way and which provide effective flood defence to substantial hinterland. No doubt such materials will continue to prove effective in the right circumstances.

Foreshore or dune sand is another fill material that may be available at the site and needs to be considered with the strong proviso that the engineer ensures that such use will not be environmentally detrimental. Materials taken from the foreshore may be subject to a dredging licence. Generally, granular materials are less troublesome than soft clay but are more dependent on revetment integrity and effective drainage.

Locally produced fill materials, that might be economically available, can comprise the unwanted products of other activities. The overburden excavated for access to new sand and gravel workings is an example. Domestic refuse has been used to form a seawall in a location where the high land-take could be redeveloped, a plentiful supply of refuse was available and landfill sites for disposal were at a premium.

It is possible to harness a demand for the dispersal of general fill materials from the development of an adjacent area, but this can be uncertain. The nature of the fill available will be variable and its characteristics will require conservative treatment at the design stage as selective acceptance is rarely practical. The timing of availability is usually random and often production is slow, requiring storage with consequent double-handling. One example known to have been economic is the use of clay taken from the development of a new town in south-east England and used to build flood banks to the same new town.

In selecting sources of fill the engineer is faced with a complex set of variables from which to identify an optimum solution. In looking at a particular possibility, it can be helpful to answer three questions in sequence:

1. Can an effective seawall be built from this fill?
2. Is there a cost advantage?
3. Is the result environmentally acceptable?

As each question is resolved, confidence limits should be established. It is probable that the confidence limits on cost will be wider than is desirable. Experience suggests that a conservative approach should be taken.

7.3.9 Other materials

Widely used materials have been discussed in Sections 7.3.1–7.3.8. Other areas not covered are:

- Innovative use of existing or new materials;
- Minor materials used in seawalls for secondary purposes;
- Materials used in ancillary works.

Almost by definition, a list of innovative material cannot be provided in a book of a general nature, but innovation should be encouraged within the limits of good practice. If preliminary investigation indicates suitability, extensive research and intensive testing will be necessary before unproven materials can be used with confidence that the design life will be attained. Further, the conventional tests designed to classify materials presently in use may not serve to prove new materials. If time is available and the cost justified, then testing by the use of a model should be investigated, but the accelerated testing of materials in this way is difficult and may not be possible. Foreshore trials may be the only way to ensure that the performance required can be obtained.

Conversely, the list of secondary materials that might be used to achieve particular results is almost endless. Many will perform only a minor role in aiding construction or enhancing appearance, and it is unlikely that the stability will depend on such materials. Examples are additives to concrete for various purposes, fillers to expansion joints, grouts used for anchoring fixtures, mortars for seating precast units, etc. Reference is made in Section 6.5 to the use of some of these materials.

The ancillary works and equipment provided to complete the functional performance of a seawall are not usually fundamental to its stability or life. However, the use of materials that rapidly degrade can destroy the appearance and in doing so damage the social and visual environment. Examples are handrailing, steps on a sloping wall, floodboards to openings, landscaping including the flora, access ramps both to the foreshore and for the activities adjacent to the wall. The criteria for the choice of ancillary equipment is substantially the same as that for other materials in the seawall. However, much of it will be accessible for maintenance or replacement. Designed to facilitate repairs or renewal is necessary if safety and appearance is to be maintained to the chosen standards without unnecessary cost.

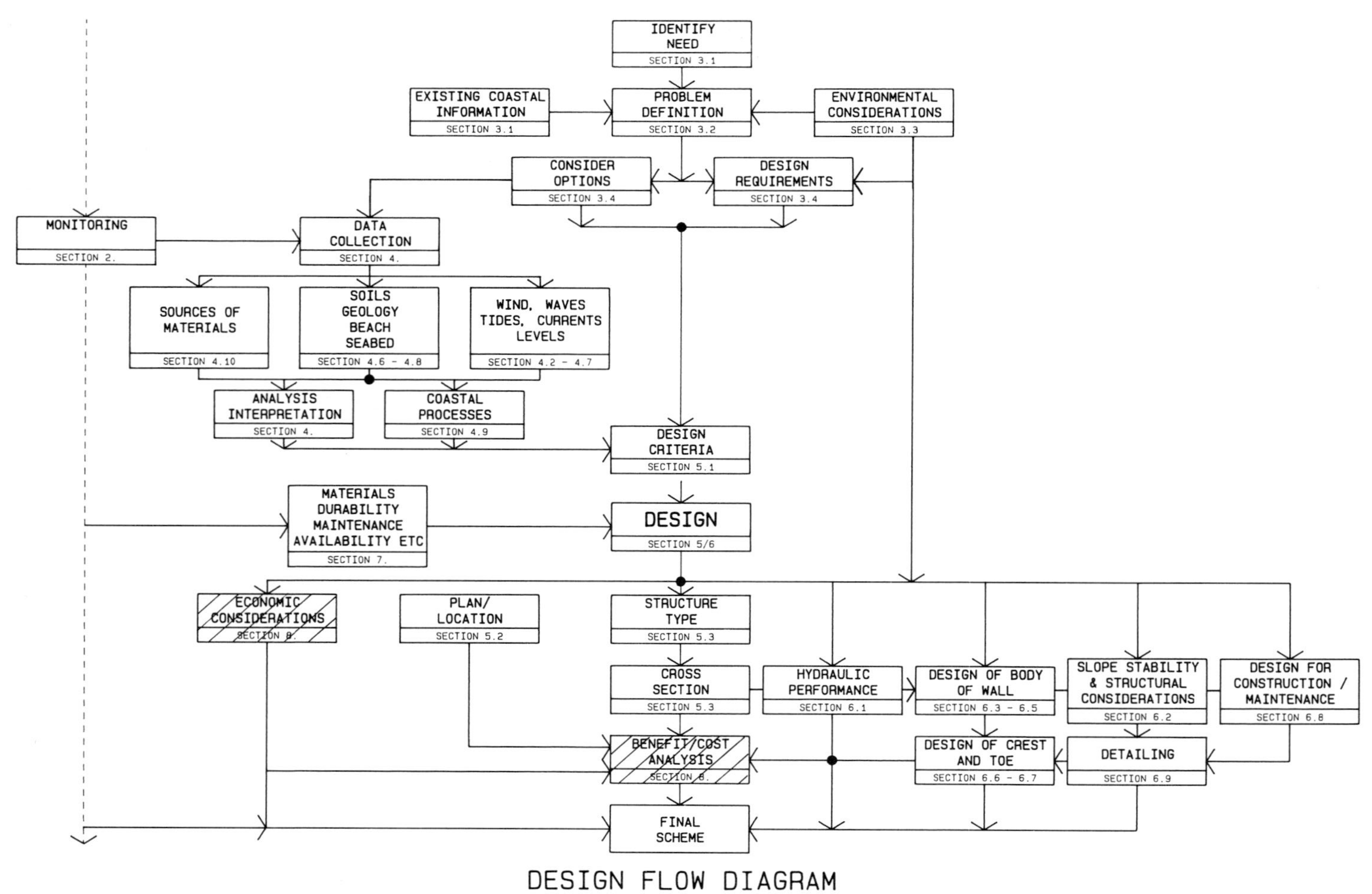

DESIGN FLOW DIAGRAM

8 Financial and economic considerations

Planning, design, construction and maintenance of seawalls are likely to be major undertakings. In appraising a scheme it is therefore necessary to estimate in advance how much it is going to cost and the benefits that will accrue from it.

This chapter deals with the estimation of costs and benefits. Section 8.1 outlines the principles of economic appraisal which allows the economic 'worthwhileness' of the scheme to be assessed. In essence, the benefits accruing from protection (to prevent erosion) or sea defence (to prevent flooding) are the avoidance or reduction of damages. Section 8.2 gives guidance on estimating likely failure scenarios (timing and extent of areas subject to damages) and Sections 8.3 and 8.4 describe methods of assessing the economic costs of such damage. Section 8.5 discusses the costs and in particular assists the engineer in identifying true overall costs as distinct from those of simple capital construction.

8.1 Economic appraisal

8.1.1 The need for economic appraisal

Society invests in the construction and maintenance of seawalls in order to reduce future losses caused by flooding or erosion. Economic appraisal tries to answer two questions:

1. Does the reduction in losses represent sufficient return on the investment (as opposed to, say, hospitals or railways)?
2. Does the proposed scheme represent the most cost-effective way of achieving its objectives?

The technique most commonly used and which will be described in detail later is cost-benefit analysis (CBA). Using a method known as discounting, CBA provides answers to the questions posed above by comparing the 'present values' (PVs) of streams of future scheme costs with future scheme benefits.

In practice, CBA is often carried out, both in the UK and elsewhere, in order to demonstrate beyond reasonable doubt that a scheme meets funding criteria. In many instances the case for investment will be a strong one, and it will only be necessary to identify and evaluate the principal costs and benefits. In others a good case may depend on evaluating benefits over which there may often be little consensus, e.g. reductions in anxiety levels.

Two aspects of CBA deserve emphasis:

1. The investment perspective must be clear: in the UK it is *national* benefits which must be assessed when seeking MAFF grant aid (although local and regional impacts, if severe, can be advanced as supporting evidence);
2. 'Do nothing' or 'do minimum' are nearly always options and should be included both as base cover against which benefits are judged and as alternative 'schemes'.

In the UK, readers should consult MAFF guidelines[3] and HM Treasury[2] for general guidance on project appraisal. In addition, MAFF regional engineers in England (or their equivalents in other parts of the UK) can be consulted as to recommended cost-benefit approaches and techniques.

The methods to be used in the economic appraisal of coast protection and sea defence works are the subject of continuing research at Middlesex Polytechnic, which is carrying out research to quantify the benefits of this type of investment. Interim Guidelines[11] have been published from initial work on that project. Final guidelines will be issued following completion of the project in 1991. This chapter is therefore designed to be an interface with that research and a guide to those Interim Guidelines, to which interested parties are referred for matters of detail. The methods described in the Interim Guidelines are considered to be theoretically sound but there remain many gaps in the current state of the art (at the time of publication).

Economic appraisal should be used to evaluate a number of possible uses of economic resources and a range of possible solutions to coast protection problems. With respect to seawalls, consideration should be given to different standards of protection, different standards or levels of upgrading or renovation of defences, different dates from when schemes could commence, and to doing nothing. Environmental costs and benefits may be involved in coast protection using seawalls if a more refined analysis is warranted. An 'extended' form of cost-benefit analysis may be used to evaluate distributional (e.g. beach users may lose but shopkeepers gain) and environmental impacts alongside economic aspects (see reference 11, Table 1).

When assessing the economics of alternatives it is necessary not only to establish that a scheme is cost-effective in terms of the coastal defence objective but also to weigh variations in cost against consequential variations in benefit. For example, a more expensive scheme may produce additional environmental benefits. The issue may further be affected by cash flow, available funds and any conditions attaching to the award of grant aid. Given that grant aid is usually provided by central government for such investment, it is important that it is adequately appraised from the national perspective, always bearing in mind the state of knowledge and the extent of uncertainties that will always remain in investment appraisal.

Formal application of cost-benefit analysis provides a disciplined framework within which design can proceed, although its limitations should be appreciated[4]. Coastal engineers need to consider carefully, both at the outline stage and in detailed design, the exact economic effects of their schemes, in terms of the flooding that is alleviated and the erosion prevented. The monetary benefits of these effects can thereby be quantified – in whole or in part, depending on the state of available knowledge – and compared with the costs of construction and maintenance with or without the proposed scheme.

The Interim Guidelines produced by Middlesex Polytechnic are not the last word on this subject and research is continuing. Techniques and data sources will thereby improve, to assist further the improvement of seawall design.

8.1.2 The value of investment in seawalls

The value to the national economy of investing in seawall construction lies in the damage (or losses) the wall will avert. When assessing these benefits care must be taken (1) to avoid double-counting (e.g. by including the existing seawall as a benefit) and (2) to include only those losses which are truly national economic losses. Detailed assessment is discussed later, but the main categories are likely to be:

- Complete loss of or recurrent damage to property or stock;
- Disruption of traffic;
- Loss of utilities;
- Marginal emergency service costs;
- Loss of recreational benefits.

It should be noted that many business (including tourism) losses, while having a severe local impact, are not true national losses as the business may relocate elsewhere in the UK (see MAFF Red Manual for guidance on this point).

8.1.3 Historic and future costs

In order to assess the overall cost of the scheme for economic appraisal the present value of these costs should include all costs that will be incurred in the future, i.e.:

- All costs associated with initial construction;
- All maintenance and other operational costs;
- Possible cost of major repairs.

Costs already incurred or to which the nation is already committed should be regarded as 'sunk costs' and omitted from the economic analysis. Costs should make no allowance for inflation, but should use the same base data as those used for the benefits.

8.1.4 Scheme comparison

The benefits of investment in coastal defences are the difference in national economic assets with and without the scheme. Cost-benefit analysis allows the comparison of all possible different schemes, and the comparison of any one with the 'do nothing' situation, on the basis of those benefits that are calculable.

Schemes may be phased in order to spread the capital cost over a period of years. The spreading of the capital cost should be set against increased overall costs which may arise from issues such as multiple mobilization and administration costs. Higher initial construction costs may lead to lower maintenance costs and to a longer structure life. Scheme comparison is illustrated in Figure 8.1.

A substantial proportion of seawall works in the UK involves rehabilitation (see Section 5.7). As a potential alternative option, consideration should always be given to the relative economy of maintenance, renovation, upgrading and reconstruction. This requires the assessment of the residual life of the existing structure. The alternatives are illustrated in Figure 8.2.

A number of measures of scheme worthwhileness may be computed and used for comparison. Where alternative schemes have the same benefits then a direct comparison of the costs, on a present value basis, is adequate. If alternative schemes have different benefits, then the difference between the present value of benefits and costs –

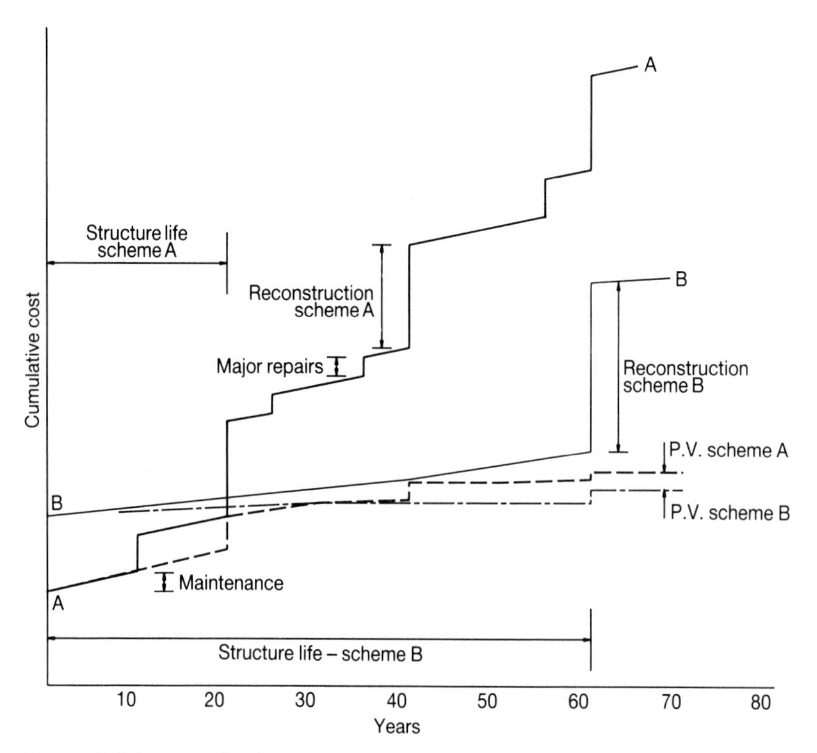

Figure 8.1 An example of cost comparison

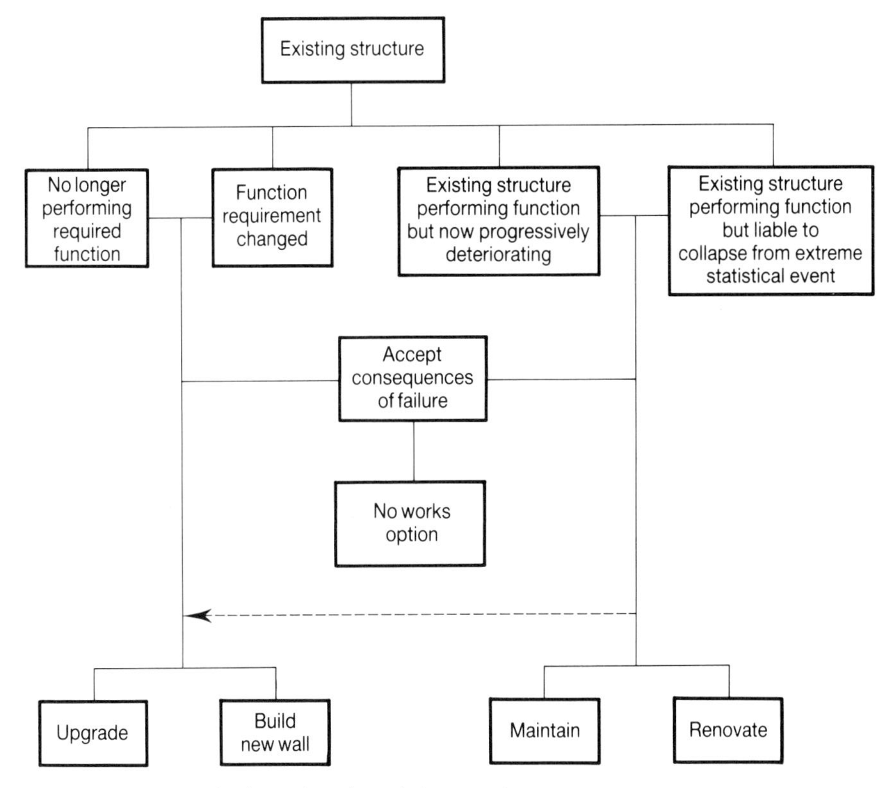

Figure 8.2 Economic alternatives for existing structures

the net present value – should be used as the basis for comparison[2]. The ratio of benefits to costs may be considered for economic comparison of alternatives. International agencies often use the internal rate of return (the discount rate at which present benefit equals present cost) which is derived from the investment.

8.1.5 Discounting

The procedure of discounting enables the present value of £1 (say) to be calculated at some future date. Thus £1 invested at an interest rate of 5% will yield a total of £1.05 in one year's time. Conversely. £1/£1.05 = £0.952 invested now would yield £1 in one year's time. The interest rate therefore becomes the discount factor for the present value of £1 one year hence.

In this manner a comparison of benefits and costs which occur at different dates can be carried out. This is normally expressed as a net present value (the difference between the present value of costs and the present value of benefits), but other measures allow the same type of comparison (see Section 8.1.4)

In the UK, the discount rate for economic appraisal of government-funded schemes is set by the Treasury and is currently (1989) 6%. This is referred to as the test discount rate. The present value of £1 for *n* years hence at this and other rates is given in Appendix C. It can be seen from this Appendix that costs incurred in the long-term future have little effect on economic analysis unless the amounts are very large.

8.1.6 Inflation

The object of discounting is to arrive at a common base date at which all costs and benefits may be assessed and compared. Cost-benefit analysis assumes that both costs and benefits will suffer the same rate of inflation in the future. They may, however, have different rates of inflation, and if a strong case can be made for such a difference it may be included in the economic analysis or tested at the sensitivity stage (Section 8.1.8). The base date commonly used is that at which the first investment is expected to be made.

8.1.7 Loss and damage probability

If the timing of an event which involves loss or damage cannot be predicted, then it can be assumed that it has an equal chance of occurring in any year in the future. The present value of such loss or damage is assessed on the basis of a loss or damage probability relationship. The method of evaluation is described in Section 8.4 in the context of flooding.

Depending on the level of protection selected and implemented, a risk of loss or damage may remain, arising from extreme environmental conditions exceeding those for which the scheme was designed. In the case of losses such as those due to flooding from the overtopping of a seawall, the present value of these losses should be assessed and deducted from the benefit.

8.1.8 Sensitivity analysis

There may be a considerable variation in the reliability and accuracy of input data for economic appraisal. In many instances adequate data are not available and assumptions have to be made based on engineering judgement. Where there is doubt as to the impact of likely variations in data (or a range of assumptions is possible) then the sensitivity of the results to such variations should be examined.

The results of the economic analysis are often particularly sensitive to:

- Erosion rate;
- Probability of overtopping or breach of an existing structure;
- Sea level/return period relationship.

Upper and lower likely data values should be used to evaluate the upper and lower results that could be obtained. Where the results are found to change significantly within the likely range of data, then refinement to the data can be sought while those results showing only tolerable change can be adopted without further effort. Such a sensitivity analysis leads both to greater effectiveness in data collection and a better appreciation of the strengths and weaknesses in the cost and benefit comparisons made.

In making a comparison between initial construction and subsequent costs the relative accuracy of the estimates should be considered. Operational and replacement costs are usually less well defined both in timing and extent than initial construction costs. In the case of projects with a particularly long construction period, especially those including a substantial foreign exchange element, the justification should be sufficiently robust to withstand reasonable exchange rate fluctuations.

8.2 Failure scenarios

An essential part of scheme appraisal is an assessment of loss and damage that would occur without intervention by the provision of a seawall. This avoidance of potential loss, modified if necessary by any loss which may still occur, represents the benefit of the works provided.

Situations commonly fall into one of three categories:

- Erosion of unprotected coastlines with loss of land and property and perhaps some flooding;
- Erosion and/or flooding following damage to, or breaching of, existing works;
- Overtopping of existing defences resulting in flooding.

The causes of coastal change may be in the form of:

- Progressive events in which deterioration is continuous (generally due to wave action);
- An isolated event such as extremes of sea level and/or storm waves;
- A combination of progressive and isolated events.

While variations in situations and causes will require modified assessment, the principles and procedures are common to all.

8.2.1 Procedure

In order to assess the probability and/or timing of the loss or damage which is avoided by the provision of coastal defences the general procedure listed below is recommended. It will be seen that much of the data collection and analysis is also required for the design process, and reference should be made to Chapters 3 and 4 as appropriate.

1. Establish the background to, and reasons for, the economic appraisal for which the information is required.
2. Make a general appraisal of the existing coastal situation in the frontage in question and in adjoing coastal areas.

3. Collect historical data for the frontage including information on coastal structures.
4. Identify any existing or potential problems which may, or will, lead to ongoing or new loss or damage.
5. Collect available meteorological and hydrographic data relating to such problems.
6. Postulate future scenarios including any failures or collapses leading to loss or damage.
7. Make an initial assessment of timing and/or probability of loss or damage.
8. Identify and carry out any investigations or further data acquisition required for a detailed assessment.
9. Make a detailed assessment as 7 above.

Steps listed in 1 to 5 above will in any case be required for new seawall design and will therefore form part of the overall scheme design procedure.

8.2.2 Erosion of unprotected frontages

The mechanisms of erosion are described in the previous sections concerned with the design process (see Section 4.9). In considering the prevention of loss of land it is important to understand the interaction between foreshore loss and the destruction of backshore or coastal escarpment. The rate of erosion may be cyclic and vary as the alignment of the coastline is changed. However, it is the rate of loss of useable land and damage to buildings or amenities that will be relevant to the assessment of benefits obtained by the provision of defence.

As erosion is a slow process, short-term records should be augmented by reference to older surveys and maps of the area. Comparison of such records should give an acceptably accurate figure for the average erosion rate provided consideration is given to changes in coastal regime and other variations which accompany the erosion. It should also be borne in mind that relatively large cliff falls may occur intermittently and that spatial variations in soil conditions may be significant.

Where historical records are inadequate or irrelevant because of changes to the coastal regime, erosion rates should still be estimated. Comparisons with similar frontages may be of assistance provided any differences in the forces causing erosion or in the geology are allowed for. A considerable degree of engineering judgement is necessary.

Erosion following the collapse of a seawall is initially likely to be very high. In most such cases, beach levels will be lower than at the time of the seawall construction so that the exposure of the now unprotected face to wave action is generally increased. The rate of erosion may subsequently decrease as the eroding face recedes relative to the collapsed seawall.

8.2.3 Residual life of seawalls

The effectiveness of an existing seawall together with its residual life will be relevant in appraising the options available for a coastline. Extensive information on types of damage and failure of seawalls is published in CIRIA TN 125[12]. The engineer should consider possible future modes of failure which are likely to occur as a result of progressive deterioration of the wall. This can result from:

- Abrasion and errosion of elements of the wall (Section 7.3);
- Foreshore lowering which will allow more severe wave loading (Section 6.2.3);
- Foreshore lowering which leads to instability in the wall (possible modes of failure and analysis are outlined in Sections 6.2, 6.3, 6.4 and 6.5 as appropriate).

Rates of foreshore lowering are discussed in Section 4.9. Based on this work, the engineer should estimate how long it will be before the wall fails (i.e. its residual life) as a result of progressive deterioration (see also Section 8.2.5 below).

8.2.4 Overtopping and flooding

Given the availability of reasonable data, it is usually possible to calculate a probability relationship with various levels of overtopping discharge and consequential flooding (see Section 6.1.3). The formation of breaches in, say, a clay floodbank cannot be precisely estimated and is therefore more a matter of engineering judgement. The extent of flooding will be related to the volume of water overtopping defences or passing through breaches.

8.2.5 Presentation of data

In assessing the residual life of a coastal defence structure or system, an attempt should be made to predict the rate at which the structure and foreshore, etc. will continue to degrade and to define critical environmental conditions and their probability of occurrence. As degradation proceeds, the structure may become increasingly vulnerable to damage and the probability of a damaging event will increase. In some cases reasonable estimates of progressive change can be made by extrapolation from previous records such as gradual fall in beach levels or reduction in steel sheet piling thickness due to corrosion/abrasion. This in turn may enable a reasonable prediction to be made as to when a catastrophic event might take place such as a seawall sliding forward or a sudden wash-out of filling due to perforation of the sheet piling.

In other cases it may be possible to arrive at reasonable damage/probability relationships from available data for certain isolated events which could lead to failure such as wave pressure overturning a cantilever floodwall or wave action that would lead to failure of an armoured revetment. Generally, however, failures will result from various possible combinations of progressive and isolated events for which precise estimation of timing and probability is complex. In such cases the coastal engineer may need to rely on his experience and engineering judgement.

Under these circumstances a range of values between possible maxima and minima may represent the best estimate. In choosing a value from such a range, consideration should be given to the immediate consequences of a collapse. A failed structure may still be affording some protection to the shoreline or to other coastal structures, and this should be taken into account in assessing the residual life or damage probability of the frontage as a whole. Two general methods have been proposed for the presentation of data for incorporation into a cost-benefit analysis of coastal defence works:

- Estimation of erosion rates, etc. and hence the residual life of property, roads, services, etc. without the proposed scheme so that the value of the losses avoided by the protection works can be calculated;
- Estimation of the probability of exceedance of extreme environmental hazards (wave, water level, etc.) and of the severity of consequential damage (flooding, etc.) leading to loss/probability relationships from which the average annual value of damage avoided may be calculated.

The former method is useful for evaluation of benefits accruing from prevention of progressive events (e.g. erosion), the latter from prevention of isolated ones (e.g. flooding).

Initial presentation of both types of data is usually in graphical form. Erosion may be represented by a series of contours at given time intervals related to a common base date while flooding may be represented by various areas affected at differing probabilities. In the case of frontages with existing coastal defences which are subject to failure, it is necessary to describe or tabulate the possible sequence of events and estimated timing leading to progressive failure. The timing may be given as a range of dates. Erosion subsequent to failure will be a matter for erosion contours.

Cliffs and coastal slopes subject to landslip, which is not directly related to erosion rates, may require a hazard-zoning map delineating zones at different levels of risk. Property, land, services, etc. should then be tabulated against residual life or damage/probability for the assessment of discounted benefit values.

Where vulnerability varies with time (for example, as a result of continuing erosion) or for other reasons, a series of event/probability relationships could be established. These would show either the variation with time of the probability of a damaging event or the variation in damage boundaries caused by an event of a given probability.

8.3 Assessment of erosion benefit

The categorization shown in Figure 8.3 is the basis of the recommended methods of benefit assessment in the Interim Guidelines produced by Middlesex Polytechnic[11]. Different analytical techniques are available for the different types of benefit arising from seawall construction, as well as different data sources to calibrate that analysis.

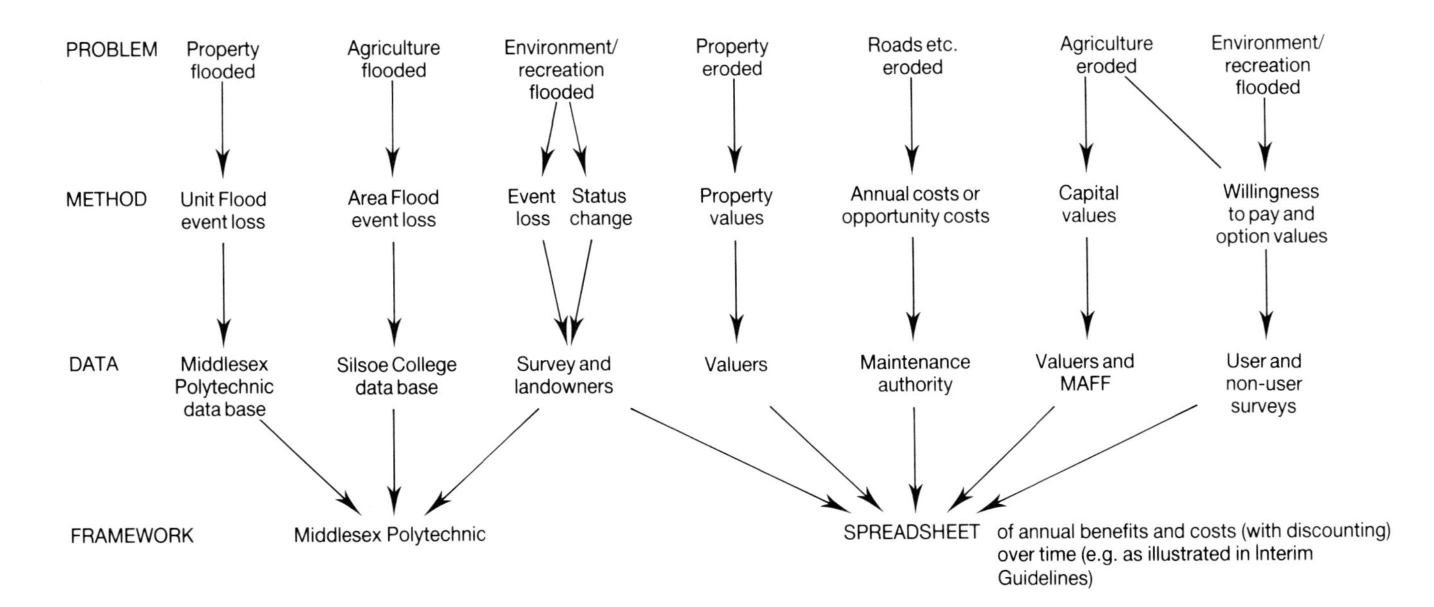

Figure 8.3 Evaluation of benefits

8.3.1 Property at risk from erosion

Erosion is a progressive or sequential process which is normally irreversible. Erosion losses are 'once and for all', except in the case where seawalls protect reclaimed land. Seawalls, and other works, can thus generally only delay erosion and protect property at risk for the effective life of the scheme, not prevent it altogether.

A theoretically appropriate value of the benefit of this protection from erosion is the difference in market price for that property with and without the scheme, over the period for which protection is given. The Interim Guidelines give detailed background on the method for assessing these benefits.

For the purposes of these guidelines the following simplified but numerically correct approach should be used. The benefit (B) obtained by extending the life of a property from an expected life of E years to a scheme life of $E + S$ years is:

$$B = MV \,.\, D_E - MV \,.\, D_{E+S}$$

where MV is the property's market value in the absence of erosion risk and D is the appropriate discount factor at time E or $E + S$ years in the future.

8.3.2 Data sources and analysis: property at risk from erosion

The first requirement in the analysis of scheme benefits is the extent and effect of erosion that will occur without the seawall scheme. The Interim Guidelines recommend the construction of five-year erosion contours, based on historic erosion rates or other calculations (see Section 4.9), to cover at least the lifespan of the scheme.

Theoretically, a further period after the end of the proposed life of the scheme should also be included. This is because even the properties outside the area that would be protected over the scheme's lifespan will benefit from the scheme. However, these benefits discounted to present values will generally be small and can be ignored except where scheme life is short or for very large schemes protecting substantial urban areas.

Second, property values for the types of property at risk will be needed, and are obtainable from District Valuers' offices, the Inland Revenue or estate agents. Local sources should be used to determine these typical local prices for property not subject to the erosion risk.

The Interim Guidelines provide an example of a simple spreadsheet framework with which the complete analysis can be undertaken (incorporating both capital and maintenance costs so as to calculate appraisal indices such as cost-benefit ratios). Use of this framework will ease the quite considerable problems involved with hand calculation, and allow rapid sensitivity analysis to show the effect on the results of alternative data, such as for property prices, and different assumptions (for example, concerning erosion rates).

8.3.3 Land at risk from erosion

The Interim Guidelines provide recommendations about assessing the benefits of protecting open land from erosion. Such land includes uses for agriculture, roads and promenades, recreational land, nature reserves and other space including that for informal recreation.

For agricultural land, roads, promenades and sewers the method for property erosion loss is recommended, suitably adapted. For the recreational use of land there is a number of approaches, and this is the subject of continuing research at Middlesex Polytechnic. At present it is recommended that user surveys of recreational areas are only undertaken to calculate the likely benefits of major schemes. For more minor works there should be a simple but full description of the extent of recreational use and the possible impacts of the likely erosion, together with the situation with the proposed scheme, to accompany the cost-benefit analysis.

In the case of important ecological, geological or archaeological features proposed for protection (or adversely affected by a seawall scheme) there are techniques available for assessing their economic worth to the nation. However, these techniques are complex and relatively untested. The current recommendation in the Interim Guidelines is therefore for a detailed description of the likely environmental changes with and without the scheme, rather than any attempt of monetary assessment, to complement the cost-benefit analysis incorporating the economic aspects that can be quantified.

8.4 Assessment of flooding benefits

The Interim Guidelines give advice on the assessment of flood damages to be avoided by seawall construction. This advice reflects both the standard procedures accepted by the Ministry of Agriculture, Fisheries and Food[3] for urban fluvial flooding and sea defence, and gives additional insight into the particular problems to be encountered in a coastal situation.

In this respect it is important to note that flood damages are recurrent rather than one-off (as is the case with erosion losses) and that any appraisal should take into account the incidence of floods of different magnitudes throughout the life of the structure or structures being appraised. However, a particular feature of coastal schemes, especially with rising sea levels, is that areas may become permanently inundated or subject to repeated tidal flooding if not protected by seawalls. The property may therefore become uninhabitable, or agricultural land uncultivatable, in which case the methods appropriate to erosion loss become applicable.

The standard method of calculating the benefits of alleviating flooding is to determine the damage caused by a range of events of different severity and magnitude and to construct thereby a relationship between future losses and the annual probability of those losses – the loss-probability curve[3,6,13]. The area under this curve represents the average annual flood damages, which need to be discounted to present values over the anticipated life of the proposed scheme. The following parameters are relevant to the situation:

r = discount rate;
n = number of years (= scheme life);
x = average annual benefit in the form of flood damage avoided.

The present value of the stream of equal annual benefits is therefore given as follows:

$$\text{Present value} = \frac{x}{r}\left[1 - \left(\frac{1}{r+1}\right)^{n}\right]$$

Applying this approach to the situation where sea levels are rising (or any other case where the probability of severity of specific events in the future is changing) requires the annual average values of future flood damages to be calculated individually (or for five- or ten-year intervals) and then summed:

$$\text{Present value} = \frac{x_t}{(1+r)^t}$$

where x is the annual benefit, r is the discount rate and t is the number of years before that benefit is gained.

8.4.1 Data collection and analysis: urban risk from flooding

Those appraising seawalls to prevent flooding will need to collect data on the extent and depths of water in the area likely to be affected by flooding (the benefit area). This is likely to involve predictions of the area affected by flooding if existing seawalls are not renovated, or fail in some other way, or the rates and duration of overtopping of existing structures which result in the accumulation of floodwaters on the landward side of such structures.

These data will not be easy to obtain but are crucial to the analysis. Flood elevations will be required for a range of flood magnitudes for different points throughout the benefit area. The data need to reflect the longitudinal profiles of watercourses feeding into this area, if appropriate. Ideally the data should cover eventualities such as the failure and overtopping of existing and proposed structures, so that the 'with scheme' and the 'without scheme' difference can be evaluated.

The appraisal will also require information on the land use and other characteristics of the benefit area, and the data on the potential flood damages that will result, obtainable from Suleman *et al.*[10] and Thompson *et al.*[11] The latter contains data and techniques for assessing indirect flood losses, which in the coastal situation will be the disruption of roads and other communication systems, of retail trade (although this is likely to be small and financial rather than economic in character[11]) and of manufacturing production by flooding, if this is relevant.

Applying these methods is straightforward, and computer programs[8] can be used to automate the necessary calculations. It is unlikely that the indirect effects of flooding will be substantial unless major roads or major industrial plants are likely to be affected by flooding. The appraisal should therefore concentrate in the first instance on assessing potential direct flood damage within the area likely to be affected.

A particular coastal problem is damage caused by spray and waterborne debris such as shingle, and an example of the application of methods to calculate the approximate magnitude of these benefits will be found in Parker and Penning-Rowsell[7]. Care should be taken, however, to ensure that the works being appraised will actually prevent or alleviate this damage; the benefits to be set against costs are obviously only allowable if the scheme can be designed to realize those benefits.

Protection from flooding with seawalls or other measures will result in the reduction of 'intangible' losses (loss of life or of personal memorabilia; stress and ill health caused by floods; disruption caused by evacuation of property, etc.). No data are available in the Interim Guidelines in this respect, although research on this topic is continuing at Middlesex Polytechnic. Examples of the magnitude of these intangible benefits are provided by Green and Penning-Rowsell[1], where references can be found to research reports describing detailed case studies. It should be noted that in the UK the Ministry of Agriculture, Fisheries and Food will require strong supporting evidence for any claimed monetary quantification of intangible losses. In any case, the listing, categorization and full description of such potential benefits of flood-protection works should be included.

8.4.2 Flood impacts on open (non-urban) land

Seawalls are generally constructed to protect high-value urban areas but open land may also warrant protection, especially as part of a comprehensive scheme affecting both urban areas and open land. The methods devised by Morris and Hess[5] should be used to assess the benefits of alleviating the flooding that would occur on agricultural land without protective works. Their approach and technique is to assess the effect of flood alleviation and drainage on farm economies, using crop and livestock gross margins adjusted to eliminate their subsidy element. Their techniques include a series of computer programs, with associated data sets, which assess the difference in economic inputs and outputs if agricultural land suffers flooding and/or poor drainage. For seawater flooding it is also important to allow for the contamination of land following flooding.

For non-agricultural open land potentially affected by flooding, the cost of repairs to that land and its features following the potential flooding could be used as the benefit of its protection. Alternatively, benefits could be gauged as the extra costs that would be incurred over and above normal costs to maintain the current use and value of the site given the changes expected with the proposed scheme.

The benefits of protecting open land can either be in the form of annual sums (particularly for agricultural benefit) or as lump sums per flood event or for the scheme as a whole. The Interim Guidelines give advice as to how these different values should feature in the overall analysis. However, it should be noted that while seawalls can enhance the use of open land, they can also be harmful. Many of these benefits and costs will be 'intangible', in which case they cannot be included in the cost-benefit analysis, but should be recorded fully, especially if the changes with the proposed scheme are likely to be irreversible.

8.4.3 Secular changes in sea level

A particular problem with assessing flood damage avoided by coast protection works is the secular rise in sea level (see Section 4.2.4). This phenomenon can have a major effect on the probability of overtopping or failure of existing or proposed works, and thus on the benefits of seawall construction, as illustrated in the appraisal of the Hengistbury Head scheme.

The Interim Guidelines recommend assessing flooding potential for ten-year intervals into the future and an analysis thereby undertaken of the likely rise in annual average flood damages with rising sea level. In this way the discounted annual benefits can be calculated, and illustrated with a loss-probability curve or set of curves, based on the changing severity of flood potential through time.

8.5 Scheme costs

Scheme costs as viewed in the economic assessment are likely to be different from those required for budgetary purposes on the part of a local authority. On the one hand, the economic assessment looks at benefits and costs from a national perspective and, on the other, estimated costs in terms of actual expenditure are likely to be required for a local authority. For example, cost of land for temporary works may be a legitimate cost for budgetary purposes. It is not an 'economic' cost since it is merely the transfer of assets from one party to another. Costs which are not allowable in the economic appraisal are identified as such in the following section.

Scheme costs accrue from every aspect of a project from initial conception, through planning and construction, to subsequent monitoring, and maintenance. A cost can be attached to each step.

The major elements in the cost of any coastal defence scheme is usually that of the construction itself. The initial stages comprising planning, design, investigation and studies, etc. often accrue relatively minor costs in relation to the scheme as a whole. However, investment in good investigation and design can greatly benefit construction cost and programme.

There will be incidental costs associated with the construction of most schemes to provide land either for the works or for temporary use during construction or in compensation to those adversely affected by the works. Such costs are extremely variable from scheme to scheme but may be significant in determining the most cost-effective option. It is often convenient to schedule the costs in five parts:

- Preliminaries;
- Planning and design;
- Construction;
- Land and property;
- Operational and maintenance costs.

The boxed section shows typical elements of cost set out in this way.

Typical elements to the cost of a seawall

Subject	*Costs to be included*
Preliminaries	Project coordination, management and administration
Planning and design	Survey, data collection and investigations Model studies Design and contract preparation Statutory procedures and licences Economic appraisal Environmental impact assessment
Construction	Contract payments including adjustments, claims, etc. Supervision and administration costs Ancillary works for environmental improvement, amenity or services
Land and property	Purchase or lease of land and property* either as part of the works or for construction Compensation payments to affected owners
Operation and maintenance	Operational activities Monitoring and maintenance, including replacement of elements having a shorter life than that of the overall scheme Repairs

*These are legitimate costs for budgetary purposes. Depending on circumstances (e.g. whether the land is removed from use or merely transferred from one party to another) they may not be an 'economic' cost to the nation.

8.5.1 Preliminaries, planning and design costs

Project planning and design costs can be assessed either by estimating the actual cost and the time incurred, or as a percentage of the estimated overall cost of the scheme, or as a combination of both. Small schemes usually incur proportionately higher design costs than larger ones.

Costs arise in respect of surveys, the collection of information and data and special investigations. Those which are likely to be most significant concern site surveys, subsoil investigations and model tests.

The environmental impact assessment – whether a formal survey or less formal consideration of expected change – will be a cost to be included at this stage. Works to mitigate unacceptable effects or improve the environment are likely to be included with construction costs.

Although the incidental costs of land acquired or leased will be identified separately, the administrative costs of acquisition will be included in this stage together with costs of statutory procedures, approvals and licences.

8.5.2 Construction costs

In some instances it may be possible to make a very preliminary estimate of cost based on unit rates for completed structures or lengths of coastline. Such an approach should be treated with extreme caution. Upper and lower limits should be applied to a cost estimated in this way.

Estimates of scheme costs may be arrived at by:

- Calculating preliminary quantities and applying unit rates based on similar work;
- Assessing the cost of labour, plant and materials and summing;
- Combinations of the above.

It is important to identify all issues which might have an effect on cost. These might include:

- Access problems;
- Level of work in relation to the tide and the balance of high- and low-level work available;
- Seasonal factors;
- Tidal range and exposure of site;
- Phasing;
- Availability of resources and materials;
- Environmental and planning constraints.

Supervision costs will arise from the provision of site staff and from the need for contract administration. The former relates to salary, on-costs, equipment, accommodation and expenses of supervisory staff, i.e. resident engineer and assistance. Contract administration may normally be assessed in a manner similar to project planning and design.

Some works included in the construction costs will arise from either the project planning stage or as a means of reducing incidental costs. Examples are:

- Additional survey or investigation for subsequent phases;
- Works to minimize environmental impact;
- Accommodation works to mitigate compensation claims;
- Roads for access to land purchased.

8.5.3 Land and property

In some cases it may be necessary to obtain land or property either on a temporary or a permanent basis in order to allow the scheme to proceed. Costs may accrue as a result either of purchase or renting the necessary area. Situations where this might arise include:

- Requirements for access;
- Areas required for temporary works;
- A need for ownership by the authority undertaking the work;
- Requirements for maintenance following completion of the work.

As mentioned earlier in the boxed section these will not necessarily form part of the economic cost. Costs may also arise as a result of compensation for damage to property or disturbance or from the provision of accommodation works.

8.5.4 Operational and maintenance costs

Operational costs arise on completion of construction from monitoring, maintenance and routine operations. Monitoring costs may include:

- Routine inspections;
- Special inspections after storms;
- Beach level surveys;
- Other routine records, e.g. wave heights, piezometer levels.

Many of these activities are necessary for effective coastal management and do not flow solely from the provision of a new seawall. Coastal authorities – in association with other civil authorities – advise the public urgently as to possible flooding, disruption of services and risk from the sea to property and inhabitants. Many also manage beaches for leisure and provide amenity works to promote recreation. Maintenance works will be planned on the basis of beach surveillance among other considerations. The extra monitoring costs occasioned by a new seawall are therefore likely to be small.

Maintenance involves the work necessary to keep the completed scheme in good order against normal wear and tear. Costs may be arrived at either by estimating the extent of work necessary at intervals in the future or by taking percentage costs derived from similar work. The annual cost can be expected to increase with time. Work may include:

- Minor repairs, pointing, etc. arising from expected conditions such as abrasion and weathering;
- Replacement of minor components;
- Lubrication of moving parts;
- Painting;
- Cleaning drains and manholes;
- Cutting grass;
- Shingle clearance.

Routine operations include such items as opening and closing floodgates and penstocks and seasonal erection of access steps. Integration of monitoring, maintenance and routine operations will usually enhance the effectiveness of each.

8.5.5 Major repairs

Major repairs may arise from events for which the works are not designed or from unforseen environmental change. The design parameters used will have probability figures associated with them and so form a basis for estimating the possible costs of major repairs caused by extreme events. Future costs of this nature should be discounted to present values for comparison purposes (see Section 8.1.5).

8.5.6 Funding and cost control

Most seawall construction in the UK benefits from central government grants. Eligibility to receive grant aid can be ascertained from the appropriate government department (see Appendix A) who will also advise as to procedure and the rate of grant aid applicable. In general terms, while maintenance costs should be included in the economic analysis, at present in the UK they are unlikely to be eligible for MAFF grant aid. Where commercial frontages receive particular benefit from the works, contributions to the cost may be sought but each case should be treated on its merits. The balance of cost must be met by the promoter.

Cash flow of outgoing funds will require analysis. Costs need to be met as they arise, whereas financial support from grant aid or contributions will generally be paid as the works are completed.

Seawalls are constructed in a harsh environment and the design involves many judgements, some of which concern the frequency of random or extreme meteorological events. In these circumstances absolute certainty as to costs can never be achieved. Costs are therefore, of necessity, based on estimates in which the events are allowed for in the light of their probability. Budgets need to provide for all facets of expenditure with confidence in their overall accuracy as to both magnitude and timing. As the works proceed, those elements costing more than the provision made in the budget can be subject to scrutiny and the budget continuously updated to predict cash flow and final cost.

The merit of design to facilitate construction is clear and methods are shown in Section 6.8. The concept may be extended by giving consideration as to how the construction activities should be shared between the parties involved. Clearly, the promoter (if a local authority) will be well placed to deal with Town Planning consent, diversion of roads or footpaths, provision of land for temporary and permanent use, wayleaves, access and perhaps the provision of power and water to the site. Additionally, site clearance, fencing and preordering of scarce materials may be advantageous. If construction is heavily dependent upon the circumstances revealed as the work proceeds then a more flexible form of contract may also be advantageous. Seawalls are generally designed as site-specific entities, and this should be reflected in the procedures adopted.

Appendix A: Statutory framework in the UK

This appendix discusses the primary legislation relating to coastal defences in the UK, coastal defences being either coast protection or sea defence as discussed below. The legislation is current at the time of writing but will undoubtedly be amended from time to time. Legislation relating to Town and Country Planning and to environmental impact assessment is also of importance and is discussed in Section A.2. When undertaking works the engineer should seek specialist advice as to the precise current statutory framework if there appears to be any doubt.

A.1 Primary legislation

A.1.1 Coast protection

The Coast Protection Act 1949 empowers maritime district councils, regional councils adjoining the sea and islands councils, known as coast protection authorities (CPAs), to construct works to protect land against erosion or encroachment by the sea, subject to government approval. Neither of the terms 'erosion' or 'encroachment' is defined in the Act but erosion is taken to mean the loss of land while encroachment concerns the permanent occupation of land by the sea. Works constructed to resist these effects are known as 'coast protection works'. Seawalls may occasionally be constructed under other legislation which makes appropriate general or specific provision. The Coast Protection Act 1949 does not extend to Northern Ireland.

A.1.2 Sea defences

In the case where the primary function of the seawall is to prevent or alleviate flooding by the sea it is defined as 'sea defence works'. Such works may be carried out under:

- England and Wales —Land Drainage Act 1976 (as amended by the Water Act 1989)
- Scotland —Flood Prevention (Scotland) Act 1961 for non-agricultural land

—Land Drainage (Scotland) Act 1958, and the Farm and Conservation Grant Scheme (National) for agricultural land

- Northern Ireland —Drainage (Northern Ireland) Order 1973

'Sea defence works' in England and Wales may be undertaken by the National Rivers Authority, internal drainage boards or local authorities. Private landowners may also carry out work on their own land.

A.1.3 Administration of the Acts

England and Wales

Prior to 1 April 1985 the administration of the Coast Protection Act 1949 in England was carried out by the Department of the Environment (DoE) while the Land Drainage Act 1976 was administered by the Ministry of Agriculture, Fisheries and Food (MAFF). Since the above date the government has transferred responsibility for coast protection in England from the Secretary of State for the Environment to the Minister of Agriculture, Fisheries and Food. The Secretary of State for Wales already had responsibility for both Acts in Wales.

Scotland

In Scotland the Scottish Development Department administers the Coast Protection Act 1949 and the Flood Prevention (Scotland) Act 1961. The Department of Agriculture and Fisheries for Scotland administers the Land Drainage (Scotland) Act 1958 and the Farm and Conservation Grant Scheme (National).

Northern Ireland

In Northern Ireland the responsibility for coast protection is not defined and, in the absence of any clear statute has, through custom, become the responsibility of the landowner who is liable to suffer damage from continued erosion. The Coast Protection Act 1949 does not extend to Northern Ireland. Departmental interests are as follows:

1. The Department of Economic Development – schemes related to tourism and harbours;
2. The Department of the Environment – schemes where there is road or promenade interest in which DED is not involved;
3. The Department of Agriculture – any essential scheme not falling under 1 or 2.

'Sea Defences' are the responsibility of the Secretary of State for Northern Ireland and are carried out under the Drainage (Northern Ireland) Order 1973, administered by the Department of Agriculture. This order is an amalgam of earlier Drainage Acts including the Drainage Act 1947 and the Sea Defences Act.

The Department of Agriculture for Northern Ireland is empowered under the Drainage (Northern Ireland) Order 1973 to maintain designated Sea Defences to prevent flooding of land or property by the sea. The Order revises the law relating to drainage in Northern Ireland by replacing with amendments previous Drainage Acts and other associated enactments including the Drainage (Sea Defences) Act (Northern Ireland) 1955.

A.2 Planning and environmental legislation

A.2.1 England and Wales

Works carried out as coast protection under the Coast Protection Act 1949 require approval (planning permission) under the Town and Country Planning Act 1971 and the advertising of each scheme is specified. Sea defence works carried out under the provisions of the Land Drainage Act 1976 may have deemed planning consent but the definitions for this purpose are complex and expert advice or consultation with the planning authority is recommended. Improvements, maintenance and repairs using the powers of this Act have permitted development rights under the Town and Country Planning General Development Order (1988) but consultation is considered prudent.

From July 1988 proposals for certain projects require 'environmental statements'. Regulations relating to the assessment of environmental effects are contained in Statutory Instruments (1988) No. 1199 for works requiring planning permission under the Town and Country Planning Act and No. 1217 for works under the Land Drainage Act.

SI 1217 relates to improvement works which have permitted development rights. This requires that the drainage body consider whether the works are likely to have significant environmental effects and thus whether an Environmental Assessment (EA) is required or not. They must publish notice of the improvement scheme and state if an EA is to be carried out. If not, and where representations are made requesting an EA or objecting to the environmental impact of the scheme, the matter may be referred to the appropriate government department for resolution.

Both SI 1199 and 1217 specify the areas that are to be covered by the EA, and also indicates those parties, such as the UK Joint Nature Conservation Committee (JNCC),* the Countryside Council, the Countryside Council for Wales and the Scottish Natural Heritage (the Countryside Council for Scotland becomes a part of this last in April 1992) who must be kept informed.

* See page 32.

A.2.2 Scotland

In Scotland, works carried out as coast protection under the Coast Protection Act 1949 require to be approved under the Town and Country Planning (Scotland) Act 1972. Approval under this Act is also required for flood protection works carried out under the Land Drainage (Scotland) Act 1958 and the Flood Prevention (Scotland) Act 1961. The Environmental Assessment (Scotland) Regulations 1988 (Statutory Instrument 1988 No. 1221) requires certain projects listed in the schedules to be subject to environmental assessment. Seawalls are not included within these schedules and would only be the subject of an environmental assessment if forming part of a scheduled project. Part I of the Regulations applies to projects which are subject to planning consent and Part V applies to projects authorized under the Land Drainage (Scotland) Act 1958. The Secretary of State for Scotland may give a direction on the requirement for an environmental statement in the event of a dispute.

A.2.3 Other legislation

Further statutory protection to the environment is given by a number of other Acts including the National Parks and Access to the Countryside Act 1949, the Countryside (Scotland) Act 1967, the Wildlife and Countryside Act 1981 and the Food and Environmental Protection Act 1985 Part II. These include, *inter alia,* requirements for appropriate licences, approvals and consultations with bodies such as the UK Joint Nature Conservancy Committee (JNCC)* and other bodies as listed in section A.2.1. Some guidance on consultation is given in the Conservation Guidelines for Drainage Authorities.

* See page 32.

Appendix B: Physical and numerical hydraulic models

The purpose of this appendix is to provide the engineer with sufficient information on hydraulic models so that he can identify potentially useful types of study. It is not intended to provide guidelines for those seeking to design or conduct such studies.

The detailed techniques used in hydraulic modelling, in both physical and mathematical models, are advancing continually. The engineer using this book is therefore advised to contact a specialist at an early stage in the design studies. Use of an experienced specialist is also advisable from the point of view of cost. Full studies of all processes will be very costly. The model investigations, if necessary at all, may be tailored so that only those aspects that are likely to be significant are modelled in detail. In this way a cost-effective study can be produced.

Until the 1970s, hydraulic models were physical models which simulated steady flows (rivers), tidal flows or the wave action specific to a given site. Latterly, computer models were increasingly available with a proliferation of mathematical modelling programs. The scope and capability of mathematical models is largely governed by the analytical and empirical understanding of the processes, which in turn depends on the complexity of the processes and the level of research that has been undertaken in the particular aspect.

Of particular importance, mathematical models involve fairly complex analytical techniques. Whereas ideally, physical models actually reproduce the physical processes that are being studied, this is not the case with numerical ones which, in many cases, produce a numerical analogue. The numerical model should therefore be used with caution. It should not be treated as a black box which will simulate all factors in all cases. There are many instances where numerical models have been used for applications subtly different from those for which they were developed, only to be substantially wrong. It is recommended that, when using mathematical models, the engineer should employ only the organizations with sufficient experience and expertise to allow them to understand the latest research, to be aware of their limitations, and to choose the most appropriate models.

Mathematical models cannot substitute for physical ones in every case, but physical models also have limitations. The use of models falls into three main areas:

- Shallow water effects;
- Coastal processes;
- Seawalls.

B.1 Calibration

All models, whether physical or mathematical, require calibration. This means running the model with a known set of conditions and checking various parameters (e.g. water elevation or current) against the values obtained from measurements made on-site at the time that the given conditions prevailed. Some variable aspect of the model is adjusted to make the model parameter match the prototype value. In the case of a tidal model the bed friction may be the calibration variable whereas in a physical wave model the wave-generating mechanism may be adjusted to produce waves of the required amplitude. All this assumes that the calibration data are available. Often, satisfactory data do not exist and hydrographic survey work must be commissioned in advance of the model studies. Ideally, the requirements of the hydraulic modelling contractor should be sought beforehand, and this obviously requires careful planning in order to allow time for the measurements to be made, this being especially important where the collection of wave data is required.

B.2 Shallow water effects

Shallow water effects are discussed in Section 4.4.6. Computer models are increasingly being used in preference to hand or graphical methods. They are quicker, more accurate, and can incorporate the effects of combined wave processes, i.e. not just refraction and shoaling but also, possibly, bed friction, breaking and increase in wave height due to wind acting on the waves during refraction. A variety of computer models exist, each with different advantages and limitations. The choice of which type of computer models to use for a given coastal engineering problem needs to be made with some care. The most important types of model are described below, and their advantages, limitations and range of applicability are summarized in Tables B1 and B2. The models are all fairly complex and should normally run for a discrete number of wave conditions (i.e. significant height, significant period and wave direction combinations) covering the range of wave conditions likely to occur offshore. The results can be used to establish a transfer function to allow inshore wave climate to be derived from that offshore.

Depending on location, an important factor in wave propagation is the tide and tidal streams. To give a good description of tidal streams, mathematical models can be used. In many situations, except for those with the most complex bathymetry, two-dimensional models are well proven and reliable. They cease to be valid when current variation with depth is complex, and not the normal exponential variation. These models are widely used in pollution and recirculation studies and are of value in assessing shallow water wave effects and in providing the necessary input to refraction models when current refraction is likely to be significant.

The models discussed below are a selection of those which deal with shallow water effects on waves and are available in the UK at the time of writing. Model technology is advancing rapidly and new models which are more efficient, more thorough or more precise are being developed. The engineer should consult the necessary specialist to receive guidance as to the most appropriate model for his requirements.

Table B1 Shallow water computational models: wave processes incorporated

	Wave processes modelled							
Computational model	*Depth refraction and shoaling*	*Current refraction*	*Internal diffraction*	*External diffraction*	*Reflections*	*Bottom friction*	*Wave breaking*	*Energy gain due to local wind*
Forward-tracking ray model	Yes	Yes	Not modelled, but numerical smoothing by ray-averaging process	Yes for long slender structures (e.g. breakwaters or long wedge-shaped obstacles: e.g. some natural headlands)	Yes	Yes, but not for intersecting wave trains	Yes, but not for intersecting wave trains Approx. energy loss in shallow water only	No
Back-tracking ray model	Yes	Yes	Not modelled, but numerical smoothing by spectral representation	No	Yes	No	No, apart from check at inshore point	No
Finite-difference model	Yes	Yes	Not modelled, but numerical smoothing if offshore spectrum used	No	No Back-scattered waves of any type cannot be modelled	Yes	Yes Approximate energy loss in shallow water only	No
Parabolic model	Yes	Yes	Yes	Yes, but difficult to incorporate in general manner	No Back-scattered waves of any type cannot be modelled	Yes	Yes Approximate energy loss in shallow water only	No
One-dimensional	Yes	Yes	No	No	No	Yes	Yes	Yes

Table B2 Shallow water computational models: parameter determining model suitability

	Coastal parameters				
Computational model	*Type of bathymetry*	*Extent of sea area*	*Type of coastline*	*Number of inshore points per run*	*Offshore wave conditions*
Forward-tracking ray model	Reasonably gentle and regular depth variations. Poor for shoal systems	Unlimited. Element size determined by depth variations	Any	Many, covering entire modelled sea area	Single period and direction. Spectrum can be covered by multiple runs
Back-tracking ray model	Reasonably gentle depth variations	Unlimited. Element size determined by depth variations	Any, except where external diffraction important (e.g. shelter by headland)	One	Homogenous ray period and direction spectrum
Finite-difference model	Reasonably gentle and regular depth variations. Poor for shoal systems	Unlimited. Element size determined by depth variations	Reasonably straight coast facing open sea	Many, covering entire modelled sea area	Period and direction spectrum. (Need not be homogenous)
Parabolic model	Reasonably gentle depth variations	Limited to few kilometres at most, often considerably less. Element size determined by minimum number of elements per wavelength	Reasonably straight coast facing open sea	Many, covering entire modelled sea area	Period and direction spectrum. (Need not be homogenous)
One-dimensional model	Straight parallel contours	Unlimited	Straight coast	Unlimited	Spectrum (unidirectional)

Forward-tracking ray model

This model involves tracing a set of closely spaced rays (orthogonals to wave crests) from deep water towards the coast over a gridded array of depth values. Each set of rays represents one long-crested, single-period, single-direction wave. This type of computer model can determine the effects of refraction and shoaling by depth variation along each ray, and can also include the effects of refraction by currents, reflections from structures and channels, bottom friction and wave breaking. A major drawback is that diffraction cannot be included in a general manner. Nevertheless, external diffraction by breakwaters can be incorporated and the effects of internal diffraction due to waves focusing can be estimated by computationally averaging the effects of rays over grid squares, although this will not be sufficient if internal diffraction is particularly strong. Ray averaging also allows intersecting wave trains (such as direct and reflected wave) to be modelled properly, and will give results in the useful form of spot values of wave height and direction in a regular array over the sea area under study. The forward-tracking ray method is limited to single-period and single-direction input waves. Wave spectra can be modelled by repeated running of the model for different wave heights, periods and directions, but this can be expensive, and is theoretically unsound if bottom friction and breaking are present to an important extent.

The forward-tracking ray method is best used for regular incident wave spectra (which can be approximated by an average incident wave height, period and direction) and regular depth contours.

Back-tracking ray model

In the back-tracking ray model, rays are traced outwards, opposite to the direction of wave travel, from an inshore point of interest to deep water. The effects of refraction and shoaling by both depth variations and currents are included. Reflections from structures and channels can also be introduced. This type of model overcomes two of the most important drawbacks to forward-tracking since it can include wave spectra and wave diffraction. Input to the back-tracking ray model takes the form of a wave spectrum of period and direction, which is assumed to apply along the seaward boundary of the model. Although the process of diffraction is not modelled in the back-tracking method, its smoothing effect is represented by considering the refraction of spectra (which are generally regular) rather than refraction of individual components of the spectrum (which are commonly irregular). The main disadvantage of the back-tracking ray method is that bottom friction and breaking cannot be included. The omission of these processes means that predicted wave heights are usually higher than the true values. A further limitation is that each run of the model determines inshore wave spectra at only one point, and so the model can be inefficient if results are required at a large number of points.

Finite-difference refraction model

This is an alternative method to ray tracking which uses the same basic set of equations. In this method, input wave conditions are specified at each point along the grid row at the seaward edge of the grid. Wave conditions are then calculated at grid points along each row successively until the row furthest inshore is reached. The wave processes modelled are shoaling and refraction by depth variations and currents, bottom friction and wave breaking. In addition, it is possible to have spectral wave input which can vary along the offshore row. Drawbacks are that wave reflections and diffraction are difficult to incorporate, although recent work by Yoo and O'Conner has incorporated diffraction with some success[2]. A limitation of the model is that it can be readily used only for reasonably straight coastlines facing the open sea, and it becomes difficult to use in the shelter of a headland or at the side of an estuary.

Parabolic model

Parabolic models are a relatively new type in which development work has been done in the 1980s. Southgate[1] contains a literature review. These models solve a more complex set of equations and some diffraction effects are included. The method of solution is similar to the row-by-row 'marching' technique used in the finite-difference models above. As well as diffraction, the other effects that can be incorporated are shoaling and refraction by depth variations and currents, bottom friction, wave breaking and spectral input. Wave reflections are difficult to include.

The inclusion of diffraction is achieved at the expense of some limitations to the model's range of applicability. One limitation is that a much finer grid mesh is needed compared with the other models. In practice, this limits parabolic models to fairly small coastal areas, no more than a few kilometres wide at most. A further limitation is that wave directions are limited to an angular sector (typically, about 45°) either side of the grid direction perpendicular to the coastline. A reasonably straight coastline facing the open sea is required.

One-dimensional (profile) model

At the expense of precision in application to real coastlines, the one-dimensional model is a useful comparative tool. It can evaluate the effect of shoaling and refraction by depth variation and currents, bottom friction, wave breaking, and energy gain due to local wind. It allows for spectral input to the extent that it is assumed that the wave climate can be described by its peak period and energy density. The model calculates wave and current parameters along a single ray assuming a straight coast with contours parallel to the shore. This means that diffraction is ignored, but it can provide a relatively simple means of assessing the significance of breaking, currents and bed friction. As such, it is powerful when used in parallel with other models such as the back-tracking ray model above.

B.3 Coastal processes

Either mathematical or physical modelling, or a combination of both, can be used to refine the understanding of an existing coastal situation and to predict future developments. Both types of modelling usually require specialists, and both have disadvantages as well as advantages. In most situations tidal modelling is the first option considered. Even if a physical model of a stretch of coast is built, it is usually important to combine it with some mathematical modelling.

The advantages of mathematical modelling are that a long length of coast can be considered, a large number of different wave conditions can be used, there are no scaling effects and the model can be stored after use without difficulty. It is also easier to calibrate. The major disadvantages of such a model are that the prediction of sediment transport relies on the accuracy of the equations used, and that studying fine detail (say, in groyne bays) can become very time consuming. Problems also arise if a shoreline has a strong curvature (for example, in the lee of a breakwater).

The numerical coastal process models tend to fall into two groups, analytical and engineering time scale. Engineering time scale models (see below) are simpler and less detailed. Subject to good calibration, they can, using a time series of wave data, run repeatedly to produce a time series estimate of beach changes over periods of many years. This can help to identify the range of beach movement (landwards and seawards) and so identify worst design conditions. Analytical models (see below) are more complex and require more time to run. They are therefore limited to examination of discrete conditions, but in much more detail and giving a more detailed understanding of the coastal regime. The engineer, assisted by specialists, should evaluate carefully whether both, either, or any models are necessary for his particular project.

One-line numerical model

This is the simplest form of numerical coastal model. The evolution of a beach (e.g. accretion or erosion) is represented by the changing position of a single contour, usually the high water line. The major sediment transport mechanism modelled is the alongshore drift of beach material, although it is possible to add or subtract material to represent, say, beach nourishment or offshore losses.

Because of the inherent simplicity of such a technique, it is relatively easy to adapt a model to a variety of different coastal situations. For example, algorithms to represent the efficiency of a groyne system can be developed, or mechanical by-passing of sediment across a harbour mouth could be represented. Of particular relevance here is the ability to represent the effects of a seawall on the plan shape development of a beach. An attempt to develop a one-line model to include a seawall was introduced by Ozasa and Brampton[4], and this performed reasonably well. A more recent paper by Hanson and Kraus[5] also discusses this issue and reviews several other approaches.

N-line numerical models

A one-line model cannot incorporate onshore/offshore transport or predict the steepening or flattening of a beach profile. To overcome this difficulty, models have been developed which represent the beach by several contours, and calculate the changing positions of each. These models are known as multi-line or *N*-line models[6]. A problem with using such models has been the specification of the onshore/offshore transport which, for example, occurs when a large storm flattens a beach profile. Progress is now being made on this front, although the added complexity of the model adds to its cost. There is also considerable debate at present on how the introduction of a seawall, for example, will alter a beach profile.

Numerical flow models

The models described above deal with the modelling of a beach. In a number of cases this is not sufficient and it is required to model the seabed some way offshore to gain a full understanding of processes at work. In this respect, flow models which simulate tidal flow can be of value. When wave-induced currents are of significance these can be introduced, as can wind-induced currents. It has been found that residual currents, i.e. the magnitude of the current averaged over a full tidal cycle, can give very valuable data on the pattern of sediment circulation. These data are calculated at grid points throughout the model area. Such flow models tend to be two-dimensional (i.e. assuming a normal and constant velocity distribution with depth) to minimize computational effort. However, this does give errors where flows are not two-dimensional, e.g. in a breaking wave. Developments are being made to allow for this in numerical models by de Vriend[3] without recourse to the complexity of a fully three-dimensional model.

Numerical morphological models

Research is progressing on models based on those above which, by using sediment transport formulae, will calculate progressive changes in seabed contours. For the moment such models are valuable as indicators of trends and possible developments. They should not, however, be considered as an absolute means of assessing coastal processes but used as a useful tool to assist in interpretation.

Physical models of coastal processes

In many situations, especially when dealing with a complicated stretch of coast, the use of a scaled physical model of a beach can provide very useful guidance to the engineer. The advantages of such a technique are that:

- The area of interest can be studied in detail, without restrictions imposed by having to choose a grid size;
- Many processes are automatically included without extra effort on the part of the modeller;
- Results from the model can be very readily appreciated visually.

It is not possible, however, simply to scale down all natural processes in a constant manner, and physical models therefore suffer from several problems and constraints.

For example, although water motions (waves and tides) are relatively easy to reproduce, it is much more difficult to introduce a material into the model which will act like beach material in the prototype. As a consequence, some distortion will occur when comparing the reproduction of, say, alongshore transport and beach profile changes. In addition, physical modelling generally requires rather substantial laboratory facilities. Even with large model basins, only a limited length of coast can be modelled (say, up to 1 km) and it can be time consuming to consider a large number of wave and tidal conditions. A range of physical models can be used to investigate coastal processes. For example, a wave flume or channel can be used, with a fixed seabed, to investigate the reflection characteristics of a proposed seawall as well as run-up or overtopping. Such a model could then be extended by replacing the fixed beach with one of granular material, and observations made on the effect of the wall on beach profiles and the possibility of scour at the base of the wall. Care has to be taken, of course, in choosing the model sediment and running a sufficient number of tests for an overall picture to emerge.

More complicated three-dimensional models can be carried out in wave basins, again with or without mobile beach sediment. A model without sediment can be useful in examining the water motions (for example, currents caused by waves in a groyne field or behind a breakwater). Models with a mobile beach can demonstrate the interaction of a coast with a seawall or any other structure, although parallel computations using a mathematical model are often useful in putting physical model results into a broader perspective.

B.4 Seawall models

Seawall models are useful for studying:

- Wave forces and pressures;
- Wave run-up, overtopping and reflections;
- Armour stability;
- Local toe scour.

Physical models

Physical models can be broadly divided into two-dimensional and three-dimensional. To examine seawall and beach cross-sections (two-dimensional), tests in a wave channel (or flume) can be used. Originally tests were carried out with regular waves, but in the 1970s it became standard practice to use the more representative irregular wave generators. Detailed information about the performance of seawalls can be obtained from large-scale tests on sections contained within a flume. The flume should also contain an adequate extent of the foreshore and seabed to ensure the correct wave forms at the structure. Observations can include measurements of run-up and overtopping, and methods are available for determining the reflection coefficient of a given section. In the case of rigid structures, sensors can be installed to measure pressures and hence determine wave forces. In sections with flexible slope protection systems, rip-rap or concrete armour, the stability of the armour is a primary consideration in the experimental work. The majority of concrete armour units are available at model scales suitable for flume studies. The scale of model sections in flume studies tend to be of the order 1:30 to 1:50, being dictated largely by the physical constraints of the test equipment. Obviously, depending upon the actual size of the prototype, the model scale can be above or below this range.

With any physical model, scale effects have to be considered. For wave shoaling, breaking run-up, reflection and rock stability, a flume study can represent all these aspects simultaneously with simple geometric scaling. Flow within underlayers, overtopping, armour unit breakage and sediment transport, however, can be subject to scale effects which can lead to considerable errors. The engineer should therefore ensure that the laboratory is suitably experienced in these aspects.

Certain features such as oblique wave approach are not adequately represented by two-dimensional flume studies. For these, three-dimensional studies in a wave basin are required. While allowing a more realistic simulation of the prototype, three-dimensional studies are inevitably more costly because of their greater size. Visual inspection is also not so easy as with a flume study, where a good deal of information can be gleaned from photographs and viewing through side windows in the flume.

Numerical models

Numerical models of seawalls are as yet in their infancy. An empirical model of wave run-up and overtopping of simple seawalls is commonly available from Hydraulics Research Limited and hydrodynamic models of wave pressures and flows in permeable seawalls have been developed by Bezuijen, Wouters and Laustrup[7]. This allows the stability of the revetments to be assessed provided wave conditions (including run-up and run-down) at the wall are known, which can often require physical model studies. More sophisticated models of wave action on smooth, composite and armoured slopes are under development.

Appendix C: Discount tables

The present value of £1 *n* years hence, when discounted at interest rate *r* per annum = $(1 + r)^{-n}$

Interest % (= 100*r*)

n (*years*)	*1*	*1.5*	*2*	*2.5*	*3*	*3.5*	*4*	*4.5*	*5*	*5.5*
1	0.99010	0.98522	0.98039	0.97561	0.97087	0.96618	0.96154	0.95694	0.95238	0.94787
2	0.98030	0.97066	0.96117	0.95181	0.94260	0.93351	0.92456	0.91573	0.90703	0.89845
3	0.97059	0.95632	0.94232	0.92860	0.91514	0.90194	.088900	0.87630	0.86384	0.85161
4	0.96098	0.94218	0.92385	0.90595	0.88849	0.87144	0.85480	0.83856	0.82270	0.80722
5	0.95147	0.92826	0.90573	0.88385	0.86261	0.84197	0.82193	0.80245	0.78353	0.76513
6	0.94205	0.91454	0.88797	0.86230	0.83748	0.81350	0.79031	0.76790	0.74622	0.72525
7	0.93272	0.90103	0.87056	0.84127	0.81309	0.78599	0.75992	0.73483	0.71068	0.68744
8	0.92348	0.88771	0.85349	0.82075	0.78941	0.75941	0.73069	0.70319	0.67684	0.65160
9	0.91434	0.87459	0.83676	0.80073	0.76642	0.73373	0.70259	0.67290	0.64461	0.61763
10	0.90529	0.86167	0.82035	0.78120	0.74409	0.70892	0.67556	0.64393	0.61391	0.58543
11	0.89632	0.84893	0.80426	0.76214	0.72242	0.68495	0.64958	0.61620	0.58468	0.55491
12	0.88745	0.83639	0.78849	0.74356	0.70138	0.66178	0.62460	0.58966	0.55684	0.52598
13	0.87866	0.82403	0.77303	0.72542	0.68095	0.63940	0.60057	0.56427	0.53032	0.49856
14	0.86996	0.81185	0.75788	0.70773	0.66112	0.61778	0.57748	0.53997	0.50507	0.47257
15	0.86135	0.79985	0.74301	0.69047	0.64186	0.59689	0.55526	0.51672	0.48102	0.44793
16	0.85282	0.78803	0.72845	0.67363	0.62317	0.57671	0.53391	0.49447	0.45811	0.42458
17	0.84438	0.77637	0.71416	0.65720	0.60502	0.55720	0.51337	0.47318	0.43630	0.40245
18	0.83602	0.76491	0.70016	0.64117	0.58739	0.53836	0.49363	0.45280	0.41552	0.38147
19	0.82774	0.75361	0.68643	0.62553	0.57029	0.52016	0.47464	0.43330	0.39573	0.36158
20	0.81954	0.74247	0.67297	0.61027	0.55368	0.50257	0.45639	0.41464	0.37689	0.34273
25	0.77977	0.68921	0.60953	0.53939	0.47761	0.42315	0.37512	0.33273	0.29530	0.26223
30	0.74192	0.63976	0.55207	0.47674	0.41199	0.35628	0.30832	0.26700	0.23138	0.20064
35	0.70591	0.59387	0.50003	0.42137	0.35538	0.29998	0.25342	0.21425	0.18129	0.15352
40	0.67165	0.55126	0.45289	0.37243	0.30656	0.25257	0.20829	0.17193	0.14205	0.11746
45	0.63905	0.51171	0.41020	0.32917	0.26444	0.21266	0.17120	0.13796	0.11130	0.08988
50	0.60804	0.47500	0.37153	0.29094	0.22811	0.17905	0.14071	0.11071	0.08720	0.06877
55	0.57853	0.44093	0.33650	0.25715	0.19677	0.15076	0.11566	0.08884	0.06833	0.05262
60	0.55045	0.40930	0.30478	0.22728	0.16973	0.12693	0.09506	0.07129	0.05354	0.04026

Interest % (=100*r*)

n (years)	6	6.5	7	7.5	8	9	10	12	15	20
1	0.94340	0.93897	0.93458	0.93023	0.92593	0.91743	0.90909	0.89286	0.86957	0.83333
2	0.89000	0.88166	0.87344	0.86533	0.85734	0.84168	0.82645	0.79719	0.75614	0.69444
3	0.83962	0.82785	0.81630	0.80496	0.79383	0.77218	0.75131	0.71178	0.65752	0.57870
4	0.79209	0.77732	0.76290	0.74480	0.73503	0.70843	0.68301	0.63552	0.57175	0.48225
5	0.74726	0.72988	0.71299	0.69656	0.68058	0.64993	0.62092	0.56743	0.49718	0.40188
6	0.70496	0.68533	0.66634	0.64796	0.63017	0.59627	0.56447	0.50663	0.43233	0.33490
7	0.66506	0.64351	0.62275	0.60275	0.58349	0.54703	0.51316	0.45235	0.37594	0.27908
8	0.62741	0.60423	0.58201	0.56070	0.54027	0.50187	0.46651	0.40388	0.32690	0.23257
9	0.59190	0.56735	0.54393	0.52158	0.50025	0.46043	0.42410	0.36061	0.28426	0.19381
10	0.55839	0.53273	0.50835	0.48519	0.46319	0.42241	0.38554	0.32197	0.24718	0.16151
11	0.52679	0.50021	0.47509	0.45134	0.42888	0.38753	0.35049	0.28748	0.21494	0.13459
12	0.49697	0.46968	0.44401	0.41985	0.39711	0.35553	0.31863	0.25668	0.18691	0.11216
13	0.46884	0.44102	0.41496	0.39056	0.36770	0.32618	0.28966	0.22917	0.16253	0.09346
14	0.44230	0.41410	0.38782	0.36331	0.34046	0.29925	0.26333	0.20462	0.14133	0.07789
15	0.41727	0.38883	0.36245	0.33797	0.31524	0.27454	0.23939	0.18270	0.12289	0.06491
16	0.39365	0.36510	0.33873	0.31439	0.29189	0.25187	0.21763	0.16312	0.10686	0.05409
17	0.37136	0.34281	0.31657	0.29245	0.27027	0.23107	0.19784	0.14564	0.09293	0.04507
18	0.35034	0.32189	0.29586	0.27205	0.25025	0.21199	0.17986	0.13004	0.08081	0.03756
19	0.33051	0.30224	0.27651	0.25307	0.23171	0.19449	0.16351	0.11611	0.07027	0.03130
20	0.31180	0.28380	0.25842	0.23541	0.21455	0.17843	0.14864	0.10367	0.06110	0.02608
25	0.23300	0.20714	0.18425	0.16398	0.14602	0.11597	0.09230	0.05882	0.03038	0.01048
30	0.17411	0.15119	0.13137	0.11422	0.09938	0.07537	0.05731	0.03338	0.01510	0.00421
35	0.13011	0.11035	0.09366	0.07956	0.06763	0.04899	0.03558	0.01894	0.00751	0.00169
40	0.09722	0.08054	0.06678	0.05542	0.04603	0.03184	0.02209	0.01075	0.00373	0.00068
45	0.07265	0.05879	0.04761	0.03860	0.03133	0.02069	0.01372	0.00610	0.00186	0.00027
50	0.05429	0.04291	0.03395	0.02689	0.02132	0.01345	0.00852	0.00346	0.00092	0.00011
55	0.04057	0.03132	0.02420	0.01873	0.01451	0.00874	0.00529	0.00196	0.00044	0.00004
60	0.03031	0.02286	0.01726	0.01305	0.00988	0.00568	0.00328	0.00111	0.00023	0.00002

Chapter 5

1 BS 6349, Code of Practice for Maritime Structures
2 CIRIA TN 125, *Seawalls: Survey of Performance and Design Practice* (1986)
3 COPPIN and RICHARDS, *Use of Vegetation in Civil Engineering*, CIRIA/Butterworths, London (1990)

Chapter 6

1 GUNBAK, A. R.,'Rubble mound breakwaters', *Report 1*, Norwegian Institute of Technology (1979)
2 SAINFLOU, G., 'Essai sur les digues maritimes verticales', *Ann. des Ponts et Chaussées*, **98,** No. 4 (1928)
3 ALLSOP, N. W. H., FRANCO, L. and HAWKES, P. J., 'Wave run-up on steep slopes – a literature review', *Report SR1*, Hydraulics Research, Wallingford, March (1985)
4 AHRENS, J. P., 'Irregular wave run-up on smooth slopes', *CETA 81–17*, CERC, Fort Belvoir, December (1981)
5 LOSADA, M. A. and GIMENEZ-CURTO, L. A., 'Flow characteristics on rough, permeable slopes under wave action', *Coastal Engineering 4*, Elsevier, Amsterdam (1981)
6 ALLSOP, N. W. H., HAWKES, P. J., JACKSON, F. A. and FRANCO, L. 'Wave run-up on steep slopes – model tests under random waves', *Report SR2*, Hydraulics Research, Wallingford, August (1985)
7 *Shore Protection Manual*, US Army Corps of Engineers, Coastal Engineering Research Center, 4th edn (1984) (periodically updated)
8 GODA, Y., 'Expected rate of irregular wave overtopping of seawalls', *Coastal Eng. in Japan*, **14** (1971)
9 GODA, Y., *Random Seas and Design of Maritime Structures*, University of Tokyo Press, Tokyo (1985)
10 OWEN, M. W., 'Design of seawalls allowing for wave overtopping', *Report EX 924*, Hydraulics Research, Wallingford, June (1980)
11 OWEN, M. W., 'Overtopping of sea defences', *Proc. Conference Hydraulics Modelling of Civil Engineering Structures*, BHRA, Coventry (1982)
12 OWEN, M. W., 'The hydraulic design of seawall profiles', *Proc. Conference Shoreline Protection*, ICE, Southampton (1982)
13 DOUGLASS, S. L., 'Review and comparison of methods for estimating irregular wave overtopping rates', *Draft Techn. Report CERC-85*, WES, Vicksburg, March (1985)
14 DOUGLASS, S. L., 'Irregular wave overtopping rates', *Proc. 19th Coastal Eng. Conference*, Houston (1984)
15 SEELIG, W. N., 'Wave reflection from coastal structures', *Proc. Coastal Structures*, ASCE, Arlington, March (1983)
16 ALLSOP, N. W. H. and HETTIARACHCHI, S. S. L., 'Wave reflections in harbours: the design, construction and performance of wave absorbing structures', *Report OD 89*, Hydraulics Research, Wallingford, March (1989)
17 ALLSOP, N. W. H. and CHANNELL, A. R., 'Wave reflections in harbours: reflection performance of rock armoured slopes in random waves', *Report OD 102*, Hydraulics Research, Wallingford, March (1989)
18 *Shore Protection Manual*, Vol. II, Chapter 7, US Army Corps of Engineers (1984)
19 THOMPSON, D. M. and SHUTTLER, R. M., 'Design of rip-rap slope protection against wind waves', *CIRIA Report 61* (1976)
20 VAN DER MEER, J. W., 'Stability of breakwater armour layers – design formulae', submitted for publication in the *Journal of Coastal Engineering*, February (1987)
21 VAN DER MEER, J. W., 'Stability of cubes, tetrapods and accropode', in *Design of Breakwaters*, Thomas Telford, London (1988)
22 PILARCZYK, K. W., 'Prototype tests of slope protection systems', *Proc. Conf. Flexible Armoured Revetments*, ICE, London (1984)
23 VELDHUIZEN VAN ZANTEN, R. (ed.), *Geotextiles and Geomembranes in Civil Engineering*, A. A. Balkema, Rotterdam (1986)
24 PIANC, 'Guidelines for the design and construction of flexible revetments incorporating geotextiles for inland waterways', Supplement to *Bulletin No. 57* (1987)
25 BROWN, C. T., 'Armour units – random mass or disciplined array', *Coastal Structures 79*, Volume 1, A Speciality Conference on the Design Construction, Maintenance and Performance of Port and Coastal Structures, ASCE, March (1979)
26 BROWN, C. T., 'Gabion report', *Report No. 156*, Water Research Laboratory, University of New South Wales, October (1979)
27 CIRIA TN 125 *Sea Walls: Survey of Performance and Design Practice* (1986)

28 *Seawalls – a Literature Review*, Report No. 1490, Hydraulics Research on behalf of CIRIA, September (1988)
29 HUDSON, R. Y., 'Laboratory investigation of rubble mound breakwaters', *Jnl. of Waterways and Harbours Division*, Proc. ASCE, September (1959)
30 'Design of concrete block revetments subject to wave action', *Report No. SR54*, Hydraulics Research Ltd, Wallingford, June (1985)
31 DUNSTER, WILKINSON and ALLSOP, 'Single layer armour units' *Design of Breakwaters*, 177–188, Thomas Telford, London (1988)
32 BISHOP, A. W., 'The use of the slip circle in the stability analysis of slopes', *Geotechnique*, **5**, 7–17 (1955)
33 BISHOP, A. W. and MORGENSTERN, N. R. 'Stability coefficients for earth slopes', *Geotechnique*, **10**, 129–150 (1960)
34 BROMHEAD, E. N., *The Stability of Slopes*, Surrey University Press (1986).
35 BROMS, B. B., *Foundation Engineering Handbook*, Chapter 11, 'Landslides', 373–501, Winterkorn and Fang
36 COPPIN, N. J. AND RICHARDS, I., *Use of Vegetation in Civil Engineering*, Butterworths, London (1990)
37 HUTCHINSON, J. N., 'Assessment of the effectiveness of corrective measures in relation to geological conditions and types of slope movement', *Engineering Geol.*, No. 16, 131–155 (1977). (Reprinted in Norwegian, *Geotech, Inst. Pub.*, No. 124, 1–25 (1978))
38 HUTCHINSON, J. N. 'Slope failures produced by seepage erosion in sands', *Proc. Int. Seminar on water-related exogenous geological processes and prevention of their negative impact on the environment*, UNESCO and UNEP in collaboration with USSR Acad. of Sciences, Alma-Ata, USSR, October 1981, 250–268 (1982)
39 HUTCHINSON, J. N., 'The geotechnics of cliff stabilisation', *Proceedings of Conference on Shoreline Protection*, ICE, Thomas Telford, London (1983)
40 HUTCHINSON, J. N., *Canadian Geotechnical Journal*, **21** (1984)
41 JANBU, N., 'Slope stability computations', in Hirschfield and Poulos (eds), *Embankment Dam Engineering, Casagrande Volume*, Wiley, New York (1973)
42 MORGENSTERN, N. R. and PRICE, V. E. 'The analysis of stability of general slip surfaces', *Geotechnique*, **15**, 79–93 (1965)
43 SARMA, S. K., 'Stability analysis of embankments and slopes', *Proc. ASCE*, **105**, GT 12, 1511–1524 (1979)
44 TOMLINSON, M. J., *Foundation Design and Construction*, 5th edn, Longman, Harlow (1986)
45 VARNES, D. J., 'Slope movement types and pressures', in Schuster, R. L. and Krizek, R. J. (eds), *Landslides: analysis and control*, Transportation Research Board, Special Report 176, Washington DC, NAS (1978)
46 BS 6031: 1981, Code of Practice for Earthworks
47 BS 6349, Code of Practice for Maritime Structures
48 BS 8004, Code of Practice for Foundations
49 TECHNICAL ADVISORY COMMITTEE ON WATER DEFENCES COMMUNICATIONS, *The Use of Asphalt in Hydraulic Engineering*, No. 137, Rijkswaterstadt, Delft, The Netherlands (1985)
50 BS 5493, Code of Practice for Protective Coating of Iron and Steel Structures against Corrosion
51 CIRIA TN 128, *Civil Engineering Sealants in Wet Conditions*
52 BS 8110, Structural Use of Concrete
53 BS 6322, Specification for Seamless and Welded Steel Tubes for Automobile, Mechanical and General Engineering Purposes
54 BS 5135: 1984, Specification for Arc Welding of Carbon and Carbon Manganese Steels
55 BS 6399: 1984, Loading for Buildings
56 DoE, *Review of Research in Land Sliding in Great Britain*
57 TYHURST, M. F., 'Coastal vegetation work at Highcliffe on Sea', *Conference of River and Coastal Engineering*, MAFF Flood Defence Division, Loughborough (1989)
58 BS 449, The Structural Use of Steel
59 THOMPSON, D. M., 'Hydraulic design of sea dykes', *Report No. DE6*, Hydraulics Research Ltd, Wallingford (1973)
60 TECHNICAL ADVISORY COMMITTEE ON WATER DEFENCES, 'The use of asphalt in hydraulic engineering', *Communication No. 37*, Rijkswaterstadt, Delft, The Netherlands (1985)
61 MARSLAND, A., 'The shrinkage and fissuring of clay in flood banks', *Note No. IN39/68*, Building Research Establishment, Watford (1968)

Chapter 7

1 FOOKES, P. G. and POOLE, A. B., 'Some preliminary consideration on the selection and durability of rock and concrete materials for breakwaters and coastal protection works', *QJEG,* **14** (1981)
2 ALLSOP, N. W. H., BRADBURY, A. P., POOLE, A. B., DIBB, T. E. and HUGHES, D. W., 'Rock durability in the marine environment', *Report SR 11*, Hydraulics Research Ltd, Wallingford, March (1985)
3 LEEMING, M. B., Co-ordinating report on the UEG. 'Concrete in the Oceans' programme (to be published)
4 BS 6349: Part 1: 1984, Maritime Structures: General Criteria
5 HESTOR, J. D. S., 'Timber in shoreline protection', *Proc. Conf. Shoreline Protection*, ICE, Southampton (1982)
6 DAVIES, C. D. and HARRISON, J. G., 'Coastal revetments – rock, concrete and asphalt', *Proc. of River and Coastal Engineers Conference*, MAFF, Loughborough (1988)
7 MORLEY, J., WAITE, D. and O'BRIEN, J. E., 'Sheet piling in coast protection works', *Proc. Conf. Shoreline Protection*, ICE, Southampton (1982)
8 PIANC, *Guidelines for the Design and Construction of Flexible Revetments incorporating Geotextiles for Inland Waterways*, Supplement to Bulletin No. 57 (1987)
9 RANKILOR, P. R., *Membranes in Ground Engineering*, Wiley, Chichester (1981)
10 VELDHUIJZEN VAN ZANTEN, R. (ed.), *Geotextiles and Geomembranes in Civil Engineering*, A. A. Balkema, Rotterdam/Boston (1986)
11 OLIVER, A. C., *Timber for Marine and Freshwater Construction*, Timber Research and Development Association, High Wycombe.
12 TECHNICAL ADVISORY COMMITTEE ON WATER DEFENCES COMMUNICATIONS, *The Use of Asphalt in Hydraulic Engineering*, No. 37, Rijkswaterstadt, Delft, The Netherlands (1985)
13 BS 812: 1975, Testing Aggregates
14 BS 12: 1978, Portland Cements
15 BS 146: 1973, Portland Blast Furnace Cement
16 BS 4027: 1980, Sulphate-Resisting Portland Cement
17 BS 882: 1983, Aggregates from Natural Sources
18 BS 4449: 1978, Hot Rolled Steel Bars
19 BS 4482: 1985, Cold Reduced Steel Wire
20 BS 4483: 1985, Steel Fabric Reinforcement
21 BS 4466: 1981, Bending Dimensions for Reinforcement
22 BS 5337: 1976, The Structural Use of Concrete for Retaining Aqueous Liquids
23 BS 8110: 1985, The Structural Use of Concrete
24 BS 5328: 1981, Specifying Concrete
25 BS 4360: 1986, Weldable Structural Steel
26 BS 5756: 1980, Topical Hardwoods Graded for Structural Use
27 BS 5589: 1978, The Preservation of Timber
28 BRE Digest 258, *Alkali Aggregate Reaction in Concrete*, Building Research Establishment, Watford

Chapter 8

1 GREEN, C. H. and PENNING-ROWSELL, E. C., 'Evaluating the intangible benefits of a flood alleviation proposal', *Journal of the Institution of Water Engineers and Scientists*, **40**(3), 229–248 (1986)
2 HM TREASURY, *Investment appraisal in the public sector: a technical guide for government departments*, London (1984)
3 MINISTRY OF AGRICULTURE, FISHERIES AND FOOD, *Investment appraisal of arterial drainage, flood alleviation and sea defence schemes – guidelines for drainage authorities*, London (1985)
4 MISHAM, J., *Cost-benefit Analysis*, Allen and Unwin, London (1971)
5 MORRIS, J. and HESS, T. M., 'Farmer uptake of agricultural land drainage benefits', *Environment and Planning*, **18** (12), 1649–1664 (1986)
6 PARKER, D. J., GREEN, C. H. and THOMPSON, P. M., *Urban Flood Protection Benefits: a project appraisal guide,* Gower Technical Press, Aldershot (1987)
7 PARKER, D. J. and PENNING-ROWSELL, E. C., *Whitstable Central Area Coast Protection Scheme: benefit assessment*, Middlesex Polytechnic Flood Hazard Research Centre, Enfield (1981)

8 PENNING-ROWSELL, E. C., CHATTERTON, J. B., DAY, H. J. (and others), 'Comparative aspects of computerised floodplain data management, *Journal of Water Resources Planning and Management*, American Society of Civil Engineers, **113** (6), 725–744 (1987)
9 PENNING-ROWSELL, E. C., THOMPSON, P. M. and PARKER, D. J., 'Coastal erosion and flood control: changing institutions, policies and research needs', in Hooke, J. (ed.), *Geomorphology and Public Policy*, Wiley, Chichester (1988)
10 SULEMAN, M., N'JAI, A., GREEN, C. H. and PENNING-ROWSELL, E. C., *Major Update of Middlesex Polytechnic Flood Damage Data*, Middlesex Polytechnic Flood Hazard Research Centre, Enfield (1988)
11 THOMPSON, P. M., PENNING-ROWSELL, E. C., PARKER, D. J. and HILL, M. I., *Interim guidelines for the economic evaluation of coast protection and sea defence schemes*, Middlesex Polytechnic Flood Hazard Research Centre, Enfield (1987)
12 CIRIA TN 125, *Sea Walls: Survey of Performance and Design Practice* (1986)
13 PENNING-ROWSELL, E. C. and CHATTERTON, J. B., 'Assessing the benefits of flood alleviation and land drainage schemes', *Proc. ICE*, Part 2 (1980)

Appendix B

1 SOUTHGATE, H. N., 'The parabolic method for numerical modelling of water waves', *Rep. No. SR81*
2 YOO and O'CONNOR B. A., 'Ray model for caustic gravity waves', *5th Congress Asian and Pacific Regional Division*, AIHR, Seoul, South Korea (1986)
3 H. J. DE VRIEND, 'Two and three dimensional modelling of coastal morphology', *Delft Hydraulics Communication No. 377*, January (1987)
4 OZASA, H. and BRAMPTON, A. H., 'Mathematical modelling of beaches backed by sea walls', *Coastal Engineering 4*, Elsevier, Amsterdam (1980): 'Models for predicting the shoreline evolution of beaches backed by seawalls', *Report IT 191*, Hydraulics Research Ltd, Wallingford (1979)
5 HANSON, H. and KRAUS, N. C., 'Seawall Constraint in Shoreline Numerical Model', Journal of Waterway, Coastal and Ocean Engineering, Vol. III, No. WW6, pp. 1079–1083, (1985)
6 PERLIN, M. and DEAN, R. G., 'A Numerical Model to Simulate Sediment Transport in the Vicinity of Coastal Structures, Miscellaneous Report No. 83–10, U.S. Army Engineer Waterways Experiment Station, Coastal Engineering Research Centre, p. 119, (1983)
7 BEZUIJEN, A., WOUTERS, J. and LAUSTRUP, C., 'Block revetment design with physicial and numerical models', *Proc. 21st International Conference on Coastal Engineering*, ASCE, New York (1988)

Index